MILLERS
ANTIQUES
PRICE GUIDE

FIRST PUBLISHED OCTOBER 1979

I S B N   0   86134   020   5

Made and Printed in Great Britain by
Redwood Burn Limited,
Trowbridge, Wiltshire.

MILLERS
ANTIQUES
PRICE GUIDE

Compiled and Edited by

Martin & Judith Miller

M. J. M. PUBLICATIONS
Finchden Manor
Tenterden,
Kent.

Acknowledgements

Editorial

Barbara de la Haye
Valerie Gatward
Carolyn Johnsen
T. Deere
E. Sanderson
S. J. Miller
A. Wells
J. Dingley, Megaron Studios Limited

Photographic

A. Bernadino
S. MacAuliffe
G. Strand

The publishers would also like to acknowledge the great assistance given by:

John S. Herbert, Public Relations Director, Christie's
Fiona Ford, Press Officer, Sotheby's Belgravia
Rhona Gorringe, Sotheby King and Chasemore
Richard Davidson, Petworth

Introduction

The Antiques Price Guide is an annual publication which is designed to meet the growing needs of the collector, dealer and enthusiast alike. It is aimed particularly at assisting with the areas of identification, dating and giving a general price guide.

The volume contains over **6,000** photographic illustrations with full descriptive captions, dimensions and a price range. It also denotes whether a particular piece sold at auction or through a dealer and in which part of the country. These all aim to give the reader a clear aid to the identification of a piece. Comparisons can then be made between different styles and factories, all of which aids immensely in the learning process essential to the full enjoyment and profit of dealing in antiques.

The editorial aim of this volume has been a very practical one in that it was felt that it was essential to collect data and photographs from as wide an area as possible, and to ensure that the book was crammed with photographs and information.

We have made it a general policy to keep away from museum pieces which are dealt with in great detail in a large number of excellent volumes on specialist subjects. We felt it important to concentrate on the pieces which are available to the dealer or collector in auction rooms, antique markets and dealers shops. These are the pieces which are on general display and may be viewed and examined. This is an extremely important area especially for the new collector and this volume is an invaluable asset, covering as it does the main areas of collecting. The volume is very consciously called a 'guide' as it is in this area it can be put to best use.

The volume is also consciously a 'guide' when we deal with the price. It was decided to have a price range rather than a single price as prices do vary from area to area and from one sale to the next; demand changes and hence the price of a piece may rise or fall. It is therefore extremely difficult to give a price which is truly representative. It is however a fact that anyone coming into the antique field desperately needs to have some guidance as to a price estimate. Hence the need for

the price range, which takes into account subsequent movements and regional variations. This need for a price guide is, of course, equally true for a general dealer who may specialise in a particular area and yet may be offered pieces which are outside his sphere of knowledge.

The increase in public awareness of antiques over the past few years has led to more and more people seeking information and hence the demand for a reference book increases.

Not all pieces which appear in the first edition were in fact sold in the immediate twelve months prior to publication. Any which have been included to extend the comprehensive nature of this volume, have had their prices readjusted to bring the valuations up to date.

Antiques do not have a monetary value which can be expressed as a set price. Value is always informed guesswork. In discussing the value of a piece one must consider such points as how much is original? what is the quality of the craftsmanship? how scarce is it? how much demand is there? what is the condition of the piece? In dealing with auction prices one must always keep in mind that conditions in a sale room may considerably affect the price achieved. If, as has happened often in the past year, a famous collection is sold by one of the major sale rooms, then some seemingly outrageous prices are paid due to the geneology of the pieces. This in itself does not destroy the worth of the prices fetched. Frequently the market responds by a general increase in price to correspond with the new price.

After saying all this the reader may be left wondering what is the point of having a price guide. The point is that a guide of this nature forms a sound foundation on which to expand your awareness of current values in an ever-changing market.

In our experience with material collected during the compilation of this guide, one becomes only too well aware of variations of price. What we have attempted to do, is to even out these variations and provide you, the dealer or collector, with a 'norm'. We would be foolish to suggest that this, or any price guide should put a direct value on any piece. The value of a piece is the much quoted "what a willing buyer pays a willing seller".

It is perhaps also valuable at this time to discuss how to use this guide. Our main intention regarding the design of the guide has been to facilitate fast visual recognition and identification. If you take the porcelain section as an example, and in particular if you are trying to identify a plate which is either unmarked or, the mark unknown to you, in most other reference works you would normally have to plough through factory after factory of assorted items of porcelain. In this guide however you go directly to the section covering plates and thumb through, all the factories being in alphabetical order where possible. If, however, you recognise the mark you can check this by going directly to the particular plates from that factory. We also include various recognition points to assist your identification.

In this edition many more identification points are included in the Porcelain and Pottery section and it is our intention to concentrate each year on a particular section without wherever possible, any duplication in subsequent editions.

Key to Illustrations

Adams Antiques — AA
Aldridge of Bath (Somerset) — AA
Alonzo, Dawes & Hoddell (Avon)
Anderson & Garland (Tyne & Wear)
Barlow Antiques — BA
Biddle & Webb (West Midlands)
J.W. Blanchard — JWB
William Brown & Son (Lincolnshire) — WB
Buckell & Ballard (Oxfordshire)
Burrows & Day (kent)
Burtenshaw walker (East Sussex)
Butler & Hatch Waterman (Kent)
Christies, St. James — CStJ
Christies, South Kensington — CSK
Churchman Auction Galleries (West Sussex)
Clarke Gammon (Surrey)
Clinkers Antiques Ltd. — CAL
S.W. Cotte & Son (Dorset)
Cubitt & West (Surrey)
Dacre, Son & Hartley (West Yorkshire)
Clifford Dunn & Partners (East Sussex)
R. Davidson — RD
Dolphin Galleries
Henry Duke & Son (Dorset)
J.R. Edmiston (Glasgow)
Edwards, Bigwood & Bewlay (West Midlands)
Ensors (Dorset)
Folly Antiques — FA
Caroline Foord Antiques — CFA
Fox & Sons (West Sussex)
B. Frith — F
Geering & Colyer (Hawkhurst) — GC

Georgina Antiques — GGA
Rowland Gorringe & Co. (East Sussex)
Graves, Son & Pilcher (East Sussex) — GSP
Greenmill Antiques —GA
Hill House Antiques — HHA
Hoff Antiques — HA
House of Antiques — HOA
Mary Howard — MaH
Jackson, Stops, Staff, Taylor Fletcher (Gloucestershire)
The Johnson Collection — TJC
Lita Kaye, Lyndhurst — LKL
G.A. Key (Norfolk)
Klaber & Klaber — KK
W.H. Lane & Son (Cornwall)
Langlois (Jersey) — LJ
Lawrence of Crewkerne (Avon)— LC
Locke & England (Warwickshire) — LE
Lutley Blower Antiques — LBA
Victor Mahy — VM
J. & J. May — JJM
Messenger, May Baverstock (Surrey)
Morphet & Morphet (North Yorkshire) — MH
Neales of Nottingham (Notts) — NN
Dennis H.B. Neal (Suffolk) — DHBN
Olivers, Sudbury — OS
Ormiston, Knight & Payne — ORM
Outhwaite & Litherland, Liverpool
Parsons, Welch & Cowell (Kent) — PWC
Petersfield Galleries — PG
Michael Pidgeon Antiques — MP
Phillips, London — PL
Phillips at Hepper House, Leeds

Phillips at Knowle (West Midlands) — PK
Phillips Marylebone — PM
Phillips & Jollys of Bath (Avon) — PJ
Phillips in Scotland, Edinburgh
Sir Francis Pittes & Son (Isle of Wight)
John H. Raby — JHR
Regina Antiques — RA
Riddetts of Bournemouth (Dorset) — RB
Robson Lowe Ltd. (London)
Russell, Baldwin & Bright — RBB
Sotheby's New Bond Street (London) — SBS
Sotheby Humbert — HKC
Sotheby King & Chasemore — KC
Sotheby's Belgravia (London) — SBel
Sotheby's at Hill House Scotland — SatHH
Sotheby's in Ireland — SIre
Somervale Antiques — SA
Spear & Sons (Suffolk)
Henry Spencer & Sons (Notts)
Laurence & Martin Taylor, Honiton
Joseph & Earle Vandekar — JAV
Vidler & Co. — VC
Wallis & Wallis
Weller & Dufty (West Midlands)
D. Whitelaw — DW
Mrs. Wildish — MW
Peter Wilson & Co. (Cheshire)
Woolley & Wallis (Wiltshire) — WW
Worsfolds (Kent) — W
Norman Wright & Partners (Northants)
J.M. Welch & Son, Dunmow, Essex

6

CONTENTS

A Capodimonte (Carlo III) group
of lovers dancing modelled by
Guiseppe Gricci, the youth with
cream jacket and black breeches
and shoes, his companion with
lilac bonnet, pale blue bodice
and with iron-red and blue
border to her white skirt, her
right arm restored, 8½", 21.5 cm.,
c.1750 **£2,800-2,900** CStJ

PORCELAIN & POTTERY

Porcelain is the most recent innovation in ceramic wares. It appeared in recognisable form in the Yuan dynasty (1280-1368) in China.

There are three quite distinct catergories, hard porcelain, soft porcelain and bone-china. Soft porcelain was only made in Europe and America in the 18th and early 19th century.

'Hard' porcelain (sometimes known as 'true' porcelain) was first made in China using kaolin and a substance called "petuntse". The secret of its manufacture was well kept and it did not arrive in Europe until 1700. It was first made at the Meissen factory in Germany, then at Vienna in 1720 but it took another fifty years before it reached the French and English factories, initially being made at Bristol and Plymouth.

Soft porcelain was highly prized from the time of its arrival in the Middle Ages. This porcelain was translucent when held up to light. Many factories in Europe attempted to emmulate this soft-paste porcelain, the most successful being in France in the late 17th C. It was extremely difficult to work with due to the critical nature of the firing process. In England this was to some extent resolved by the addition of bone-ash although this certainly affected the quality. After 1770 most factories purely made 'hard' porcelain.

English Porcelain

Divided into 3 main catergories:

(1) soft porcelain made at Longton Hall and Chelsea until 1755, Derby until 1775.

(2) 'bone ash' porcelain made at Bow, Lowestoft, Derby and Chelsea.

(3) 'soaprock' porcelain was made at Bristol, Worcester, Liverpool and Caughley.

A Bow figure of a flower-seller, c. 1755, 5¾", 14.5 cm., £240-260 MW

A Bow Figure of a Seated Bag-piper, slight chips to hat, 8½", 21.5 cm. high, c.1758/60. £600-670 CStJ

A Bow Figure of a Girl, restoration to hat, 5½", 14 cm. high, c.1755/58. £500-560 CStJ

An 18th C. Bow figure of Autumn, square aperture at rear, 5¼" high, 13 cm. £180-210 HKC

An 18th century Bow group, painted in bright enamel colours, 7", 17.5 cm., (restored) £340-400

BOW PORCELAIN

- factory established in 1747
- translucency poor
- heavy for its size
- brownish-orange colour by transmitted light
- on unglazed parts; strong absorbency
- very similar body to early Lowestoft
- used a great deal of under-glaze blue
- much painting in the Kakiemon style
- factory closed in 1776.

A Rare Bristol (Champion's) Figure of a Sportsman's Companion, right arm repaired, 6¾", 17 cm. high, c.1775. £900-990 CStJ

A Chelsea Group of The Tyrolean Dancers after the model by J.J. Kaendler, restoration to arms and legs, 7", 18 cm. high, red anchor mark, c.1758/60. £750-820 CStJ

A pair of continental male and female groups, 5", 12.5 cm. £90-130 VC

An exquisitely decorated Chelsea Gold Anchor set of the Four Seasons. 6¼", 16.0 cm., £2,925-3,000 JEV

A pair of Derby figures in bright colours on turquoise and gold-scroll moulded bases, 10" 25.5 cm., incised cross marks. £380-420 pair CSJ

A fine quality pair of Derby figures of Shakespeare and Milton, incised No. 305 under base, companion (Milton) red marks but incised No. 297. £450-500 KC

EARLY DERBY

- dates for early Derby generally taken as c 1750-1775

- in early days mainly concentrated on figures

- Duesbury attempted to emulate the Chelsea factory and hence most wares are unmarked

- Duesbury bought the Chelsea factory in 1770

- with early figures up to 1760, body is glassy and light in weight

A pair of 18th century Derby Mansion House Dwarfs, both bearing incised numeral marks No. 221, 6¾", 17.1 cm., **£440-500** KC

A rare Doccia figure of a Turkess, c. 1765, note the typical Doccia large hands. **£250-300** KK

A large Doccia musical group. 10¾", 27 cm., printed crowned N, late 19th C. **£160-180** SBel

'Sir Walter Raleigh'. A Royal Doulton Figure, 12", 30.5 high, impressed 2.4.36. **£220-250** PL

A large Derby figure of Sir James Quin as Sir John Falstaff. Turquoise breeches, iron-red and gilt jerkin, blade replaced, 20¼", 51.9 cm., incised number 271, early 19th century. **£110-140** SBel

'Priscilla'. A Royal Doulton Figure, 8¼", 21 cm. high, impressed 4.10.33. **£140-160** PL

A pair of Dresden equestrian groups, 11", 28.1 cm., crossed swords in underglaze-blue, late 19th C. **£170-190** SBel

A pair of Dresden groups, 10", 25.4 cm., mid-19th C. **£500-600** LC

William Billingsley (1758-1828) was the famous flower painter at Derby, Pinxton, Worcester and Nantgarw. Due to his high kiln wastage (sometimes put as high as nine-tenths) his venture at Nantgarw ran out of money. He then moved to Swansea, and under Dillwyn of the Swansea Pottery factory had a great deal of success. Some exceptionally fine porcelain was made from 1814-17.

Billingsley then returned to Nantgarw and produced some fine quality, highly decorated porcelains.

A pair of large Royal Dux figures, 30" and 32", 76 cm and 81 cm., applied pink triangle, c.1900. **£1,150-1,300** SBel

A pair of Royal Dux figures, 19¾" and 18¾", 49.7 and 47.2 cm. applied pink triangle, c.1910. **£350-390** SBel

A Dresden group, 18¼", 45.7 cm. crossed swords mark in underglaze-blue. **£440-500** LC

A Royal Dux group, 13", 33 cm., overall, applied pink triangle, impressed numerals, c.1910. **£150-170** SBel

A pair of large Royal Dux figures, monogrammed incised artist's initials 'A.H.' to reverse, applied triangular mark to base, 21", 50.3 cm., **£350-375** KC

A pair of Royal Dux porcelain figures, painted in muted tones of brown and green highlighted with gilding, raised mark to bases, 21", 53 cm., **£480-530** KC

A Royal Dux porcelain figure of a Charioteer, 11½", 29.5 cm., **£75-100** KC

A Royal Dux figure group, painted in green and brown with gilded highlights, signed Hampel with impressed mark to base, 18", 46 cm., **£220-250**

A Royal Dux porcelain dish in the form of a Lily-Pond, and figure, painted in gold and pink, impressed mark to base, 13¼", 33.5 cm., **£180-220** KC

PINXTON

- factory started c.1796 and closed c.1812
- emulated Derby designs
- William Billingsley set the factory up in 1796 and worked there until 1799
- body has good translucency
- some good flower painting and local views predominate

A Frankenthal group of 3
children, blue crowned interlaced
CT mark and 86, incised AC 3 X
Former's mark for Adam Clair,
1786, 9″, 23 cm.
£1,300-1,400 CStJ

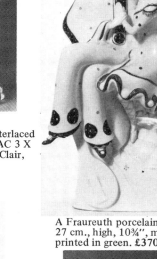

A Fraureuth porcelain group,
27 cm., high, 10¾″, marks
printed in green. £370-400 PL

A pair of French figures, crossed
swords, late 19th C., 13¾″ and
13¼″, 35 and 34 cm.
£240-280 SBel

A coloured and glazed Gille
Jeune figure, 9¼″, 23.4 cm.
applied blue mark impressed and
incised J.S., c.1900. £100-150
SBel

A Hochst figure of the Bauer am
Taubenschlag. Dove-cot missing,
chips, impressed 10H mark,
c.1753, 7½″, 19 cm.
£1,100-1,200 CStJ

A Longton Hall Figure of Winter,
restoration to hands, collar and
base, 4½″, 11.5 cm. high, c.1755.
£250-280 CStJ

A Kloster Veilsdorf figure, firing
crack to base, c.1770, 6″, 15 cm.
£3,800-4,000 CStJ

A pair of large Leboeuf and
Milliet coloured biscuit figures
16¾″, 42.4 cm. impressed mark,
late 19th C. £600-700 SBel

A pair of Jacob Petit portrait
figures and stands, in underglaze-
blue, incised D, mid 19th C.,
12¼″ or 11¼″, 31 or 28.5 cm.
£400-450 SBel

LONGTON HALL

- factory founded by Jenkin-
  son and Littler c 1750 and
  closed in 1760
- porcelain glassy soft-
  paste type
- very similar in some ways
  to Plymouth: it is thought
  that Longton moulds were
  sold to Cookworthy

- Duesbury worked at Longton before going to Derby
- pieces often thickly potted
- porcelain generally un-
  marked
- if marked usually 2 crossed
  'L's with dots below

A Longton Hall Figure of Minerva, helmet, arm and leg repaired 7¾", 19.5 cm. high, blue XI mark, c.1755. **£280-320** CStJ

A Meissen group of 3 putti, minor chips, blue crossed swords mark, c.1755. 11½", 29 cm. **£550-600** CStJ

MEISSEN
- harbour scenes popular in late 1720's and through 1730's
- battle scenes popular in late 1730's and through 1740's
- scenes from Italian Comedy popular in late 1740's and through 1750's
- pastoral subjects popular in 1750's
- putti also fashionable in 1750's

A pair of Meissen figures of a gardener and companion, 7½" and 7⅛", 19.1 and 17.8 cm., cancelled crossed swords in under-glaze-blue, late 19th C. **£390-420** SBel

A pair of Meissen figures, 7¾", 19.3 cm. crossed swords in under-glaze-blue, late 19th C. **£500-580** SBel

A pair of Meissen figures, crossed swords, late 19th C., 6½" and 7¼" 16.7 cm and 18 cm. **£480-560** SBel

A Meissen figure, crossed swords, late 19th C., 6¼", 16 cm. **£170-200** SBel

A pair of Meissen figures, 6", 15 cm., cancelled under-glaze-blue crossed swords, late 19th C. **£270-300** SBel

A Meissen group from the Four Seasons, minor chips, blue crossed swords mark at back, c.1755, 5¼", 13 cm. **£350-380** CStJ

A Meissen group, crossed swords, late 19th C., 9″, 22.8 cm. **£430-480** SBel

A Meissen figure, crossed swords, late 19th C., 7″, 18 cm. **£220-250** SBel

2 Meissen child musicians, crossed swords, 19th C., 5½″ and 4¾″, 14.3 and 12.2 cm. **£190-250** SBel

A Meissen group of a mother and child, by J.J. Kandler, repair to base, blue crossed swords mark, c.1750, 9¼″, 23.5 cm. **£1,500-1,600** CStJ

A Meissen group, crossed swords, late 19th C., 5½″, 14 cm. **£320-350** SBel

A Meissen figure, crossed swords, late 19th C., 7¼″, 18.4 cm. **£250-270** SBel

A Meissen figure of a young woman, 7½″, 19 cm., cancelled crossed swords in underglaze-blue, late 19th C. **£230-260** SBel

A late 18th C. Meissen group of the Academic period, underglaze crossed swords with dot. 8¼″ high, 21 cm. **£400-500** HKC

A Meissen group, incised triangle and crossed swords, late 19th C., 8¾″, 22.5 cm. **£360-400** SBel

---

MEISSEN MARKS

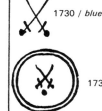

1730 / *blue*

1731 / *blue*

after 1750 / *blue*

1774—1830 / *impressed*

beginning of 19th cent.

1774 / *blue*

after 1766, medium quality *blue*

1st half of 18th cent., with mark of Master Moebius / *blue*

A late 18th C. Meissen group. Underglaze-blue crossed swords mark, 7" high, 17.5 cm. £750-850 HKC

A late 19th C. Meissen Silenus group, 7½" wide, 19 cm. £400-450 HKC

A Meissen figure modelled by Elias Meyer, crossed swords mark, c.1752, 5¾", 14.5 cm. £360-400 LC

A Meissen figure, gilt rose mark, late 19th C., 6¼", 15.5 cm. £80-100 SBel

A pair of Meissen 'Japanese' figures, 5¾" and 6⅛", 14.7 cm. and 15.2 cm., underglaze-blue crossed swords, late 19th C. £380-420 SBel

A late 19th C. Meissen pastoral group, underglaze-blue crossed swords mark, 8" high, 20 cm. £440-500 HKC

A Meissen figure of a Turkish Dignitary, 16½", 41.9 cm. crossed swords in underglaze-blue, late 19th C. £620-700 SBel

A Meissen group, 11¼", 28.5 cm. cancelled crossed swords in under-glaze-blue, late 19th C. £800-890 SBel

---

MEISSEN

- the most important 18th C. factory
- first porcelain made c.1709
- body was hard with slightly yellowish tinge
- displays a strong Chinese influence

- up to c.1720 influenced by J.F. Bottger
- from c.1720-1734 influenced by J.G. Herold, famous for applying brilliant enamel colours to hard paste porcelain
- porcelain now based on Japanese Kakiemon style

- Kaendler started in the Meissen factory in 1731 and began the period of the finest Meissen figures of the Baroque period
- 'Crinoline' groups painted in strong colours, were made from 1740-1745

A rare grey pottery head of a Lady, 2¾", 7.0 cm., Han Dynasty, wood stand, £500-600 SBel

A pottery figure of a lady, well modelled, robe decorated with vertical black lines, scarf picked out in red, 11½", 29.0 cm., T'ang Dynasty, £2,200-2,400 SBel

A pair of 'Famille-Verte' porcelain figures of boys, painted in iron-red yellow, green and aubergine enamels, 7⅝" and 7½", 19.5 and 19.0 cm., 2nd half 17th century, £500-550 KC

A pair of famille-verte models of smiling boys, painted with flowers on a black and seeded green enamel ground, square bases, 12¾", £1,200-1,400 NN

A famille verte biscuit standing figure of a bearded immortal, slightly chipped. 5½", 14 cm., K'ang Hsi. £130-150 CStJ

A good famille rose figures of a Mandarin, Turquoise enamel base, 19½", 49 cm. high, 19th C. £220-240 NN

A group of standing lovers, chipped, 6¼", 16 cm., late Ch'ien Lung. £175-195 CStJ

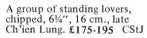

A Japanese standing figure wearing a cloak, an iron-red floral robe with gold and green enamel waistband, 14¼", 36.3 cm., 17th century, £440-500 LC

FAMILLE ROSE

- used in the decoration of porcelain at the end of the K'ang Hsi period (1662-1722)
- the colour varied from a pale pink to a deep copper brownish-red
- the highest quality famille rose is a beautiful rose-pink
- the best period for famille rose was the Yung Cheng period (1723-1735)
- most rose enamel work was done in Canton

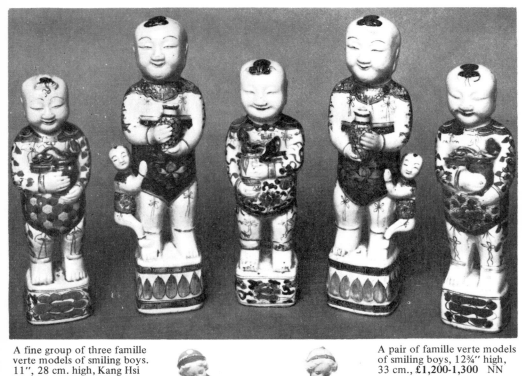

A fine group of three famille
verte models of smiling boys.
11″, 28 cm. high, Kang Hsi
£1,000-1,200   NN

A pair of famille verte models
of smiling boys, 12¾″ high,
33 cm., **£1,200-1,300**   NN

Grey pottery figure of a Lady,
well modelled in standing attitude.
9″, 23.0 cm., Chin/Yuan Dynasty,
brocade stand. **£300-400**   SBel

A pair of Mintons tinted Parian
classical figures, the details picked
out in salmon pink, lilac and dark
brown, minute chips, 16⁷/₈″,
43 cm., impressed Mintons and
date code for 1874 **£390-450**
SBel

A pair of Paris figures, mid 19th C.,
12½″, 31.8 cm. **£360-400**   SBel

A pair of Paris porcelain figures
17½″, and 18″, 44.8 cm. and
45.7 cm., crossed swords and
dot in blue, impressed DP, late
19th C. **£380-420**   SBel

A fine group of three famille-
verte models of smiling boys.
Floral painted attire differing in
detail, on square bases, 11″, Kang
Hsi, **£1,000-1,200** NN

A Plymouth figure of Autumn, c. 1770 5½", 14.0 cm., **£190-220** MW

A large Ridgway Parian group of Venus and Cupid after the original by J. Gibson, R. A., impressed, hairline cracks, chip to base and a toe, 18⅝", 47.3 cm., impressed Art Union of London, J. Ridgeway, Bates & Co., 1858 **£170-200** SBel

A Rockingham Biscuit Figure of Paysanne De S. Angelo, 7¾", 19.5 cm. high, impressed griffin mark, and Rockingham Works Brameld and incised no. 120, 1826-1830. **£220-240** CStJ

A pair of Samson 'Chelsea-Derby' figures. 7⅛", 17.8 cm., painted D and anchor, late 19th C. **£110-130** SBel

A pair of Samson Sweetmeat figures and covers, 7¼", 18.5 cm., painted crossed lines, late 19th C. **£320-400** SBel

A set of five Samson 'Chelsea-Derby' figures, 6¾", 17 cm. high, gilt D and Anchor mark. **£145-155** HKC

A pair of Samson 'Chelsea' Bocage candlestick holder groups, 8¼" and 9", 21 and 23 cm., gilt anchor, late 19th C. **£200-230** SBel

A Scheibe, Thuringia, group, 7¾", 19.05 cm., incised crossed S, c.1870. **£100-120** SBel

A rare Spanish Buen Retiro Figure of Africa, c. 1770, £900-1,000 KK

A pair of Sitzendorf figures of a shepherd and shepherdess in 18th century costume, 7" and 6½", 18 and 16.5 cm., crossed parallel lines in gilding, impressed 38, late 19th century. £130-160 SBel

A rare Strasbourg faience figure of L'Abbe de Cour, minor glaze chips, firing crack, 1745-48, 13", 33 cm. £11,500-13,000 CStJ

A Vienna figure, minor chips, blue beehive mark, c.1780, 8¾", 22.5 cm. £240-260 CStJ

An Eckert & Co. Volkstedt group, 8¾", 22 cm., painted crossed swords and EC, late 19th C. £140-160 SBel

A Volkstedt figure, minor chips, incised mark, c.1770, 7¼", 18 cm. £550-600 CStJ

A pair of Royal Worcester figures, minor damage, printed crowned circle marks, 1876, 10¾" and 9¾", 27.3 and 24.8 cm. £150-200 SBel

A pair of Volkstedt figures of a gallant and companion, 16½" and 16", 41.6 and 40.5 cm., sunburst mark in underglaze-blue, c. 1900 £180-220 SBel

A Royal Worcester figure, printed crowned circle mark, 1894, 6", 15.2 cm. £105-125 SBel

A pair of Royal Worcester cream-glazed figures, 9¾" and 10", 24.7 cm and 25.4 cm., printed and impressed crowned circle marks, pattern number 880, one with date code for 1883. £100-120 SBel

A Hadley's Worcester porcelain figure group depicting Paul Kreuger and Neville Chamberlain, c. 1903, 8¾", 22 cm., £100-130 KC

A Royal Worcester porcelain figure of a Water Carrier, painted in shot enamels of brown and green signed Hadley, printed mark to base, dated 1910, 20¾", 52.5 cm., £240-280 KC

A Royal Worcester figure, decorated in honey gilt, ivory body, 7", 17.5 cm., £100-150 LE

A pair of Royal Worcester figures after models by Hadley, cast signature. The robes tinted in imitiation gilt-metal, the figures portraying 'Music' and 'Dancing'. 12¼" and 12½", 31.5 and 31.5 cm., printed retailer's mark Townsend Newcastle-On-Tyne, crown and circle mark, pattern number 1828 and 1827 date for 1924 and 1923. £210-250 SBel

A large Royal Worcester porcelain figure of A Lady in Classical Pose, converted for electricity. £640-680 KC

A Hadley Worcester figure, painted in tones of peach and blue, impressed Hadley to rear, printed and impressed marks to base, No. 1249 dated 1893, £125-175 KC

A Royal Worcester figure of John Bull after a model by James Hadley, moulded signature, in apricot with gilt details, hat chipped, 6¾", 17.3 cm., printed crowned circle mark, impressed 5C and 31, date code for 1894. £70-100 SBel

A Royal Worcester Bone China model of The Privy Chamberlain of the Sword and Cape, after a model by Frederick Gertner, 11", 27.1 cm., printed mark and title, date code for 1967, framed certificate for number 93 from a limited edition of 150, wood stand. £170-200 SBel

23

A Royal Worcester figure of a Yankee after a model by James Hadley, the whole coloured in pastel shades and lightly gilded, 6¾", 17.1 cm., printed and impressed crowned circle marks, impressed numerals, 1891 **£120-150** SBel

A Royal Worcester figure of an Irish girl, the whole decorated in bronzed 'shot' enamels, 6½", 16.5 cm., printed crowned circle mark, pattern number 1874, date code for 1914, **£130-160** SBel

Pair of Royal Worcester Parian figures of a Japanese Lady and Gentleman, decorated in pastel shades and heightened in gilding, 16 and 16¼", 40.6 and 41.2 cm., printed and impressed crowned circle marks, one with date code for 1874 **£270-300** SBel

A set of three Royal Worcester figures of Great Britain after models by James Hadley, representing England, Ireland and Wales, 6½", 7", and 16.5 and 17.8 cm., printed and impressed crowned circle marks, date codes for 1900, 1899 and 1895, **£350-380** SBel

A pair of French coloured biscuit figures, c.1880, 14¾", 37.8 cm. **£320-360** SBel

A pair of French biscuit figures 19½" and 19¾", 49 and 49.5 cm., impressed numerals, late 19th C. **£260-290** SBel

A Royal Worcester group, 7", 17.8 cm., 1882, incised mark Hadley. **£150-180** LC

A German white biscuit group, minor chips, 1 foot repaired, c.1760, 8¾", 22 cm. **£220-240** CStJ

A 'Girl-in-a-Swing' Chelsea scent bottle with patch box on base, with gold mounts and gold lettering on enamel bands on collar and base. c. 1752-4 **£1,550-2,000** HA

A Bow Figure of a Green Parrot, restoration to tail feathers and flowers, 5½", 14 cm. high, c.1763/65. **£800-870** CStJ

A Blanc-de-Chine porcelain model of a Buddhistic Lion, 34.5 cm., 13½", c. 1700, **£120-140** KC

A pair of white and gilt continental porcelain parrots, 7", 17.5 cm. **£70-90** VC

A pair of Bow Lions, one with body crack, 4" long, 10.0 cm., **£2,400-2,750** pair JEV

A Bow Figure of a Green Parrot, restoration to the eyes, tail feathers, 4⅛", 10.5 cm. high, c.1760. **£300-340** CStJ

Early pair of Derby sheep, uncoloured, c. 1758, **£100-150** pair KK

A miniature Derby sheep, No. 109 on base, c. 1790-1800, **£60-80** KK

A pair of Bow Pug Dogs, 4" wide, 10.0 cm., **£4,800-5,000** JEV

A pair of Bow birds, Cormorants, one with neck damaged, 4½", 11.5 cm., **£1,800-2,000** JEV

A Rare Chelsea Figure of a Duck, restoration to tree stump and wing, 4¼", 11 cm. high, raised red anchor mark, c.1750/2. **£350-390** CStJ

A Derby figure of a pug, c. 1775, 3½", 9.0 cm., **£60-80** MW

Derby grazing sheep, c. 1765
£210-240 RD

A pair of Meissen Golden Orioles,
9$\frac{1}{8}$", 25 cm., crossed swords in
underglaze-blue, late 19th C.
£420-480 SBel

A pair of famille verte figures
of cockerels, restored. 13½",
34.5 cm. **£680-750** CStJ

A large Dresden hound, its coat
dark brown, 12¼", 31 cm., last
quarter of 19th century, **£150-180** SBel

A Meissen jay, crossed swords,
late 19th C., 15¼", 38.4 cm.
£300-350 SBel

A pair of Samson Lions, with
finely striped tawny bodies, 13",
33 cm., cross and S mark, in
underglaze-blue, last quarter of
19th century. **£300-350** SBel

A Martin Bros. Bird, with half
smiling expression, incised and
painted brown, green and blue,
detachable head and base both
incised and dated 18th April,
1905, 9¼", 23.3 cm., **£900-1,000** KC

A Nymphenburg model of a
parrot, impressed mark, c.1850-62,
7¼", 18.7 cm. **£48-58** SBel

A pair of ormolu-mounted
Chinese porcelain models of
parrots. 8½", 21.5 cm. 18th C.
£300-340 CStJ

A pair of Chinese pottery figures
of Geese, brown ground on black
bases, 7½", 19.0 cm., **£42-50** AB

A Meissen Parrot, 16½", 42 cm.
underglaze-blue crossed swords,
c.1900. **£120-140** SBel

A good pair of Samson 'Compagnie-Des-Indes hounds, 15¼",
38.8 cm., Samson seal marks in
red, c. 1880 **£530-600** SBel

A grey pottery fabulous animal,
for use as a lamp base, traces of
white slip, 9", 23.0 cm., Han
Dynasty, wood stand. **£700-800**
SBel

Staffordshire figure group, £12-15
RA

Miss Nightingale, a well-coloured
group of the nurse, beside a
seated officer, slight chip, 10",
25.5 cm., £160-190   SBel

Omer Pacha (sic), blue coat with
yellow facings, and orange fez,
gilt title, restored. 12¾", 32.5
cm., c. 1854 £110-130

The Vicar and Moses, a Ralph
Wood glazed group, in shades of
manganese, impressed 'The Vicar
and Moses', 9½", 24.0 cm.,
£400-500   NN

PR Alfred and PR of Wales, a
pair of Figures, well-coloured,
gilt raised titles, one chair rubbed,
10¾", 27.5 cm., c. 1858 £120-
140   SBel

Turkey, England, France, an
alliance group of Queen Victoria,
Sultan Abdul-Medjid and Napoleon III, details gilt and coloured.
11", 28 cm., c. 1854 £40-50
SBel

A pair of Staffordshire figures
of Sailors, 10½", 26.5 cm., £42-
55   WW

Gnl. Simpson, a well-coloured
equestrian figure of the Crimean
commander, 13", 33.5 cm., £150-
170   SBel

Miss F. Nightingale, a rare figure
of the heroine in a green dress
repaired, 10¾", 27.5 cm., c. 1855,
£200-300   SBel

A rare Staffordshire figure of
Napoleon, gilt 'N', 8½", 21.5 cm.,
c. 1845 £140-160   SBel

Miss Nightingale, the Reformer,
repaired, 14¼", 36.3 cm., c. 1856
£110-130   SBel

An Astbury-type figure of a girl
with yellow skirt, purple coat,
with bird, 6¾", 17.0 cm., £90-
120   WW

27

Wemyss ware pig, white and black, c. 1850, with imprint R.H. & Son, **£95-110** PG

A pair of 'Famille-Verte' porcelain models of Buddhistic Lions, in the K'ang Hsi style, in green, yellow, aubergine, iron-red and black, 5½", 14 cm., long, 19th century, **£180-200** KC

A straw-glazed pottery figure of a Camel, unglazed rectangular base, the pale pottery covered with a somewhat degraded glaze with details picked out in black, 13¼", 33.5 cm., early T'ang Dynasty, **£3,500-4,000** SBel

A Victorian white china elephant, Reg'd. mark, 8", 20.0 cm., **£12-15** WW

Green Wemyss ware pig, (repaired) **£75-85** PG

18th century Staffordshire group by Ralph Wood, **£250-280** VM

Staffordshire figure of S. Sebasti, **£39-45** JC

Staffordshire, c. 1830 **£30-35** RA

Staffordshire figure group, **£20-25** RA

Staffordshire figure group, **£15-20** RA

Staffordshire equestrian figure of General Havelock, **£78-90**

Master M'Grath and Pretender, a rare pair of figures of the two greyhounds, 9½", 24 cm., c. 1871, **£220-250** SBel

A pair of Staffordshire models of seated lions on oblong bases, painted and natural colours, 4", 10.0 cm., high **£42-55** AB

Manx Cottage, Laxey, straw coloured thatched roof, green creeper, pale blue detail, 2.3", 5.5 cm., printed title, impressed and falcon marks. **£46-55** LC

A pair of large Italian earthenware figures and stands, 55¼" and 58½", 140 and 148 cm., early 20th C. **£620-700** SBel

An unusual earthenware group of a naked woman standing behind a screen, 6¼", 16 cm., third quarter of 19th century. **£120-180** SBel

Anne Hathaway's Cottage, straw coloured thatched roof, black beams, pale blue detail, unglazed, 2.3", 5.5 cm., printed title, impressed and falcon marks, **£32-40** LC

St. Iltyd's Font, Llantwit Major, 3.5, 8.0 cm., brown, printed inscription reading model of Norman Font in St. Iltyd's church, Llantwit Major and with falcon mark. **£1,250-1,400** LC

Llandaff Cross, 5.7", 14.0 cm., brown, impressed on front Llandaff and with printed falcon mark. **4540-600** LC

Shakespeare's house, brown tiled roof, black beams, pale blue detail, unglazed, 3.1", 7.5 cm., printed title, impressed and falcon marks. **£32-40** LC

S. O'Brien, from the Alpha factory, a rare figure of the insurgent, indented gilt title, the neck restored, 7'', 18 cm., **£220-260** SBel

Sir R. Peel, a figure of the politician, brightly coloured, gilt scroll and title, 8'', 21 cm., c. 1846 **£80-100** SBel

R. Cobden, from the Alpha factory, the Free Trader, gilt indented title, neck restored, 7¼'', 18.5 cm., c. 1846, **£65-80** SBel

Bust of Whig 'Weeping over the Calamities and Oppressions of the Poor', (socle broken) 5½'', 14.0 cm., **£20-35** WW

'Bull Beating', a Staffordshire group, perhaps by Obadiah Sherratt, flanked by two labels, 'Bull-Beating' and 'Now Captain Lad', 9'', 22.8 cm., high, 14'', 35.5 cm., wide. **£480-530** LC

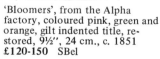

'Bloomers', from the Alpha factory, coloured pink, green and orange, gilt indented title, restored, 9½'', 24 cm., c. 1851 **£120-150** SBel

19th century Staffordshire group of Garibaldi and horse, named on base, 15'', 38.0 cm., **£230-250** WW

A rare Staffordshire Courtship group, 7¾'', 19.7 cm., **£330-390** LC

Late 18th century Staffordshire group of shepherd and shepherdess, 7½'', 19.0 cm., **£125-150** WW

A Goss Shetland pony, cream-glazed, the base bearing the arms of Chagford, 4¼", 10.7 cm., printed goshawk. £120-150 SBel

Guillemot Egg, 3.3", 8.0 cm., armorials of Tenby and with printed title and falcon mark. £70-85 LC

'How's your poor feet?'. A rare fairing depicting an old sailor, titled in black script, anchor damaged, 4¼", 10.8 cm., c. 1890 £110-130 SBel

A Ming Dynasty pottery shrine, applied with turquoise and aubergine glazes, 18½" high, 47 cm., 16th century (repaired) £240-280 KC

Pegwell Bay (Shrimping) a medium lid without a margin (Clarke 33) £110-140 SBel

A pot lid and base with view of Shakespeare's house, £20-25 AB

A pot lid — The Times, £22-25 AB

A pot lid — High Life, £24-26 AB

A pot lid — Uncle Toby, £18-22 AB

Sebastopol, a large pot lid (Clarke 209) £50-75 SBel

Grand International Building of 1851, a large pot lid (Clarke 133) £75-85 SBel

A pot lid — Il Penseroso, £20-22 AB

A Berlin Campana vase, 16", 41.2 cm., sceptre in underglaze-blue, c.1815. £480-530 SBel

A pair of Bates, Brown, Westhead and Moore classical vases, 1859-61, 13" high, 33 cm. £60-80 HKC

A Canton vase painted with shaped panels of figures on a floral ground with po-ku and butterflies, applied chih-lung, and bird handles, 17" (43 cm) £320-350 SBel

A pair of Canton porcelain vases, 17¼" high, 2nd half of 19th century. £650-710 KC

A Canton vase painted with panels of dignitaries, birds and flowers on a gilt and green lotus-scroll ground, shoulder with gilt chih-lung. Buddhist lion handles. 24" (61 cm) c. 1870 £440-500 SBel

A pair of late 18th century Canton hexagonal vases with gilt dragon side handles, decorated in famille rose enamels, 17½" high (43.3) £700-800 PK

A Canton vase with cylindrical neck, decorated in 'famille-rose' enamels, gilt dragon handles. 24½" high (62.3 cms.) 19th century. £270-300 LC

SOME MING DYNASTY MARKS

Lung Ch'ing 1567-1572	Wan Li 1573-1619	T'ien Ch'i 1621-1627	Ch'ung Cheng 1628-1643
慶 大 年 明 製 隆	曆 大 年 明 製 萬	啟 大 年 明 製 天	年 崇 製 禎

A Chelsea vase, with birds decorated in the manner of Giles and with applied flowers. c. 1765 7¾", 19.5 cm., **£200-230** MW

An unusual Coalport vase, textured and gilt-meshed body with named view of Harthornden, 7¼", 18.4 cm, printed crown mark, numbered V.6811/LS209, c. 1900 **£300-360** SBel

A large and unusual Coalport 'jewelled' vase, the pink-ground borders similarly decorated; cracks, 17¼", 43.8 cm.. printed mark, 1881-91. **£330-380** SBel

A Copeland Garniture, painted with flowers beneath a deep scrolling ribbon and gilt border, one rim chip, 5" and 5½", 12.5 and 14 cm., printed crowned garland Copeland Garrett mark painted pattern Nos. 6392R, 6392H 1833-47 **£115-150** SBel

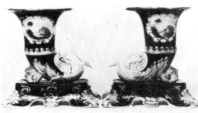

A pair of Cornucopia vases, possibly Coalport, one with hair cracks, 5³⁄₈", 15 cm., painted pattern number 2757, c. 1860 **£200-300** SBel

A pale-yellow Coalport vase, painted with a blue-tit within elaborate gilt border, 9¼", 23.5 cm., printed crown mark, numbered A9269, c. 1881-91. **£130-150** SBel

An unusual Coalport vase, each panel painted with lake-side castles, with gilt 'C' scroll handles, small enamel flakes, 5¼", 13.3 cm., printed crown mark, numbered B 881, c. 1885 **£150-190** SBel

A royal blue Coalport vase, painted by P. Simpson, signed. 10¾", 27 cm., printed crown mark, painted title, numbered V7730/D 3 m/s 232 **£120-150** c. 1900 SBel

A Coalport 'jewelled' vase, painted by P. Simpson, signed with monogram, on a gilt band with turquoise enamel dots, 5½", 14 cm., printed crown mark, numbered V5955 /m/s, 162, painted title, c. 1905. **£200-250** SBel

---

COALPORT (1796-today)

- factory founded in 1796 by John Rose when he left Caughley
- Rose bought Caughley in 1799 and had it demolished in 1814

- in 1820 Rose bought moulds from Nantgarw and Swansea and Billingsley came to work at Coalport
- best period for the Coalport factory began in 1820 when the factory produced a brilliantly white hard felspar porcelain, with a high level of translucency and a new leadless glaze

- the factory then began to imitate Sevres, Meissen to a lesser degree and also to produce some Chelsea copies (with fake marks)
- vases covered with a mass of flowers were a Coalport speciality

A pair of Coalport vases, painted with dog-roses alternating with cream bands with gilt motifs and enamel studs, slight wear, 6¾", 17.2 cm., printed crown mark, painted B323, c. 1880 **£150-180** SBel

A pair of Coalport vases, painted with 'Kate Greenaway' girls, gilt ring handles and feet, 3¾", 9.6 cm., printed crown mark, painted pattern number B2247, c. 1885, **£150-190** SBel

A pair of Copeland and Garrett ovoid vases on a turquoise ground richly gilded, 14" high, 35.5 cm. **£200-250** HKC

A garniture of Delft blue and white vases of octagonal sections painted with figure or animals within moulded reserves 9", by Gerritt Brouwer. **£160-180** HKC

18th century Dutch Delft vase 6¾". **£85-90** RD

A large Della Robbia pottery vase 25¼", 64 cm. high. galleon mark and initials RB on base. **£120-150** PL

A pottery vase, painted in ruby lustre, 12½", 31.8 cm., impressed mark WM. DE MORGAN SANDS END POTTERY, **£180-200** LC

A pair of Dutch Delft blue and white baluster vases, minor glaze chips, c.1740, 8¼", 21 cm. **£250-280** CStJ

An early 19th century Derby two handled vase with gilding by William Watson, mark in red, 4". £80-90 RD

A pair of Royal Crown Derby bases, Imari in blue, iron-red, green and gilding, 8", 20.3 cm., printed mark, incised numerals, pattern number 1443-6299, date code for 1905. £200-250 SBel

A Derby Crown porcelain company rose-pompadour ground vase of flask form. Reverse side with sprays of flowering heather attracting a butterfly, enclosed by moulded borders, 8¾", 22.3 cm., printed mark, 1878-90. £180-210 SBel

A pair of early 19th century Derby vases, decorated with wide gilt bands and foliate design on a bleu de Roi ground. Inscription to bases and crown and crossed baton marks in red, 11¾", 30 cm., £380-420 KC

A pair of Doccia polychrome vases, decorated in iron-red, blue, yellow and green, chipped, c.1745, 7¾", 19.5 cm. £280-320 CStJ

A Royal Doulton pitcher-shaped vase, painted 'Winter scene with a shepherd and sheep', decorated in colour. £38-45 RB

A Royal Crown Derby vase painted by A. Gregory, signed on a royal-blue ground 5⅞", 15 cm., printed crowned initials, incised shape number 1781, date code for 1914. £290-330 SBel

A Derby vase of rare claret ground, 3 patch marks on the base, 7", 17.5 cms., c. 1765. £160-190 DW

A Royal Doulton Lambeth stoneware vase, MB scratched monograms to base. £70-90 HKC

DOULTON (1815-PRESENT DAY)

- situated at Lambeth
- produced brown saltglaze stoneware
- from 1830's made spirit flasks
- noted for its influence on the Studio Pottery Movement
- wares by Hannah Barlow – particularly her animal sketches – are highly collectable
- faience was made by the Doulton factory from c.1870 to the First World War
- the factory moved to Burslem, Staffordshire in 1882

A Royal Doulton 'Sung' vase, ruby ground. 7½", 19 cm., high. 'Sung', Noke and F. Allen. **£160-180** PL

A Doulton vase by Edith D. Lupton, 10", 25.5 cm., 1887, incised initials E.D.L., M.D. and A.G. **£90-120** LC

A pair of Doulton vases with deep blue glaze inside, 12", 30.5 cm., **£95-120** HKC

A pair of Royal Doulton 8" vases, with blue glaze and incised floral band, bearing artist's initials. **£30-40** AB

A pair of unusual Royal Doulton porcelain 6" pedestal vases, royal blue and gilt enrichment, each signed H. Allen. **£1,540-1,800** RB

Two Donath Dresden vases, painted with flowers on a turquoise ground within gilt scroll borders, 31.8 cm., crown and Dresden mark in under-glaze blue, late 19th century. **£100-120** SBel

'Love's Melody', a Royal Doulton earthenware vase painted by Geo. White, signed. Neck and footrim gilded. Printed lion and crowned circle mark, first quarter of the 20th century. **£500-600** SBel

A Royal Doulton vase painted by George White, signed, the Sleeping Beauty. 14½", 36.7 cm., printed lion, crowned circle mark, c. 1910. **£1,050-1,300** SBel

---

SOME DOULTON MARKS

Lambeth Pottery
DOULTON & WATTS
+15+
HIGH STREET
LAMBETH

DOULTON
LAMBETH

A pair of earthenware vases, enamelled and gilt on a ground shading from yellow to striped blue and pale blue, 32 cm., late 19th century. £150-200 SBel

An earthenware vase, of depressed ovoid form, decorated in enamels and gilding, 7¼", 1st half of 19th century. £400-450 KC

A pair of earthenware vases, painted with birds amongst melon vines on a powder-blue ground, brocade borders, (46 cm) 1'6½" £100-115 SBel

A pair of French earthenware vases, the blue neck and body with red and yellow roses, 52.7 cm, incised numerals, late 19th century. £100-130 SBel

A large pair of Imari porcelain vases, each painted in underglaze blue, iron-red and gilding. 61.5 cm., late 19th century (one with repaired neck) £75-85 KC

A small pair of elaborate earthenware vases, painted in enamels and gilding. 21 cm., £330-370 KC

A pair of square-section Imari porcelain bottle vases, each painted in deep underglaze blue, iron-red and gilding, 21.5 cm., Arita in Hizen Province, c. 1700 £3,000-3,500 KC

A pair of Fukagawa Imari porcelain vases, each fluted ovoid boidy painted in enamels and gilding. 30.5 cm., 2nd half 19th century. £300-350 KC

A pair of square-section Imari porcelain bottle vases, painted in underglaze blue, iron-red and gilding, 21.5 cm., Arita in Hizen, late 17th century (repaired) £800-900 KC

A pair of Jacob Petit Cornucopiae, painted with flowers and gilt-outlined emerald panels, 9", (23 cm), J.P. in underglaze-blue, c 1830. £160-190   SBel

A pair of Jacob Petit vases, moulded with gilt leaves, applied with trails of roses and other flowers in high relief, 21.6 cm, J.P. in underglaze-blue. c. 1840 £250-290   SBel

A pair of green-ground Jacob Petit vases, body pierced at the rim and applied with coloured flowers amongst four smaller flower holders. 21.6 cm. J.P. in underglaze-blue, c. 1840 £320-360   SBel

One of a pair of Japanese vases. £85-95   LBA

A Japanese vase, the top with a dragon curled on the edge, with a running liver-colour and Chun-type glaze on shoulders, the base in under-glaze blue with splashing waves. 8¾" high (22.2 cms) £250-300   LC

A pair of Japanese vases decorated with bands of crackled glaze, converted to table lamps. 22" high. £150-170   HKC

A pair of Japanese vases, decorated in underglaze blue, iron-red, gold and enamels, with children at play in garden scenes, 10½" high (26.7 cms) 19th century. £320-350   LC

A pair of Japanese flared cylindrical vases, painted with panels of flowers in the Imari taste. 21" high. £900-1,000 pr.   HKC

Pair of Japanese vases, multi-coloured pattern on turquoise ground. £45-55   LBA

A large pair of oviform Kutani porcelain vases, 23″ high (58½ cm)., mid-19th century. £550-610   KC

A 'Ludwigsburg' vase in mid-18th C. style, 16½″, 42 cm., crowned interlaced C's and Ludwigsburg in underglaze-blue, 20th C. £120-180   SBel

A pair of Mason's Ironstone vases, in 'famille-rose' and iron-red and gilding on a blue ground with gilt leaves. 9½″, 24 cm., impressed Patent Ironstone China, c. 1825 £200-250   SBel

A pair of Kyoto vases, enamelled with numerous immortals and their attributes. 1′7″ high (49.7 cm) £300-350   SBel

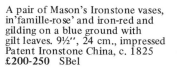

A pair of Minton vases, Scene after Flaxman from 'Homer' between gilt laurel leaf borders, with gilt snake handles and mask terminals, the body and flared foot turquoise, 20½″, 52 cm., printed puce exhibition marks, 1862. £160-190   SBel

A Kinkozan Kyoto vase enamelled and gilt. 13″ high (32.5 cm), the foot marked dai Nihon, Kyoto, Kinkozan tsukuru, c. 1870. £160-180

A pair of Maiolica melon shaped vases with Romaine heads in reserved panels on yellow ground, the rest with all-over decoration on blue ground. 11″, 28.0 cm. £800-900   LJ

Customary mark	LUDWIGSBURG, Hard paste porcelain from 1758-1824. Painted in blue 1758-1793	King William 1816-1824

A Moorcroft 'Claremont' vase in ruby, ochre, 4¾", 12 cm. high, 'Potter to H.M. the Queen' signed in blue. £150-170   PL

A vase, in olive and blue, 6¼", 16 cm. high, impressed Moorcroft, Burslem, England 85, £90-110   PL

A pair of Moorcroft saltglazed vases, with blue and lemon panels, 10¼", 26 cm. high, impressed and signed. £190-220 PL

A pair of Nagayakawa Rouleau vases, finely painted with panels of families. 3¾" (9.5 cm) gilt Nagayakawa tsukuru, c. 1900 £160-180   SBel

A Neolithic Mortuary Urn in red pottery, painted with a bold spiral pattern of black and purple, the flared mouth with a band of crosses on the exterior and arcs and lines on the interior, 13½", 34.5 cm., Pan Shan type, Yang Shao Period. £5,200-6,000   SBel

A famille verte Chinese vase, Ch'ien Lung, underglaze-blue four character mark. 23½" tall, 59.5 cm. £340-390   HKC

A splashed Yueh-Yao vase, Crackled green glaze unevenly applied and decorated in iron-brown with splashed around the rim and sides, falling short of the base showing the body which has burnt to a purplish tone in the firing, 10¾", 27.0 cm., Eastern China, wood stand £3,800-4,200   SBel

A pair of 18th Century clobbered blue and white vases, 12¼", 31 cm, painted pseudo Chinese seal, early 18th century and later. £160-180   SBel

A pair of famille-rose vases, each ovoid body painted with bands of po-ku beneath T-fret enclosing flower panels, 13½", 35.3 cm., late 19th century. £220-240 SBel

A Chinese blue and white vase, the elongated neck with a collar. 7" high, leaf mark. Kang Hsi. £19-22 HKC

A good moulded Ying Ch'ing vase, the shoulders decorated with a crackled translucent glaze of bluish tone, 10", 25.5 cm., Yuan Dynasty, £1,200-1,400 SBel

A Chinese blue and white ovoid vase with moulded vertical ribs painted with flowers, the foot rim with Symbols. 6" high, Kang Hsi. £22-25 HKC

A pair of 14" high famille verte baluster vases with figures of scholars in a garden with deer. Kang Hsi. £2,100-2,400 LJ

A small Kuan-Yao Vase, the milky grey-blue glaze with some irregular brown crackle, 4", 10.0 cm., Sung Dynasty, wood stand, £3,800-4,200 SBel

A Tz'u Chou vase painted in black with two peony sprays, beneath the unevenly applied leaf-green glaze, somewhat degraded and with a slight iridescence, 87/8", 23.0 cm., Sung Dynasty, £6,000-6,700 SBel

A pair of blue and white bottle vases, chipped. 8", 20.5 cm., K'ang Hsi. £440-500 CStJ

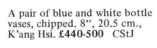

A pair of Chinese blue and white beaker vases, 7¼", 18.5 cm., high fungus mark Kang Hsi. £140-160 HKC

SOME CHING DYNASTY MARKS

K'ang Hsi 1662-1722	Yung Cheng 1723-1735	Ch'ien Lung 1736-1795	Chia Ch'ing 1796-1820
熙 大 年 清 製 康	正 大 年 清 製 雍	隆 大 年 清 製 乾	年 嘉 製 慶

A blue and white Mei P'ing, Ch'ien Lung six-character seal mark, 12¾", 32.5 cm., £550-600 CStJ

A blue and white baluster vase, chipped, K'ang Hsi, 10", 25.5 cm. £580-650 CStJ

A transitional blue and white pear-shaped bottle vase painted with 'Three Friends', pine, prunus and bamboo. 9", 23 cm., Hauan Te six-character mark. c,1640 £480-560 CStJ

A transitional blue and white pear-shaped vase, chipped. 5½", 14 cm., high. c.1650. £280-320 CStJ

A large pair of blue and white porcelain vases, 22¼"., inscribed panels, painted marks, Seto Province, late 19th century. £400-450   KC

A blue and white porcelain Yen-Yen vase, painted with panels of seasonal flowers. 17½" high (44½ cm) Kang Hsi £400-450 KC

A 22" high (55.8 cm) Oriental vase in style of the Chia Ching period. £480-520   JHR

Black-ground famille-verte vase, the body painted with falconers, hunters with a lion or figures with a kylin. 20" (50.8 cm) third quarter of the 19th century. £270-300   SBel

A 12½" high white porcelain baluster shaped vase and cover with under-glaze blue and famille verte enamelled decoration of entertainers in a garden. Ming middle period. £1,300-1,500 LJ

CHINESE CHRONOLOGY		
	960-1280	Sung Dynasty
	1280-1368	Yuan Dynasty
	1368-1644	Ming Dynasty
	1368-1398	Hung Wu
	1399-1402	Chien Wen
	1403-1424	Yung Lo
	1425	Hung Hsi
	1426-1435	Hsuan Te
	1436-1449	Cheng T'ung

A Kakiemon bottle vase, finely enamelled in green, blue, iron-red and gilt, the base unglazed, 22 cm Hizen Province, last quarter of 17th century. **£2,700-3,000** KC

A famille rose pear-shaped vase on a deep blue ground gilt with butterflies, damaged, iron-red Ch'ien Lung six-character seal-mark, 16", 41 cm., **£280-330** CStJ

A silver-mounted double-gourd porcelain vase, painted in rich underglaze blue 9 1/8" high. Kang Hsi. **£300-350** KC

A pair of famille-rose porcelain vases, of bottle form, painted in vivid enamelling, 10 1/8" high (25½ cm) Chia Ching **£300-350** KC

A pair of blue and white vases, in underglaze blue on a crackled coffee-ground, carved and bronzed biscuit bands, mask and ring handles, 1'6" (45.7 cm) incised mark, c. 1900 **£350-400** SBel

A pair of famille-rose vases painted with flowers, moulded mask and ring handles. 23½" (59.2 cm), last quarter of 19th century. **£580-640** SBel

A pair of famille rose semi-quatrefoil wall vases, one restored, Ch'ien Lung, 6½", 16.5 cm., **£220-250** CStJ

1450-1456	Ching T'ai	1621-1627	T'ien Ch'i	1851-1861	Hsien Feng
1457-1464	T'ien Shun	1628-1643	Ch'ung Cheng	1862-1873	T'ung Chih
1465-1487	Ch'eng Hua	1644-1661	Shun Chih	1874-1908	Kuang Hsu
1488-1505	Hung Chih	1644-1912	Ch'ing Dynasty	1909-1912	Hsuan T'ung
1506-1521	Cheng Te	1662-1722	K'ang Hsi		
1522-1566	Chia Ch'ing	1723-1735	Yung Cheng		
1567-1572	Lung Ch'ing	1736-1795	Ch'ien Lung		
1573-1619	Wan Li	1796-1820	Chia Ch'ing		
1620	T'ai Ch'ang	1821-1850	Tao Kuang		

A pair of Paris vases, 12½", 32 cm., interlaced L's and letters, incised z, mid-19th century. **£600-700** SBel

A pair of Paris vases, applied in high relief with flowers and gilt stems on a gilt sprig ground, 51 cm., last quarter of the 19th century, **£400-500** SBel

A pair of Paris vases, 15¼", 38.5 cm. impressed numerals, late 19th C. **£110-140** SBel

A pair of Paris vases painted by Lefranc, signed, metal mounts, marble base, 18", 46 cm., last quarter of the 19th century. **£380-420** SBel

A rare Plymouth baluster vase, tin-marked, c. 1770, 6½", 16.5 cms., **£300-350** MW

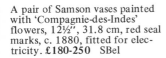

A pair of Samson vases painted with 'Compagnie-des-Indes' flowers, 12½", 31.8 cm, red seal marks, c. 1880, fitted for electricity. **£180-250** SBel

A Samson famille-rose vase painted with an exotic bird perched amongst flowers between formal borders, 45.5 cm., late 19th century. **£100-120** SBel

A Satsuma ovoid vase with animal mask handles, 6½" high, 16.5 cm. **£60-70** HKC

SAMSON

- factory began in 1845 in Paris
- they reproduced wares of virtually every factory
- they produce a list of various marks they have used

- good copies of Chinese export porcelain
- reproductions of English soft-paste porcelain easily recognisable as they used a hard-paste body
- wares made by Samson often have an 'S' contained within the mark

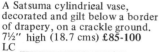

A Satsuma ovoid vase, 8¾"
high, 22 cm., £70-90 HKC

A Satsuma cylindrical vase,
decorated and gilt below a border
of drapery, on a crackle ground.
7½" high (18.7 cms) £85-100
LC

Small Satsuma vase. £35-40
LBA

A large Kinkozan 'Satsuma'
earthenware vase, the baluster-
form body painted in enamels and
gilding. 17", Kinkozan seal.
£800-900 KC

A large 'Sevres'-style yellow ground
vase painted with one Watteau
panel and another of a chateau,
24" (base restored). £100-£130
WW

A fine pair of 19th century
'Sevres'-style vases, having a blue
ground (indistinctly signed Schilt)
fitted for electricity, 22½" (57.1
cm) £1,500-1,800 KC

A pair of gilt-metal mounted
'Sevres' vases, painted with panels
amongst tooled gilt foliate scrolls,
the borders with turquoise and
ruby 'jewelling', with satyr mask
handles, 21 cm, third quarter of
the 19th century. £280-320 SBel

A Garniture of three Staffordshire porcelain vases encrusted
with brightly coloured flowers,
painted landscape scenes, dolphin-
head handles, one chipped, cracks,
15¼" and 12¾", 38.7 and 32.4
cm., c. 1840 £120-150 SBel

A pair of Taizan vases, enamelled
and gilt. 30¼" high (30.5 cm),
painted dai Nihon, Taizan sei,
late 19th century. £150-170
SBel

A Staffordshire salt glaze miniature
vase decorated in scratch blue.
3½", 9 cm., £190-220 LC

SEVRES

- factory moved to Sevres in 1756 from Vincennes where production started c.1740
- in early days copied Meissen and influenced by Kakiemon
- in 1750's factory began

producing vases in large quantities

- most sought after ground colour is the yellow (jaune jonquille)
- plaques for furniture became popular in 1760's
- factory also noted for clock-cases, small sets for

tea, coffee and chocolate, and boxes

- managed to discover the secret of hard-paste porcelain in 1770
- 'Jewelled porcelain' was introduced in 1773, used a technique of fusing enamels over gilt or silver foil

A pair of Viennese vases, three handles and with gilded claw feet, 19th century marked. 7''
£360-400 pair   HHA

A pair of 'Vienna' vases of claret, yellow and green 35 cm., printed shield in blue, late 19th century. £210-250   SBel

A Wedgwood blue spill vase with classical decoration, 5'', 12.5 cm. £11-15   RB

A Worcester Spill vase, c 1765. 5'', £240-280   MW

A pair of Royal Worcester blue-ground vases, painted by Chivers, signed. Details gilded, 8¼'', 20.9 cm, printed crowned circle mark, pattern number 1959. Rd No. 304839, retailer's mark for John Ford & Co., Edinburgh, date code for 1901. £400-480 SBel

A pair of Royal Worcester earthen-ware vases in oriental taste, set on four gilt moulded feet. 1¾'', 29.8 cm, printed and impressed crowned circle marks, date code and dated 1871. £240-280   SBel

A Royal Worcester vase, painted by H. Davis, signed. Moulded bronzed borders, green handles. 10½'', 26.7 cm, printed crowned circle mark, pattern number F100/H, date code for 1911 £490-560   SBel

A Royal Worcester vase of baluster shape, painted in poly-chrome enamels, printed mark to base and printed 1430, dated 1890, 36.5 cm, £190-210   KC

Pair of Royal Worcester vases, painted by C. Baldwyn, signed. Shaded apricot ground, the reverse with a smaller scene. Details gilded. 8'', (20.3 cm) for 1899 £728-800   SBel

---

LIVERPOOL

- main factory started c.1756
- wares frequently mistaken for Worcester
- Richard Chaffers & Co. started producing soft-paste porcelain c.1756 until 1765

- much blue and white ware made, with strong Chinese influence
- names associated with Liverpool factories: Samuel Gilbody c.1754-1761 William Reid & Co. c.1756-1761

Philip Christian & Co. c.1765-1776
Seth Pennington c.1770-1799
Wolfe & Co. c.1795-1800

A Coalport pink-ground pot-pourri vase, lid and cover, painted by F. Howard, signed. The details gilt, 6″, 15.2 cm., printed crown mark, numbered V.5146/c S3s. 236, c. 1910 **£150-180** SBel

A Coalport Royal-Blue ground vase and cover, gilt scroll handles moulded with garlands, the domed cover with quatrefoil knop, 17¼″, 43.2 cm., printed mark, Rd. No. 283665, c. 1900 **£240-300** SBel

Pair of Continental vases with covers. 19th century, 10″, 25.5 cm., **£120-140** RA

19th century pair of Chinese blue and white vases. 8½″ high. **£40-50** RA

A Cantonese enamel vase 5¾″ (14.5 cm) **£85-110** HHA

A pair of Coalport Pink-ground vases and covers, with gilt and ribbon-edged panels, gilt scrolling buttress handles, covers restored, 10⅜″, 26.3 cm., c. 1850 **£300-350** SBel

Coalport vase and cover painted with a riverscape within a gilt border on a royal-blue ground, 10¼″, 26.1 cm., printed mark, pattern number, c. 1900 **£230-300** SBel

A pair of Coalport rose-pompadour vases and covers, painted within moulded and studded borders linked and divided by strung gilt wreaths, one cover restored, 14½″, 37 cm., CBD monogram in blue enamel, c. 1854 **£800-1,000** SBel

A pair of Delft eight sided vases, with covers, having animal head handles, blue and white decoration. Painted mark to base. W/5. 21½" **£95-110** pair   AB

A Pair of Derby Crown Porcelain Company pot-pourri vases and covers, pink, silvered and gilt aquatic plants against blue and gilt bands, cover and knop pierced, one knop restored, 8¼", 21 cm., printed crowned initials, C. 1885 **£240-270**   SBel

A pair of Royal Derby Crown porcelain vases and covers, painted in underglaze-blue and iron-red with raised gilt foliage, one cover damaged, 9½", 24.5 cm., printed mark in red, date code for 1886 **£270-300**   SBel

A Dresden globular urn with cover, 16", 40.5 cm., green ground with raised floral pattern in the Chinese style. **£70-90**   AB

A pair of pierced Grainger vases and covers, each cream-glazed and details lightly gilded, 8", 20.3 cm., printed and impressed shield marks, c. 1870-89 **£180-220** SBel

Pair of French porcelain blue vases and covers, applied with flowers, 8½", 21.5 cm., **£15-20** WW

A pair of Jacob Petit 'Schneeballen' bottle-vases and covers, underglaze-blue J.P. and crossed swords and star, mid 19th century. **£180-210** SBel

A pair of Helena Wolfsohn pink – ground vases and covers, 14½", 36.8 cm., AR monogram in blue, late 19th C. **£300-400**   SBel

A pair of Jacob Petit vases and covers, encrusted with tiny florets and applied with branches of fruits, vegetables and birds, 17", 42.5 cm., **£150-180**   SBel

---

DELFTWARE

- English earthenware which was tin-glazed and fired at low temperatures
- the decoration in blues, yellows and greens tend to have a spontaneous quality as all art work had to be carried out quickly while the glaze was absorbent

- there is very little fine painting possible on Delft-ware
- one noted type is the 'blue-dash chargers'
- English Delft was made at Lambeth, Southwark, Glasgow, Dublin, Liverpool, Bristol, Norwich and Wincanton

- very fragile medium and surviving examples tend to be chipped and repaired

A pair of Chinese vases and covers in delicate 'famille-rose' enamels. 18″, 45 cm. Ch'ien Lung. £575-675   LC

A Chinese blue and white baluster vase and cover, 8″, 20.0 cm. leaf mark, Kang Hsi. £50-70   HKC

A large pair of 'famille-verte' porcelain jars and covers, painted in iron-red, green, yellow, blue, aubergine and black enamels. 12″., 30.5 cm., overall, one jar damaged, one cover repaired, Kang Hsi. £1,900-2,200   KC

A pair of shield-shaped Meissen vases and covers, in turquoise and pink, 7″, 17.3 cm. crossed swords in underglaze-blue. £620-720   SBel

A Khmer brown-glazed broad baluster vase and saucer-shaped cover, chipped, the cover re-paired. 13¼″ high, 33.5 cm., 12th/13th C. £220-250   CStJ

A large pair of ovoid-bodied Imari porcelain vases and covers, each painted in iron-red, under-glaze blue, gilding, black and green enamels. 29½″, 75 cm. Arita in Hizen, 18th century. £2,300-2,600   KC

A Mintons pate-sur-pate vase and cover, both sides on a deep-coral ground reserved on pale duck-egg blue, reverse with flowers, 13½″, 34.5 cm., printed Mintons globe, impressed 2969, Mintons date code used between 1891-04. £500-600   SBel

A Chinese blue and white baluster vase, painted with alternate panels of tubs of flowering plants and maidens, 6½″, 16.5 cm., character mark, Kang Hsi. £75-85   HKC

<table>
<tr><td>

- factory opened in 1793 at Stoke-on-Trent
- Thomas Minton had worked at Caughley and Spode
- factory first made earthenware, transferred to soft paste porcelain c.1799
- the factory is mainly famous for its bone-china

</td><td>

MINTON

- the factory suffered in reputation by many of its finest pieces being wrongly attributed to other factories, such as Worcester, Derby, Rockingham and Coalport
- Minton used fine artists and any piece which can

</td><td>

be attributed to them is highly sought after; George Hancock and Joseph Bancroft being particularly sought after

- Minton still tends to be an under-rated factory which is still scoffed at by dealers and hence there is the possibility of picking up some reasonably priced pieces

</td></tr>
</table>

A pair of Paris gilt-metal-mounted vases, on a blue ground, 15", 38.2 cm., late 19th C. £270-300 SBel

A pair of Paris vases and covers, on a bleu -celeste ground, 11", 28 cm., late 19th C. £100-120 SBel

A pair of Paris 'First Period Worcester' vases and covers, on a deep-blue scale ground, 12½", 32 cm., crossed arrows in underglaze-blue, late 19th C. £260-300 SBel

A pair of Paris ormolu-mounted vases and covers, 10¾", 27.5 cm, mid-19th century. £500-600 SBel

A pair of gilt-metal mounted Paris vases and covers, painted by Jeccatly, signed, with gilt-metal mounted rim, mask and loop handles and shaped square base, the covers matching, 17", 42.5 cm., late 19th century, £400-480 SBel

A pair of Paris vases and covers, 16", 40.7 cm., interlaced L's mark in blue, mid-19th century. £480-550 SBel

A pair of Paris porcelain 17½", 44.5 cm., covered vases, decorated within apple green and gilt borders, capital M, Paris in shield mark. £540-600 PWC

A pair of silver-mounted porcelain vases and covers of European silver form, mid-19th century Paris hallmarked silver stands, 19 cm., overall (7½") £280-340 KC

A Potschappel vase, cover and stand, 23¼", 58.7 cm. crossed lines and T in underglaze-blue, 1880's. £380-420 SBel

A fine Spode garniture of three vases, marked Spode and Pattern No. 1166 in red to each base, centre vase 10", 25.4 cm., side vases 8", 20.2 cm., £1,100-1,300 KC

A large pair of 19th century Samson vases and covers of ovoid form, having 'famille-rose' decoration, pseudo Oriental marks in underglaze blue to base, 2'6", 75 cm., £1,200-1,400 KC

A pair of Potschappel flower encrusted pot-pourri vases, covers and stands. 21½", 54.5 cm., cross and initial T marks, late 19th century. £500-600 SBel

A pair of 'Sevres' soft-paste gilt-metal-mounted and 'jewelled' vases and covers, 12½", 32 cm. c.1870. £1,000-1,200 SBel

A pair of 'Sevres' soft-paste bleu-de-roi-ground vases and covers, 10", 25.7 cm., painted interlaced L's, mid 19th C. £380-420 SBel

A pair of Sevres apple-green-ground gilt-metal mounted vases and covers, 1 cover repaired, 1 handle cracked, c.1785, 14¾", 37.5 cm. £600-670 CStJ

A pair of 19th century 'Sevres' ormolu mounted vases and covers, having white beaded surround and gilt scrolling to the blue ground, the covers with ormolu bud mounts (restored), 13", 33 cm., £400-450 KC

A pair of 'Sevres' Champleve and gilt-metal-mounted vases and covers, painted by Delys, signed, 15½", 39.3 cm. mount stamped L. Henry, late 19th C. £520-600 SBel

A pair of Sevres vases and covers, painted by E. Sieffert, signed, 13¼", 34.3 cm., late 19th C. £190-210 SBel

51

A pair of 'Sevres' vases and covers, painted with court portraits, reverse with the arms of Bourbon reserved on a bleu-de-roi ground. 10¼", 20 cm., interlaced L's and 1, mid-19th century. **£1,000-1,300** SBel

A pair of 'Schneeballen' vases and covers, each flower encrusted body applied with coloured branches, leaves, fruit and birds, 15", 38 cm., incised LD, second half of 19th century. **£210-250** SBel

A pair of Sevres vases, painted in a soft palette in Boucher style. Necks, covers and bases of turquoise ground champleve enamel, on gilt metal square bases with chamfered corners. 13¼", 33.7 cm., 19th century. **£380-410** LC

A Royal Worcester vase and cover of ovoid form, in enamel colours highlighted with gilding printed mark to base and No. 1515, dated 1899. **£205-250** KC

A pair of 'Vienna' vases and covers in a gilt and crimson-banded pale yellow ground. 16⅞", 42.8 cm. shields marks in blue, 1890's. **£250-280** SBel

A Royal Worcester porcelain garniture, comprising pot-pourri of bulbous form, 9¾", 25 cm., and two slender vases, 8¾", 22 cm., c. 1903 printed crowned circle to bases. **£210-250** KC

A Vienna vase and cover, painted by E. Pollach, signed. 14½", 37 cm., shield mark in blue, impressed 804, titled in German, mid-19th century. **£560-600**

VIENNA (1719-1864)

- factory opened in 1719 by Du Paquier assisted by Stolzel
- from 1719-1744 in the Du Paquier period there were no marks, except perhaps some copies of Chinese marks. This porcelain is very desirable
- in the State Period from 1744-1784 the Shield mark was used. Year marks were used from 1738-1800
- height of factories production and prosperity was under the direction of von Sorgenthal

A 19th century Bohemian bowl, with pierced edges and decorated with an exotic bird, 8½", 21.5 cm., £35-45 HHA

Blue and white Delftware bowl, Bristol or Liverpool, £125-140 CAL

Faience bowl c. 1660 by Puerto del Obispo, £420-520 CAL

A Canton bowl, decorated in 'famille-rose' enamels, 20¾", 52.7 cm., 19th C. £1,550-1,700 LC

A Dutch Polychrome Delft bowl, the outside painted in Chinese taste, 8¾", 22.2 cm., first half 18th century. £310-350 LC

An Imari bowl, 9" dia. 23 cm., £140-160 HKC

A Cantonese bowl, 18½" dia., 45.5 cm., flowers and insects to border, frieze of thirteen figures to interior, £380-420 AB

A Bristol Delft punch bowl, 10⅜", 26.5 cm., £60-70 LC

An Imari bowl, 9½" dia, 24 cm., £110-120 HKC

A Canton punch bowl, decorated in 'famille-rose' enamels, 15", 40.3 cm., 19th century, £440-520 LC

A Derby pot pourri bowl, c. 1820 3¾", 9.5 cm., £31.35 RA

An Imari bowl, 9½" dia, 24 cm., £110-120 HKC

A Japanese Imari bowl, 11½" dia., 29 cm., £200-240 HKC

A Chelsea Red Anchor bowl and cover, red anchor mark, c. 1755, £150-200 KK

A late 18th C. English bowl and cover, blue and white painted, 5¼" dia., 13 cm., £240-270 HKC

An Imari bowl, c. 1800, 6", 15.0 cm., £30-35 F

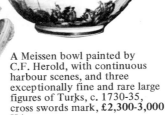

A Meissen bowl painted by C.F. Herold, with continuous harbour scenes, and three exceptionally fine and rare large figures of Turks, c. 1730-35, cross swords mark, **£2,300-3,000** HA

A late Ming blue and white bowl painted with three Buddhistic lions, Provincial, early 17th C., frit chips, 11½", 29 cm. diam., **£440-500** CStJ

A Leeds creamware bowl and cover printed in black with figure of Minerva and putti grouped round a globe, inscribed below 'Let wisdom unite us', 5¼", 13.3 cm., **£100.130** LC

Liverpool blue and white bowl painted with 'Stag' pattern, c. 1785, **£45-50** RD

A large grey pottery globular bowl with extensive ochre colouration, the rim chipped, 3-1 Millenium B.C., 7½", 19 cm., **£160-180** CStJ

A grey pottery buff-slip decorated pedestal bowl painted in red pigment. 6½", 16.5 cm., 3-1 Millenium B.C. **£110-130** CStJ

A blue and white globular bowl, 10", 26 cm. diam. K'ang Hsi. **£420-470** CStJ

Maling Fairyland lustre bowl, 8½", 21.5 cm., **£24-30** WW

A Satsuma bowl with shaped ju-i head border, painted, enamelled and gilt with petal panels, the outside blue panels of flowers, 9¾", 24.8 cm., mark the mon of Prince Satsuma in blue enamel and an inscription in gold. **£550-650** LC

A Meissen slop bowl, Pressnummer 6, c.1745, 7", 17.5 cm. **£340-360** CStJ

A Chinese 10½", 26.5 cm., crackleware bowl, decorated with figures of horses, on a carved hardwood stand. **£34-45** AB

A Celadon tripod shallow globular bulb bowl, Ming Dynasty, 12¼", 30.5 cm. diam., **£360-400** CStJ

A grey pottery buff-slip decorated globular bowl painted in red pigment, extensively worn, chipped. 6", 15.5 cm., 3-1 Millenium B.C. **£170-190** CStJ

A Choshuzan Satsuma bowl elaborately enamelled and gilt, 12¼″, 31 cm., gilt Choshuzan yaki, Satsuma Kintani Jitsushoin, jitsu seal and other marks, large Satsuma mon, late 19th century, **£440-500** SBel

A carved Tz'u Chou bowl boldly cut with radial flutes through the white slip to the buff ground beneath a translucent glaze now slightly degraded, giving a banded effect, the undecorated interior with three spur marks in the centre, 4⅝″, 11.5 cm., Sung Dynasty, wood stand, **£2,200-2,500** SBel

On octagonal fluted bowl, 8″ dia. 20 cm., K'ang Hsi. **£240-260** HKC

A good Imari bowl and cover painted in underglaze-blue, iron-red gilding and enamels 10½″ dia, 26.5 cm., early 18th century, **£420-550** HKC

A pottery bowl, the body marbled and covered with an amber-yellow glaze collecting in a deep pool in the centre of the interior, the base with traces of two spur marks, 4⅛″ 10.0 cm., T'ang Dynasty, **£1,300-1,500** SBel

A Ting-Yao bowl divided into six lobes by vertical flutes extending to the notched and correspondingly lobed rim, ivory-tinted glaze forming tear drops on underside stopping just short of footrim, 5¾″, 14.5 cm., Sung Dynasty, fitted box, **£1,400-1,600** SBel

A large famille-verte bowl painted on the interior with a rounded of figures being attacked by warriors. A wide frieze of figures in various pursuits. A diaper border rim. Exterior similarly decorated with figures, 16″, 40.6 cm., c. 1870 **£350-450** SBel

A Satsuma bowl, enamelled and gilt formal flowers, diaper patterns above a band of medallions 4⅜″, 11 cm., **£80-100** LC

A Chu-Lu Hsien bowl and cover, the interior divided by six radial ribs extending from the central medallion, 5¾″, 14.5 cm., Sung Dynasty, **£700-800** SBel

An attractive famille verte circular bowl, the curving sides in underglaze-blue and with yellow, iron-red and green enamel, interior with dragon, 5½″ diam. 14.0 cm., six character marks of Wan Li. **£85-100** NN

Samson Armorial bowl, 19th century, 11¼″ diam. 28.5 cm., **£85-95** RA

A Satsuma bowl with lobed edge, painted and enamelled with flowering iris plants, traces of gilding in the background, 4¾", 12.0 cm., **£30-35** LC

A Turner's patent punch bowl, the inside painted in the centre in bright colours and gold, the outside with a similar bold pattern, 12¼", 31 cm., printed mark Turner's Patent in brown and N 10 in red script. **£310-450** LC

Worcester blue and white basket, c. 1770, 10¾" wide, **£170-190** RA

A Sevres bowl and cover, painted by Pol, 6¼", 15.7 cm. printed double circle in blue, 1846. **£150-170** SBel

A rare Cozzi (Venice) bowl, with iron-red chinoiserie decoration, c. 1768-70 **£100-180** KK

Worcester First Period blue and white bowl, c. 1780, Dr. Wall, 6", 15.0 cm., **£55-60** RA

A Vienna blue-ground bowl, 10", 25.5 cm., impressed blue shield, late 19th C. **£240-270** SBel

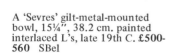

A 'Sevres' gilt-metal-mounted bowl, 15¼", 38.2 cm. painted interlaced L's, late 19th C. **£500-560** SBel

Worcester blue and white powder bowl and cover, c. 1755, 5¼", 13.0 cm., **£150-170** RD

A large blue and white Worcester bowl, painted with Oriental scene, c. 1765, crescent mark, 9¼", **£120-140** MW

A Turner's Patent bowl, painted in bright colours and gold in Chinese taste. 7", 17.7 cm., printed mark Turner's Patent in red and N 3 in red script. **£95-110** LC

A Wedgwood Flame Fairyland Lustre Imperial bowl decorated 'Fairy with large Hat' 'Woodland Bridge', and a central medallion of stylised fish, 6½", 16.4 cm., printed urn mark, Z5630, 1920's **£500-600** SBel

A Worcester moulded butter tub, c. 1768, crescent mark, 5¼", **£80-90** MW

A Wedgwood Fairyland Lustre circular bowl, the interior decorated in green and blue enriched with gilding, c. 1920, 9¾", 24.5 cm., dia. **£700-800** KC

Imari Porcelain goldfish bowl. **£800-875** RBB

A very rare Marseilles sucrier and cover, from the Robert factory marked R, c. 1770-5 **£80-100** KK

A Large Yellow Ground Deep Porcelain Fishbowl, the steeply rounded exterior sides painted in Famille Verte enamels, the interior painted with large iron-red fish, 51½ cm., 20¼" dia. 2nd half 19th century. **£740-800** KC

Coalport, c. 1810. crossed swords mark, 5¾", 14.5 cm., diam. **£180-200** RD

A Meissen sugar bowl and cover in the Kakiemon design, c. 1745, 3½" wide, 9.0 cm., marked, **£500-600** AA

A Massive Famille Verte Porcelain Fishtank, the interior with large iron-red goldfish swimming amidst water-weeds, 25¼" dia, 64 cm., 2nd half 19th century (restored). %**580-620** KC

A Coalport Sucrier, c. 1800, 5¼", 13.0 cm., **£40-45** HHA

A Meissen circular sugar-bowl and cover, minor chips, blue crossed swords mark, 4½", 11.5 cm. **£450-500** CStJ

Pair of large yellow ground circular fish tanks, enamelled and modelled in high relief. Interior painted with red-iron goldfish amidst aquatic plants, 21" dia.; 18" high; 52.5 cm., x 45 cm., 19th century. **£2,800-3,000** NN

A Newhall sucrier example of the well-known Shell pattern, c. 1820, pattern no. 811:x at bottom, 7½" wide, 19.0 cm., **£45-50** ET

A fine quality Spode sucrier and cover, marked SPODE, c. 1820, 6½" wide, 16.5 cm., **£50-55** HHA

Chamberlains Worcester sugar bowl and cover, printed mark in red. c. 1820, 6″ diam. 15.0 cm., **£58-65** RD

A Berlin Yellow-Ground Jardiniere and Stand, the whole scattered with flowers and insects, the stand matching, 20 cm., 8″, sceptre and KPM in underglaze-blue. **£220-250** S.Bel

A Limoges jardiniere decorated in enamels, three gilt supports with cameo panels, 8″ dia; 20 cm., **£65-90** AB

A Worcester scale blue sucrier and cover, decorated with the Japanese star pattern, with the square seal mark, c. 1770, 5¼″, 13.0 cm., **£320-350** MW

A Fine Pair of Chelsea-Derby Bucket-Shaped Jardinieres, 6½″, 16.5 cm. wide, c.1780. **£550-600** CStJ

A French Faience Jardiniere and stand, the whole in royal blue and cream, 37⅝″, 94.3 cm., made in France, early 20th C. **£140-160** SBel

A Salopian Blue and White Sugar Bowl and Cover, with underglaze-blue printed floral sparys, 'S' mark in underglaze-blue to base 4¼″; 10.8 cm., high, circa 1780 **£80-100** KC

A Doulton Lambeth stoneware jardiniere, scratched I.H.S. monogram, scratched monogram FH to base. 10½″ dia., 26.5 cm., **£70-90** HKC

A Chinese porcelain Jardiniere in 'famille-verte' enamels. 8¼″, 20.9 cm., diam, K'ang Hsi, **£520-600** LC

A Pair of Jardinieres probably Minton. Handles and bases with bands of white studs, 7¼″; 18.5 cm., impressed numerals, mid-19th century. **£140-180** SBel

A Pair of Minton Bleu-De-Roi Ground Jardinieres in Sevres style. Gilt scroll and floral border. 9″; 22.8 cm., circa 1850. **£320-350** SBel

A Large Minton Turquoise-Ground Earthenware Jardiniere, four mask and paw feet decorated in black outline, 23″; 58.4 cm., impressed mark, pattern number 1630, date code for 1876. **£140-180** SBel

A Tournai 2 handled bucket-shaped jardiniere, incised P mark, c.1775. 19¾", 27 cm. wide. £1,000-1,100 CStJ

A pair of Helena Wolfsohn Jardinieres, 6⅞", 17.2 cm., AR monogram in underglaze-blue, late 19th C. £150-170 SBel

A Chinese famille verte jardiniere, 11" dia. 28 cm., £120-140 HKC

A Chinese 19th century jardiniere with raised leaf pattern 10"; 25.5 cm., £60-80 AB

A Pair of Paris Jardinieres and stands, magenta base. Painted flowers, moulded mask and vine terminals. Stands with gilt and magenta band, 12"; 30 cm., third quarter of the 19th century £280-340 SBel

A Victorian Wedgewood jardiniere 10" dia.; 25.5 cm., raised decoration of birds and nest, slight damage to feet. £62-85 AB

A Famille Verte Jardiniere painted with birds and peonies. Diaper and false gadroon borders, 37.5 cm., 14¾", second half of 19th century. £450-550 SBel

A pair of Paris Jardinieres and stands with scrolling gilt foliage and rims, 22 cm., high; 8¾". £560-700 CSTJ

A Fine French Empire — Period Paris Flower Pot and Stand, the body having all-over scrolled floral gilt decoration, 8¾" 22.2 cm., high. £220-260 KC

A Samson Armorial Jardiniere 17½", 44.5 cm., late 19th C. £230-260 SBel

A Blue and White Jardiniere painted with a frieze of figures on a coarsely crackled ground between incised and bronzed borders, 33 cm., 13", late 19th century. £135-165 SBel

A pair of Sevres 2 handled bucket-shaped jardinieres, blue interlaced L marks, 1764, 6¼", 16 cm. wide. £1,200 CStJ

A Samson Bulb pot of Miniature Jardiniere Form, decorated in the 18th century Famille Verte taste, pseudo Chinese seal mark to the base, 3½"; 9 cm., high. £80-100 KC

A pair of yellow-ground Berlin Cache-Pots and Stands, 8¹/₈'', 20.5 cm., sceptre in underglaze-blue, late 19th C. **£440-520** SBel

A pair of St. Cloud white cache-pots, with mask handles, marked and incised stc circa 1725, 4½''; T 11.5 cm., **£1,000-1,300** HA

A Pair of Chamberlain's Worcester Yellow-Ground Flared Flower-Pots and Stands, one cracked, 6'', 15 cm. high, c.1805. **£520-580** CStJ

A yellow ground earthenware cache pot, applied with flowers, 8'' high; 20 cm., stamped L. Schneider, Marburg. **£42-50** WW

A Sevres 2 handled seau a verre, puce interlaced L marks, 1789, 6'', 15 cm. **£400-440** CStJ

A Pair of Worcester (Flight & Barr) Flared Flower-Pots, 6¼'', 16 cm. high, incised B and script marks, c.1800. **£320-360** CStJ

A famille rose broad globular chamber-pot and shallow domed cover, chipped, surface cracks, late Ch'ien Lung, 10'', 25.5 cm. **£180-240** CStJ

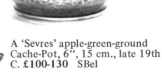

A 'Sevres' apple-green-ground Cache-Pot, 6'', 15 cm., late 19th C. **£100-130** SBel

A Pair of Worcester (Flight & Barr) Flared Flower-Pots, 6¼'', 16 cm. high, incised B marks, gilder's mark WB, C.1800. **£280-310** CStJ

A Paris Raspberry Ground Cache-pot, pail-form body painted with two panels, applied fluted shell handles, details gilt, 18.5 cm., 7¼'', circa 1870. **£120-140** SBel

A pair of Thuringian Porcelain Cachepots, with mask lifts, 5¼'' dia; 13 cm., (damaged) **£11-20** WW

A Coalport jug, painted on a cobalt blue ground; Sheffield plate cover. 10½'', 26.7 cm. £180-200   LC

A Donyatt pottery inscribed puzzle jug, covered with a yellowish glaze with brown markings, mottled with green the neck pierced with crosses and circles and inscribed 'fill me full then geat (sic) it out how you will' 1766 1766, 7¼'', 18.5 cm., 18.4 cm., £500-600   LC

A Doulton Lambeth jug with metal lid. Initials JF incised to base. 7¼'' high, 18.5 cm. £30-35 HKC

A Doulton Lambeth jug, incised monogram FCR to base. 7¼'' high, 18.5 cm., £30-35   HKC

A Doulton Lambeth stoneware quart moulded mug. scratched monogram PB. £90-100   HKC

A Doulton Lambeth stoneware quart moulded mug, scratched monogram L.W. £80-100   HKC

A Liverpool ale jug, of baluster form, with monochrome painted figure panels and verse entitled 'The Bachelor's Wish', c. 1760, 9¾'', 24.5 cm., £105-130   KC

A Lowestoft sparrow-beak cream jug, 3³⁄₈'', 8.6 cm. £100-140   LC

A Lowestoft sparrow-beak cream jug, 3½'', 9.2 cm. £70-90 LC

A Doulton Lambeth brown stoneware ½ pint mug commemmorating Queen Victoria's Jubilee (1897) £30-40   HKC

A Lowestoft Sparrow Beak jug, with typical handle, c. 1780, £50-70   KK

A rare, early Ludwigsburg jug, minus cover, raised design copied from Meissen, c. 1760, £65-85   KK

A Mason's Ironstone 5'', 12.5 cm. jug, royal-blue and gilt decoration, lizard handle. £22-28   AB

A mid 19th C. Masons ironstone jug decorated with orange panels on a deep blue ground. 7½'' high, 19 cm. £65-75   HKC

61

A Meissen jug, with mask face, pink ground, by Heroldt, c. 1735, 5″, 12.5 cm., marked (no lid), **£400-500** AA

Neolithic pottery jug, the shoulders painted in black and reddish-brown, the ware of orange tone, 10″, 25.5 cm., Pan Shan style, Yang Shao period. **£2,600-3,000** SBel

A Sevres cream-jug, blue interlaced L mark, 1770, Painter's mark PR, 3¼″, 8.5 cm. **£260-290** CStJ

A Meissen pear-shaped hot-milk jug and cover, chipped, blue crossed swords mark, 6¼″, 16 cm c.1745. **£280-310** CStJ

A gold and white Paris jug with a mask panel, c. 1820, 6″, 15.0 cm., **£80-90** HHA

A German stoneware pewter-mounted jug, covered in a brown glaze, with initials IHB, minor foot rim chip, c.1720, 13″, 33 cm. **£280-310** CStJ

A pair of Meissen jugs in 18th C. style, 7¼″, 18.4 cm., underglaze-blue crossed swords, late 19th C. **£580-640** SBel

A Pratt pottery jug, 4¼″, 10.8 cm. **£125-150** LC

A Rhenish stoneware jug, 17th C., 10¾″, 27 cm., **£200-230** CStJ

A famille-rose porcelain export jug and cover, painted with two double shield monogram panels, 9½″, 24 cm., overall, Ch'ien Lung, **£150-180** KC

A Sevres jug, blue interlaced L mark, 1763, Painter's mark, 8″, 20 cm. **£1,000-1,100** CStJ

A Rhenish stoneware Bartman-krug, covered in a mottled brown glaze, 16th C., 8¾″, 22 cm., **£220-250** CStJ

A Rhenish stoneware bartman-krug, minor rim chips, 16th C., 7", 18 cm. £160-190 CStJ

A fine Sevres jug, date letter S, c. 1771, 5½", 14.0 cm., marked, £200-250 AA

A First Period Worcester Blue and White Cream Jug and Cover of Pear Shape, decorated with underglaze-blue printed 'fence pattern', cross-hatch crescent mark in underglaze-blue to base, 5½"; 14 cm., high. £70-100 KC

A rare early Worcester 'scratch cross' type jug, c. 1755, 7¼", 18.5 cm., £500-550 RD

1st period Worcester milk jug of Chelsea-Ure type, c. 1765, 3½", 9.0 cm., £135-155 RD

A very early Worcester jug of 'scratched cross' type, c. 1755, 7", 17.5 cm., £500-600 RD

A Worcester Sparrow Beak jug, c. 1775, 3½", 9.0 cm., £70-80 MW

A first period Worcester jug, painted in colours, of unusual barrel shape, c. 1770, £90-110 KK

A Worcester jug from the Lord Stormont Service, c. 1780, £200-250 KK

TOBY JUGS

- based on the character Toby Fillpot
- Ralph Wood I (1715-1772) first produced his pottery jugs c.1761-1772, these were of excellent quality and are much sought after today
- the original jugs tended to be unglazed, with non-gaudy colours
- Ralph Wood II (1748-1795) produced jugs from 1772-1795, during this period the enamel colours became stronger and brighter
- Enoch Wood (1759-1840) produced jugs from 1790-1840 and the majority of jugs were made at this time

Hearty Good Fellow jug and cover of pratt type. Brown hat, blue jacket over yellow waist-coat, yellow and blue trousers. Base, back and handle sponged in blue and ochre, 11" high overall; 28 cm., £180-240 NN

A Staffordshire Toby jug crudely coloured. Clear complexion and brown hair, green jacket with brown buttons, plain waistcoat, brown breeches. Brown glazed chamfered base moulded with florettes. £110-140 NN

Rodney's Sailor, a large Walton type underglaze painted and enamelled figure jug. Brown ale pot. Blue jacket and trousers, black and white striped vest and black kerchief. Grassy base with branch handle, 11½″ high; impressed with initial F. **£130-160**   NN

Good Squire jug, streaked brown tricorn hat, blue jacket, rust waistcoat and streaked brown breeches. Corner elbow chair enamelled in rust. Base painted in underglaze-blue, 11″ high; 28.0 cm., **£460-540**   NN

A Pratt type Staffordshire underglaze painted and enamelled Toby jug and cover with blotched complexion. Blue jacket, plain waistcoat with green cravat, orange breeches. Textured ale jug with speckled decoration. 10½″ high overall; 26.5 cm., **£260-290**   NN

The Squire, Ralph Wood glazed jug. Hooked nose and warty features. Green jacket, white cravat and blue waistcoat with brown breeches, seated in a carved corner elbow chair, blue jug. **£580-650**   NN

A Ralph Wood Toby jug. Glazed attire of mouse coloured coat over green waistcoat and yellow breeches. Empty brown jug and full glass. 9½″ high; 24 cm., **£250-280**   NN.

Glazed Toby jug with dark manganese complexion. Blue coat over a green waistcoat with blue breeches, a green glazed base 9¾″ high; 24.5 cm., **£520-600**   NN

A Staffordshire Toby jug with blue jacket, 9½″: 24 cm., **£14-20**

A Staffordshire coloured ware Mother Hubbard jug 9″; 23 cm., **£16-24**   WW

Ralph Wood glazed 'Shield' Toby jug with pale manganese face brown jacket and breeches; Empty jug. Green shield inscribed 10″ high, 25.5 cm., **£1,700-1,900**   NN

A Wayte and Ridge Earthenware Toby Jug in the Form of a Seated Mandarin with his Tongue out, impressed mark 'W and R/L' to base, circa 1864, 30 cm., high; 11¾" £80-100   KC

A 19th century Staffordshire Earthenware Toby Jug Depicting a Standing Man, painted mark to base 26.5 cm., high; 10½", together with a 19th century Staffordshire earthenware Toby jug painted mark 'L' to base, 25 cm., high; 9¾" £85-95   KC

Small Lambeth brown ware Toby jug 3"; 7.5 cm., £15-20 WW

A Staffordshire Earthenware Toby jug of the Squire, 18.5 cm., high; 7¼". £50-60   KC

A Ralph Wood glazed Toby jug with green eyes. Brown tricorn hat mouse coloured coat, green waistcoat and lemon breeches. 9½" high; 24 cm., £220-250 NN

A Ralph Wood type figure jug modelled as the Hearty Good Fellow. Features in naturalistic tones. Brown jacket, blue-buttoned plain waistcoat, yellow breeches, brown striped stockings, brown shoes with yellow buckles. Green glazed grassy base. Handle modelled as a gnarled branch, 12" high; 30.5 cm., £380-450   NN

A Ralph Wood type glazed Toby jug. Eyes with brown pupils, brown attire and shoes, seated on a scrolling rococo chair, 9½" high; 24 cm., recessed underbase. £240-280 NN

A Ralph Wood glazed Toby jug with mouse coloured jacket, plain waistcoat, and pale lemon breeches, part full jug. 10" high; 25.5 cm., £220-250   NN

Wood glazed 'Shield' Toby jug with light brown jacket over a blue waistcoat. Brown glazed shield inscribed. 10" high; 25.5 cm., recessed unglazed underbase. £1,750-1,900   NN

A Ralph Wood glazed Toby jug with pale manganese face. Blue coat over a plain waistcoat and ochre breeches. Brown baluster jug 10½" high; 26.5 cm., underglazed recessed base. £220-260 NN

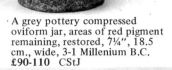

A grey pottery compressed oviform jar, areas of red pigment remaining, restored, 7¼", 18.5 cm., wide, 3-1 Millenium B.C. £90-110 CStJ

An unusual San Ts'ai glazed jar covered with a cream glaze irregularly splashed with blue and green streaks with an iridescent sheen, the unglazed base showing the pale ware and the interior covered with a thin amber-yellow glaze. 7¾", 19.5 cm., T'ang Dynasty, fitted box, £4,200-4,500 SBel

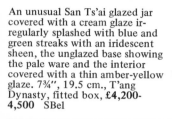

A good Lung Ch'uan jar, the short straight mouth with unglazed rim and base, the remainder covered with celadon glaze of even tone, 35/8", 9.5 cm., Sung Dynasty, wood stand, £1,300-1,500 SBel

A grey pottery buff-slip decorated oviform jar, repaired, 10¾", 27.5 cm., 3-1 Millenium B.C. £190-220 CStJ

An ovoid blue and white porcelain ginger jar, 8¼", 21 cm., K'ang Hsi, £250-300 KC

A pharmacy jar and cap cover, painted PICIS. BASILIC. U, 10", 25.5 cm., claw mark. £310-350 LC

A grey pottery buff-slip decorated inverted bell-shaped jar, repaired. 9", 23 cm. 3-1 Millenium B.C. £260-290 CStJ

A green-glazed jar, the exterior with a green glaze showing a silvery iridescence, 7¼", 18.5 cm., Han Dynasty, £1,700-1,900 SBel

A Satsuma cylindrical pot and cover, finely decorated in gold and soft colours, 3", 7.5 cm., £105-120 LC

Wedgwood black basalt pot and cover, 2¼", 5.5 cm., impressed Wedgwood, 3rd quarter of 19th century, £45-50 RD

A Cantonese enamel jar and lid, 3½" wide, 9.0 cm., £45-50 HHA

A Chinese export blue and white pot and cover, c. 1780, 3¾", 9.5 cm., £20-25 DW

Tz'u Chou Jar, carved through the dark brown glaze to the coarse buff body beneath, the glaze stopping just short of the footrim, the interior similarly glazed, 8¼" high 21.0 cm., 8½" wide, 21.5 cm., Sung/Yuan Dynasty, wood stand, £4,400-5,000 SBel

A large Dutch Delft drug jar, having blue and white armorial decoration, from the De Drye Clocken factory, with ribbed metal cover, 11¼", 28.5 cm., £420-480 KC

A green glazed pottery jar, the shoulder moulded in relief with a frieze of leaping tigers, interlaced linear scrolls between raised line borders, the glaze degraded to a silvery iridescence, the base and interior showing the red ware, 6", 15.0 cm., Han Dynasty, £1,700-1,900 SBel

A Dresden jar and cover marked, early 19th century, 14.0 cm., 5½", £60-70 HHA

Early 16th century Faenza Albarello, painted in blue on the label between ochre and blue line borders, the shoulders and foot with blue 'dash' borders, 17.8 cm., c. 1520-25 £2,000-3,000 PK

A Kinkozan jar and cover, finely enamelled and gilt with chrysanthemums, 5", 12.5 cm., gilt Kinkozan tsukuru, late 19th century, £160-180 SBel

A rare 'Proto-porcelain' jar and cover, showing traces of the green kiln gloss covering the high domed cover, the unglazed ware burnt to a reddish-purple tone, 7¼", 18.5 cm., Han Dynasty, £420-500 SBel

A large circular-section blue and white porcelain brushpot, 7½" dia. 19 cm., K'ang Hsi, £410-500 KC

A Dresden gilt-metal-mounted Ewer, 17¼", 44 cm., late 19th C. £240-280   SBel

A miniature flask moulded in crisp relief on each side with a stylised animal mask, surmounted by a 'fleur-de-lys' motif and encircled by a beaded border, the slightly degraded straw glaze falling short of the oval foot to reveal the pale buff ware, 2⁵⁄₈", 6.5 cm., Sui/early T'ang Dynasty, wood stand and fitted box, £1,300-1,500   SBel

A pair of 'Sevres' gilt-metal-mounted Ewers, on an apple-green ground, 8", 20 cm., c.1870. £160-180   SBel

A pair of earthenware ewers, 15¼", 38.5 cm., gilt crossed flags, and N, c.1880. £150-170   SBel

A Tz'u Chou Ewer with five lobes extending from the splayed footrim to a band of triple horizontal grooves encircling shoulders, covered with a crackled translucent glaze applied over the white slip, falling short of the foot, 3½", 9.0 cm., Sung Dynasty, wood stand, £1,700-2,000   SBel

A Ying Ch'ing Ewer, the lobed body incised with vertical lines along the grooves, applied overall with a crackled translucent glaze of faint greenish tone, 8", 20.0 cm., Sung Dynasty, £1,100-1,400   SBel

A large Vienna ewer and stand, the cylindrical body painted by P. Hoffmann, signed, with a scene after Rubens, 16¾", 42.7 cm., painted shield in underglaze-blue, title painted in script, 1880's. £600-700   SBel

A pair of large Paris blue-ground Ewers, 24¾", 63 cm., mid 19th C. £1,300-1,500   SBel

A Flight, Barr and Barr miniature water sprinkler and stopper, the semi-matt mid-blue ground reserving a panel painted with a named view of Warwick Castle, 4", 10.0 cm., script mark with Coventry St. address. £300-350 PK

First period Worcester mustard pot and cover, "Three flowers' pattern, (slight restoration). **£100-120 MW**

18th century faience pot **£48-55 CAL**

A fine pair of dated wet drug jars painted with coat-of-arms beneath the spout and above the oblong tablets, one inscribed – SVSINE AMOSCI, one dated 1616, 11¾", 30.0 cm., **£1,300-1,500 NN**

A large Coalport royal-blue-ground ewer, painted with scenes of Windsor Castle and Buckingham Palace, the handle and details gilt, handle restored, 18", 45.8 cm., printed crown mark, painted title and pattern mark, v.6378, L/pl49, impressed 22A1, c. 1910 **£660-750 SBel**

A Yueh-Yao waterpot, applied with four flanges, each joining a short leg, applied overall with crackled translucent glaze of grey-green tone, 2¾", 7.0 cm., Tang Dynasty, wood stand. **£500-600 SBel**

A Coalport gilt and 'jewelled' ewer, the central band with painted primroses, the ground enamelled with white and turquoise studs, gilt handle, 10¾", 27.4 cm., printed crown mark, numbered V 2500 and 32, 1890's **£300-360 SBel**

A pair of fine George III ormolu-mounted Derbyshire Spar ewers attributed to Matthew Boulton, one in deep amethyst, the other in brown and ochre, on socle bases, 19", 48 cm., c. 1772, **£19,000-23,000 SBel**

Yueh-Yao waterpot in the form of a toad, moulded in relief with incised details, the greyish-green glaze slightly degraded, 3", 7.5 cm., Chin Dynasty, **£1,000-1,200 SBel**

A pair of Doulton Lambeth ewers, 11¼", 28.5 cm. high, impressed marks, **£360-400 PL**

A pair of Grainger's Worcester ewers, pierced with scrolling flowers and foliage between gilt borders, 9", 22.8 cm., printed shield mark, shape no. 1/1928, c. 1890 £330-360 SBel

A late 19th century Royal Worcester glazed ivory-coloured ewer, 17", 43.0 cm., £270-300 RB

A faience pilgrim flask, 5½", 14.0 cm., £11-18 RB

A blue and white moon flask painted on each side with a circular panel of figures on a ground of scrolling foliage, chih -lung handles, 55.5 cm., 21¾", late 19th century, £650-750 SBel

A pair of Royal Worcester Ewers of classical shape, signed C. Baldwyn, printed Royal Worcester mark (restored) £300-400 KC

A Coalport moon flask painted with a landscape within a gilt border, pink blossoms, gilt branches and leaves, 5", 12.5 cm., printed crown mark, painted pattern number B2467, c. 1885, £100-120 SBel

A Royal Worcester reticulated ewer painted by H. Chair, signed, and pierced by G. Owen, Details lightly gilded, 6¼", 15.8 cm., printed mark, pattern no. 1581, Rd. No. 189077 date code for 1907, £180-230 SBel

A Chelsea scent bottle 3", 7.5 cm., (damaged) stopper lacking, gold anchor mark, £90-110 WW

A Japanese bottle with bevelled shoulders, painted in underglaze blue, iron-red and gold, the shoulders with green enamel reserves and diaper patterns, 7¼" high (18.4 cms) 18th century. £360-400 LC

A white-glazed bottle covered with a bubble-suffused translucent glaze of faint bluish tint falling short of the base showing the pale buff ware, 5³/₈", 13.5 cm., Sui T'ang Dynasty, £2,600-2,900 SBel

A pair of Japanese Imari square bottles with stoppers, painted in under-glaze blue, iron-red, gold, green. 6" high (15.3 cms) 18th century. £390-450   LC

Caughley blue and white tea caddy and cover, printed with 'fisherman and cormorant' pattern, circa 1780, 4¾"; 12 cm., £95-110   RD

An 18th century Meissen tea-caddy, with Ozier moulding, printing after Rugendas, with silver top, circa 1745, marked 4½". 11.5 cm., £700-750   AA

An 18th century Meissen tea-caddy, decorated with allegoric scenes, circa 1745, marked 5"; 12.5 cm., £400-450   AA

A famille verte powder-blue ground hexagonal bottle and cylindrical cover, chipped, K'ang Hsi, 7", 17.5 cm., £160-180 CStJ

A Christian's Liverpool Teapoy, circa 1775. £60-80   KK

A Hochst teacaddy and cover, pear finial painted in colours, puce wheel mark, circa 1760, 5", 12.5 cm., £700-900   HA

A Meissen teacaddy, in the Kakiemon design, circa 1735-40, contemporary silver lid. 5½" marked; 12.5 cm. £450   AA

A late 18th century Wedgwood blue jasper-ware scent bottle with raised cameos, silver top, 5", 12.5 cm., £56-75   WW

A Meissen hexagonal teacaddy and cover, with Kakiemon decoration, circa 1728, 4"; 10 cm., £800-900   HA

An 18th century Meissen tea-caddy with top, circa 1745, ochre printing, marked 5"; 12.5 cm., £500-600   AA

71

A Bow basket decorated with English flowers, painters mark, 5, 6¾", 17.0 cm., £200-230 MW

A Bristol Delft circular dish, painted in polychrome in Chinese style, 13", 33 cm., £70-90 LC

A Rectangular-Section 'Famille Verte' Porcelain Tea Caddy, 8.25 cm., 3¼", K'ang Hsi. £440-500 KC

An 18th century Chinese export teacaddy, (no cover). £30-35 DW

A Canton pierced oval basket and stand, decorated in 'famille-rose' enamels, basket 10¾", 27.3 cm., the stand 11¼", 28.5 cm., mid-19th century £150-200 LC

A famille-rose porcelain basin, in enamels and gilding, 15" diam. 38 cm., c. 1800, £280-310 KC

A pair of Caughley shell dishes, 'Fisherman and Cormorant' pattern, c. 1780, £105-120 pair, MW

A Chelsea Peony dish, painted in colours, c. 1755, red anchor mark, 8" wide, 20.0 cm., £520-600 HA

A Bow patty pan, c. 1760 £70-80 MW

A Chantilly soft paste tea dish with soft Chinoiserie decoration, red hunting horn mark, c. 1735, £300-400 KK

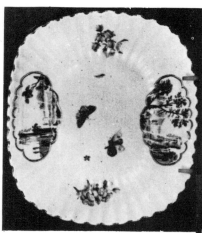

A Davenport coloured floral decorated china comport, 11", 28.0 cm., £22-30 WW

A Chelsea fluted dish, painted in colours by J.H.O'Neale, raised anchor period, c. 1751, 8" wide, 20.0 cm., £400-500 HA

A Derby basket, painted by the Moth painter, c. 1760, £300-400 KK

A pair of Dutch Delft blue and white dishes, minor rim chips, c.1720, £240-270 CStJ

A Doccia tin glaze pickle dish, decorated with fruit, c. 1770, £30-40 KK

A Chelsea Pine-Cone Moulded Dish boldly painted, 9", 23 cm. diam, gold anchor mark, c.1760. CStJ

A Dutch Delft blue and white dish, minor rim chips, script Fortuyn mark, c.1700, 13¼", 34 cm. diam., £320-350 CStJ

A Dutch Delft blue and white dish, rim chip, c.1700, 13½", 34.5 cm. diam., £600-680 CStJ

A Copenhagen pierced dish, decorated with flower and insects, c. 1840, £50-70 KK

A pair of Dutch Delft blue and white dishes, minor glaze chips, c.1740, 11¾", 30 cm., £280-310 CStJ

A Dutch Delft blue and white dish with ochre rim, minor glaze chips, Claw mark, c.1720, 13¾", 35 cm. diam., £240-270 CStJ

A Dutch Delft blue and white
dish painted in the Kraakporse-
lein style, minor rim chips, blue
No. 4 mark, c.1700. 13¼", 34
cm. diam. £240-270 CStJ

A pair of Hochst oval dishes,
painted in colours, one with people
playing skittles and the other with
'A Catch of Fish', borders with
fruit, blue wheel marks, c. 1765,
9", 23.0 cm., £1,200-1,300 HA

A Lambeth Delft polychrome
dish, painted in yellow, green,
blue and ochre. 11⅝", 29.5 cm.,
£250-280 LC

A Dutch Delft blue and white
large dish, minor rim chips
repaired, cracked, c.1720, 15¾",
40 cm. diam., £90-100 CStJ

An Italian maiolica shell shape
dish with mask handle, 11½"
wide, 29.0 cm., £20-25   AB

An 18th century tin glaze earthenware monochrome shallow dish
decorated with flowers, 12½",
diam. 32 cm., £105-125 AB

A Japanese Nabeshima dish
painted in blue, iron-red and
enamel colours, 12", 30.5 cm.,
early 19th C. £240-270 LC

A Lambeth Delft polychrome
dish, painted in mangganese,
blue, green, yellow and iron-
red. 10", 25.4 cm., £130-150
LC

A Longton Hall Mulberry Leaf
dish, with typical Longton Hall
moulding and decoration, c. 1758
£250-270 KK

French porcelain basket, blue
borders applied flowers, cupids
and doves, (damaged), £16-20
WW

A rare Longton Hall spoon tray,
very rare shape, c. 1753-7,
£400-450 KK

A fine late 18th century Loosdrecht part dessert service, (6 pieces), rims enriched with dentil gilding, blue painted MoL mark with star to reverse. Three oval and three circular dishes, each with pierced link borders of formal classical design. £1,750-2,000 HKC

A Newhall saucer dish, rare pattern, No. 427, 8″, 20.0 cm., c. 1790-95, £35-40 MW

A pair of Chinese dishes, in 'famille-rose' enamels, 10″, 25.4 cm., Ch'ien Lung; 19.7 cm., £250-280 LC

A Meissen spoon tray, c. 1790, 7″ wide, 17.5 cm., Marcolini period, with military scene, marked, £200-240 AA

A Chinese provincial Ming sauce dish, painted in underglaze blue, 9″, 23.0 cm., £45-65 DW

A famille rose dish, cracked, Yung Cheng, 15½″, 37.5 cm. diam., £140-180 CStJ

An octagonal Meissen tray, with Kakiemon decoration, crossed swords mark, c. 1745, 6″, 15.0 cm., £640-750 JEV

Hausmalerei, A Nymphenburg circular dish, painted outside the factory with the Massacre of the Innocents, 8¾″, 22.2 cm., impressed shield mark, £1,300-1,500 LC

A Mettlach dish moulded after a design by Sturke, impressed signature, 15¼″, 38.5 cm., impressed castle mark, incised 2070, c. 1900 £250-350 SBel

A pair of famille-rose lotus pattern dishes, Chien Lung, 10¼″ dia. 26 cm. £90-120 HKC

A Chinese saucer dish, decorated in famille-rose enamels with turquoise diaper borders, 10¼″, 26.0 cm., £20-30 LC

A Kinkozan dish, finely enamelled and gilt, 6¹/₈″, 15.5 cm., gilt Kinkozan, late 19th century, **£230-280** SBel

A Chinese dish, enamelled in famille-rose in star-shaped panel outlined in green on a famille-verte ground in stippled green with branches, 15¼″, 38.7 cm., Hua mark in underglaze-blue, 18th century. **£140-160** LC

A set of four famille-rose dishes, the centres brightly enamelled with an Imperial procession, border with gilt scrollwork and enamelled flower sprays, 8½″ diam. 21.5 cm., Ch'ien Lung, **£280-320** NN

A Chinese export spoon tray, with European monogram, 4½″, 11.5 cm., c. 1780, **£45-65** DW

A Chinese Armorial porcelain octagonal meat dish, 16½″, 41.9 cm., Ch'ien Lung, c. 1775 **£270-310** LC

A fine famille-rose circular dish, the curving sides pierced and the centre colourfully enamelled, 9¾″, 24.5 cm., Ch'ien Lung, **£260-290** NN

A good set of four famille-rose circular shaped-edge deep dishes, 8½″, 21.5 cm., diam., Ch'ien Lung, **£280-300** NN

A pair of late Ming blue and
white Kraak porcelain dishes,
slightly chipped, Wan Li, 11½",
29 cm. diam., **£720-800** CStJ

A late Ming blue and white
dish, cracked, Wan Li, 17½",
44.5 cm. diam., **£360-400** CStJ

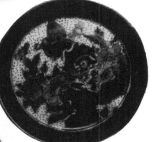

A Satsuma fluted dish, painted
and gilt with a peacock and hen,
flowering prunus and a fir tree.
8¾", 22.3 cm., **£80-90** LC

A famille rose oval octagonal
deep dish with underglaze-blue
scrolling lotus and whorl-pattern,
Ch'ien Lung, 15", 38 cm., **£150-
180** CStJ

A pale Celadon stem dish, minor
chips, 8½", 21.5 cm. diam.,
underglaze-blue, Yung Cheng
six-character seal mark. **£440-500**
CStJ

A set of four Ao-Kutani dishes,
on a seeded yellow ground, 6",
diam. 15 cm., painted Fuku
marks, 19th century, **£80-100**
KC

A pair of well decorated Ridgway dishes, 8", 20.0 cm., **£55-65**
pair.   ET

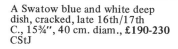

A Swatow blue and white deep
dish, cracked, late 16th/17th
C., 15¾", 40 cm. diam., **£190-230**
CStJ

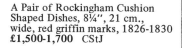

A Pair of Rockingham Cushion
Shaped Dishes, 8¼", 21 cm.,
wide, red griffin marks, 1826-1830
£1,500-1,700 CStJ

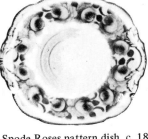

A 'Sevres' gilt-metal-mounted fruit dish, 16¾", 42.5 cm. gilt interlaced L's, late 19th C. £240-270 SBel

A Rockingham Cinquefoil Dish, slight chip to rim 10", 25 cm. wide, red griffin mark, 1826-1830 **£600-650** CStJ

A pair of Sevres bleu celeste ornithological dishes, blue inter-laced L marks, painter's mark, c.1765, 8¼", 21 cm. **£800-880** CStJ

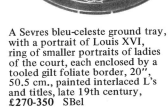

A Sevres bleu-celeste ground tray, with a portrait of Louis XVI, ring of smaller portraits of ladies of the court, each enclosed by a tooled gilt foliate border, 20", 50.5 cm., painted interlaced L's and titles, late 19th century, **£270-350** SBel

Spode Roses pattern dish, c. 1835, 10", 25.5 cm., **£30-35** RA

A Swansea Cushion-Shaped Dish, painted by William Pollard, 8½", 21.5 cm. wide, red stencil mark, c.1815. **£300-340** CStJ

A Sevres bleu celeste ornithological dish, blue interlaced L mark, Painter's mark, c.1765, 10¾", 27 cm. **£450-500** CStJ

A Sevres soft-paste tray within a royal blue border, 12¼", 31 cm. painted interlaced L's, late 18th C. **£340-400** SBel

A pair of Sevres bleu celeste ornithological dishes, blue inter-laced L marks, Painter's mark, c.1765, 8¾", 22.5 cm. **£950-1,050** CStJ

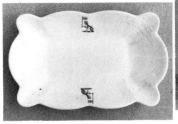

A Spode dish, red Spode mark, c. 1830, 10" long, 25.5 cm., **£25-28** ET

A pair of Tournai (Hague decorated) spirally moulded dishes, blue stork marks, c.1775, 12¼", 31 cm. **£950-1,050** CStJ

A Pair of Swansea Cushion-
Shaped Dishes 9½", 24 cm. wide,
c.1815. £250-280   CStJ

A Pair of Worcester (Flight &
Barr) Lobed Cushion-shaped
Dishes, 8¾", 22 cm. wide, full
script and incised B marks, c.
1800. £800-900   CStJ

A Tournai (Hague decorated)
saucer-dish, blue stork mark,
c.1775, 11½", 29 cm.
£500-560   CStJ

A Pair of Worcester (Flight,
Barr & Barr) Cushion-Shaped
Dishes, impressed marks, 9¼",
23.5 cm. wide, c.1820. £280-300
CStJ

A Pair of Worcester (Flight And
Barr) Lobed Oval Dishes, 11",
28 cm. wide, with full script
mark, incised B marks, c.1800.
£700-780   CStJ

1st period Worcester leaf sauce
dish, c. 1770, 8", 20.0 cm.,
£250-280   RD

1st period Worcester blue scale
circular dish painted with
European flowers, crescent mark,
9", 23.0 cm., £340-370   RD

1st period Worcester 'wet blue'
dish, c. 1770, 8¾", 22.0 cm.,
£200-220   RD

A Dr. Wall Worcester 'Blind Earl'
dish, painted in colours, with
unusual flower decoration, c.
1758-60 £250-300   KK

A Worcester junket dish with basket moulding, crescent mark, c. 1765, 9", 23.0 cm., £120-150 MW

A set of six Berlin plates, painted with a bird, sprigs and insects within a celadon border and puce-edged wavy rim, 8½", 21;6 cm., underglaze-blue sceptre and circle mark, impressed 12 and 1, third quarter of 19th century. £290-320 SBel

A very rare Caughley plate, painted by George Davis at Chamberlain's factory at Worcester, mark painted S in underglaze-blue, c. 1785, 9½", 24.0 cm., damaged £30- perfect £330-350 DW

A Worcester blue and white 'Blind Earl' dish, hand painted decoration, crescent mark, c. 1760, £180-210 KK

A Bow plate in the famille-rose style, 8¾", 22.0 cm., c. 1755 £85-95 MW

18th century Chanek Kale plate depicting ship, £200-220 CA

A Worcester leaf dish, (imperfect), c. 1768, 10", 25.5 cm., £70-75 MW

A Bow blue and white octagonal plate with the 'Image Pattern', simulated Chinese marks on the back, c. 1756, 8¾", 22.0 cm., £100-115 HA

A Chelsea Hans Sloane botanical plate, 9¹/₈", 23.2 cm., brown anchor mark. £150-190 LC

A set of three shaped circular entree dishes with covers and liners, and a matching dish base and lid handle. £135-160 HKC

A pair of early 19th C. cream ware oval dessert dishes and stands. £100-120 HKC

A small Bow blue and white plate, with the 'Jumping Boy' pattern c. 1759, 6¼", 16.0 cm., £140-155 HA

A Chelsea Hans Sloane botanical plate, 9", 22.8 cm., red anchor mark. £330-390 LC

A Chelsea Hans Sloane botanical plate, 8⅝", 21.8 cm. red anchor mark, partly obliterated. **£160-190** LC

A fake copy of a Chelsea Red Anchor plate, 9½", 24.0 cm., early 20th century, **£15-20** DW

A good Coalport dessert plate painted by F. H. Chivers, signed, on a turquoise-blue ground, rim with raised gilding, 9", 22.6 cm., printed crown mark, numbered 7218 and 54, impressed numerals, probably as date code for 1908. **£105-140** SBel

A Chelsea Hans Sloane plate, 9", 22.8 cm., **£200-230** LC

A Clewes wolf trap pattern, transfer printed blue and white plate, 8", 20.0 cm., c. 1810, impressed mark, **£32-38** MW

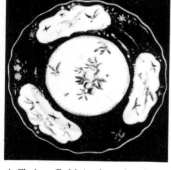

A Chelsea Gold Anchor plate in the Sevres style, 8¼", 21.0 cm., gold anchor mark, c. 1765, **£90-100** MW

A pair of Coalport plates decorated by Chamberlain, Worcester with the Jabberwocky pattern (restored) 10¼", 26.0 cm., c. 1820 **£65-75** pair (MW)

A pair of Coalport plates painted by F. Howard, signed, gilt scroll and vine borders against a royal-blue ground, 9", 22.8 cm., printed crown mark, retailer's mark for T. Goode & Co., painted title, pattern number 7918/B, impressed date code for 1914 **£150-200** SBel

A Gold Anchor Chelsea plate printed with exotic brids, gold anchor mark, 8¾", 22.0 cm., **£105-120** MW

Pair of botanical plates — Coalport, c. 1840, painted by Toulouse, 8¾", 22.0 cm., **£95-110** RA

A Pair of Derby Botanical Plates, 9", 23 cm. diam., Crown, crossed batons, D marks, pattern no. 197 in blue, c.1795. **£280-310** CStJ

A Delft charger with turnover rim, painted in blue with a naked heroic figure of a warrior. 13", 33 cm., £400-450 LC

One of a set of twelve Copenhagen plates, shaped gilt rims, 9¼", 23.5 cm., Three Belts mark in underglaze-blue. £110-130 LC

A pair of Doccia Plates, 10¼", 26 cm., crowned N in underglaze-blue, late 19th C. £150-250 SBel

A pair of Royal Crown Derby plates, by G. Harris, 9", 22.8 cm., impressed marks. £340-390 LC

A Fine Pair of Derby Blue-Ground Botanical Plates, painted in the manner of Pegg, within rich blue borders, 8¾", 22 cm. diam., Crown, crossed batons, D marks in iron-red, c.1805. £700-800 CStJ

A pair of Dutch Delft blue and white pancake-plates painted in iron-red yellow and green, c.1730, 8¾", 22 cm. diam., £600-680 CStJ

Two Carl Magnus Heuschten-Reuter plates, painted by A. Bock or Klein, signed, 9½", 24.2 cm., shield in underglaze-blue, c.1900, £200-230 SBel

A Pair of Derby Blue-Ground Botanical Plates, 8¾", 22 cm. diam. Crown, crossed batons, D marks in iron-red, c.1805. £550-600 CStJ

A pair of Dutch Delft polychrome pancake plates, minor rim chips, c.1740, 9", 23 cm. diam., £220-250 CStJ

A Davenport blue and white transfer printed plate with a view of the Imperial Park Gehol, Barrow, 9¾", 24.5 cm., c. 1810, impressed DAVENPORT Mark, £30-35 MW

A Davenport and Wedgwood dessert service of eighteen 9", 23.0 cm., octagonal plates, five comports — red, blue, gilt and grey decoration. **£320-350** AB

A Lambeth Delft polychrome plate, in blue, green, yellow and ochre, 9³/₈", 23.8 cm., **£135-150** LC

A Derby plate, c. 1780, marked with a crown and D in blue, 9", 23.0 cm., with vine borders, (chipped) **£30-33** DW

A 19th century Japanese blue and white wall plate, 24½" diam. 61 cm., **£150-180** OL

A Lambeth Delft polychrome plate, painted in green, yellow, manganese and iron-red. 9", 22.8 cm., **£45-55** LC

Part of a fine late 18th century Loosdrecht dessert service, blue painted M o L mark with star to reverse: 10 dessert plates, **£2,200-2,500** HKC

18th century Lambeth Delft plate decorated with a long tailed parrot and peony pattern, 9", 23.0 cm., **£55-65** MW

A Liverpool Delft plate, 10½", 26.5 cm., c. 1760, **£30-35** MW

A Furztenburg plate, on celadon blue ground, late 18th century, 9", 23.0 cm., marked, **£220-250** AA

Rare English Delft charger, **£195-220** CA

A Liverpool Delft plate, bright yellow, blue, ochre and pea green. 9", 22.8 cm., **£230-260** LC

A Furstenburg plate, pierced rim-mark in blue, late 18th century, 10", 25.5 cm., **£75-85** RD

An 18th century Hochst teapot stand, with 19th century ormolu surround, 9" wide, 23.0 cm., marked, **£400-450** AA

A patent iron stone china plate, 9½", 24.0 cm., marked **£20-24** ET

Part of a fine late 18th century Loosdrecht dessert service, blue painted M o L mark with star to reverse: 10 dessert plates, **£2,100-2,500** HKC

A pair of Meissen plates, with fable animals in puce and gold, from the studio of Loewenfink, c. 1740, cross swords mark, 9¼", **£850-950** (price is dependant on importance of the animal) HA

Five Limoges 8½", 21.5 cm., dessert plates, each with different decoration, (one with slight chip), **£20-25** AB

A Meissen plate, scene of Neustadt bey Dresden, Marcolini period, 9" marked, **£600-700** AA

A plate, probably Minton, c. 1860, 9", 23.0 cm., **£20-24** ET

A Marcolini Meissen plate, of a hunting scene, marked, 9", **£600-650** AA

A rare Longton Hall plate, strawberry border, c. 1760 9½", 24.0 cm., damaged **£30-35** perfect **£200-230** DW

A set of sixteen pierced dessert plates, possibly Minton, rim with gilt details, one broken, 9½", 24 cm., painted pattern No. 6303, c. 1880, **£650-720** SBel

A Mason's plate, 8", 20.0 cm., **£14-18** ET

A Meissen 'Vienna' decorated plate painted by Kray, 97/8", 24.8 cm., crossed swords in underglaze-blue, late 19th C. **£170-190** SBel

Minton green ground plate pattern No. N. 1084, c. 1840 8½", 21.5 cm., **£30-35** pair RD

A mid-19th century dinner service decorated in the Chinese style by F. Morley & Co., **£360-400** OS

An Imari plate 8½", 21.5 cm., c. 1880 **£15-18** ET

A Nantgarw Dessert-Plate, 8½", 21.5 cm. diam., impressed Nant-Garw C.W. mark C.1820. **£120-140** CStJ

A Newhall teapot stand, pattern No. 441, 6½", 16.5 cm., c. 1790-95 **£30-33** MW

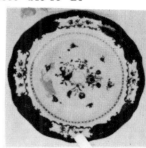

One of a matched pair of Chinese plates, gilt in the centres with Islamic characters in medallions surrounded by flowers in famille-rose enamels, 9¾", 24.7 cm., Ch'ien Lung, **£100-120** LC

A Newhall teapot stand, pattern No. 267, 8", 20.0 cm., c. 1785, **£32-38** MW

A Nantgarw plate, painted in the centre with the Country Dance by William Weston Yound. 8½", 21;6 cm., impressed mark NANT-GARW C.W. **£300-340** LC

Six Chinese Imari plates each decorated in iron-red, underglaze-blue, green and yellow enamel and gilt, chipped, three cracked, early 18th C., 8¾", 22.5 cm. diam., **£210-240** CStJ

19th century Chinese blue and white plate, 10½", 26.5 cm., **£25-30** RA

A Chinese deep plate with scalloped rim, decorated in 'famille-rose' enamels 9", 23 cm., Ch'ien Lung, **£85-100** LC

A famille verte plate, chipped. 8¼", 21 cm. diam. K'ang Hsi. **£150-170** CStJ

A blue and white plate, painted with phoenix amongst rocks and peonies within a diaper border, 14¾", 37.5 cm., four character marks of K'ang Hsi, late 19th century, **£75-90** SBel

Two blue and white plates, scale and cell-pattern ground, one chipped. 10½", 27 cm. diam., encircled six character K'ang Hsi marks. **£300-350** CStJ

19th century (Paris) Samson plate, 9¾", 24.5 cm., **£40-45** RA

A Pinxton Yellow-Ground Plate, 8", 20 cm. diam., c.1800. **£290-320** CStJ

Decorative plate, c. 1820 Paris — Feuillet Marked 'Feuillet', 9¾", 24.5 cm., **£40-45** RA

A good set of four famille-rose octagonal plates, 8½" diam. 21.5 cm., Ch'ien Lung, **£300-350** NN

19th century Samson famille-rose plate, 9¼", 23.5 cm., **£30-35** RA

An early 19th century Paris (de la Courtille) part dinner service, (39 pieces) principally in blue and aubergine, **£400-450** HKC

A Pair of Rockingham Plates,
9″, 23 cm., diam. red griffin
mark and pattern no. 409, 1826-
1830. **£1,100-1,200** CStJ

A Spode 'Death of the Bear',
blue and white transfer printed
plate, printed and impressed marks,
10″, 25.5 cm., **£50-55** MW

A pair of Staffordshire transfer-
printed plates, depicting a balloon
ascent, bordered with vines, 10¼″
26 cm., diam. English, c. 1830-35
£170-200 SBel

A fine Rozenburg stoneware
circular wall plate, decorated in
bright red, yellow, and green
enamels, printed marks and incised numerals to base, 13″, 33
cm., dia, **£460-500** KC

A Spode plate marked SPODE,
mark red painted, 9½″, 24.0 cm.,
c. 1820, **£35-40** ET

Five Swansea Plates, one cracked,
8¼″, 21 cm., diam, one with
impressed mark, c.1815. **£500-
550** CStJ

A pair of Sevres bleu celeste
ornithological plates, blue interlaced L marks, painter's mark,
c.1765, 9½″, 24 cm.
£700-780 CStJ

A Spodes Imperial plate, marked
9″, 23.0 cm., **£20-22** ET

A Spode blue and white transfer
painted plate, Tiber pattern, 8″,
20.0 cm., marked, **£25-28** MW

A Spode blue and white plate,
'Tile pattern', marked SPODE,
c. 1810, 10″, 25.5 cm., **£18-20**
ET

A Swansea Plate, 8¼″, 21 cm.
diam. impressed mark, c.1815.
£280-310 CStJ

A Swansea Plate painted in an Imari palette, 9¾", 24.5 cm. diam red stencil mark, c.1815. £300-330 CStJ

A 'Vienna' octagonal plate, 13½", 34.5 cm. painted shield in underglaze-blue, late 19th C. £420-480　SBel

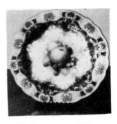

A late 19th century Worcester porcelain plate, painted decoration of fruit by A. Shuck, depicting apples and blackberries, underglaze-blue and elaborate jewelled gilt border, 8¾", 22.0 cm., £300-350

A rare Dillwyn & Co., Swansea, plate transfer-printed in black, 8⅞", 22.5 cm., impressed Dillwyn & Co., c. 1814-17 £50-60 SBel

A jewelled 'Vienna' plate by A. Becker, 9¾", 24.4 cm., shield mark in underglaze-blue, late 19th C. £180-210　SBel

Worcester blue and white 'Pinecone' pattern plate, Crescent marked, c. 1770-75, 7", 17.5 cm., £55-65　RD

A Venice (Cozzi) plate, iron-red anchor mark, c.1775, 9¼", 23.5 cm. £300-330　CStJ

An octagonal Vienna plate, stiff leaf border and foliate panels in raised gilding on a gros-bleu ground, 10¼", 26 cm., underglaze-blue shield, painted 'Jupiter and Calisto' in iron-red script, late 19th century. £180-210　SBel

A Worcester plate with pagoda and flowering tree pattern. 7½", 19.0 cm., c. 1770　MW

A Victorian blue and white banded dessert service with different floral painted panels, 12 8" plates and 2 square dishes. £75-85　AB

A Wedgwood plate with impressed Wedgwood T.G. mark, c. 1810-20 10", 25.5 cm., £20-25　ET

A Chamberlain's Worcester stone china plate of the early 19th century, (possibly made by Mason and decorated by Chamberlains and marked) £30-35　MW

A Vienna plate painted by Gritsch, signed with 'Irrlicht', the ghostly nymph rising from a pond. 9⅝", 24.2 cm., title painted shield, last quarter of 19th century. £250-280 SBel

A Franz Dorfl Vienna plate, painted by F. Tenner, signed, within an elaborate raised and acid-etched gilt rim, 10⅛", 25.8 cm., printed Vienna FD mark, painted title and 173, late 19th century. £420-500 SBel

A Vienna plate painted by Wagner signed, with a bust portrait of a curly-haired girl titled 'Fruhling', 9¾", 24.9 cm., painted blue shield and title, last quarter of 19th century. £410-500 SBel

A Wedgwood blue jasper-dip plate applied in crisp white relief with a classical man beside a winged horse, 8¾", 22 cm., impressed Wedgwood, late 19th century. £280-340 SBel

'Lisette', a Vienna plate painted by Wagner, signed, on a pale green-ground border enriched with gilt floral scrolls, 9¾", 24.3 cm., titled, painted shield, impressed marks, last quarter of 19th century, £410-500 SBel

A Wedgwood blue-jasper plate applied with a white relief of a classical scholar, 8¾", 22.1 cm., impressed Wedgwood and date code for 1887, £100-120 SBel

89

A Worcester Dr. Wall 'Blind Earl' plate. 6¼", 16.0 cm., **£670-750** JEV

A Worcester (Dr. Wall) Lobed Plate, 8½", 21.5 cm. diam., blue crescent mark, c.1770. **£250-280** CStJ

A Chamberlain's Worcester plate, Victorian registration mark, 10½" 26.5 cm., **£19-25** ET

1st period Worcester plate decorated by James Giles, c. 1765, 9", 23.0 cm., **£80-90** RD

A blue and white transfer printed plate Don Pottery depicting a 'View near Palma', 10", 25.5 cm., c. 1820, **£30-33** MW

A Flight, Barr & Barr Worcester plate (special mark) c. 1813, 8½", 21.5 cm., **£85-95** HHA

A Worcester Dr. Wall Lobed Plate from the Earl Manvers Service 8¼", 21 cm., diam. c.1770 **£450-500** CStJ

A good tazza painted with Venus and Cupid in a tree-framed glade with mountains beyond, 9¾" diam., 24.5 cm., **£800-900** NN

A pair of 9" German basket edge plates with Military figures of four different regiments, **£20-25** AB

Polychrome plate, possibly faience **£65-75** CAL

A WORCESTER (FLIGHT) DESSERT-PLATE FROM DUKE OF CLARENCE SERVICE, the centre painted en grisaille by John Pennington 24.5 cm. diam., blue crown, script and crescent mark, circa 1792. **£400-450** CStJ

An Adams 3 piece tea service in
the Wedgwood style, deep blue
ground, raised white decoration,
silver rims marked London 1906
£26-30   RB

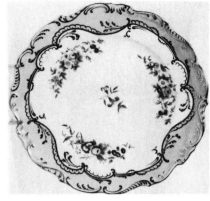

A 9 piece Coalport dessert service,
printed and painted within a grey
and gilt-scroll rim, plate, 9",
23.0 cm., painted pattern No. 308,
c. 1850   £200-250   SBel

Belleek part tea service (10 pieces)
in shell form. (inmarked) £32-40
WW

Richly decorated Coalport dinner
service. (116 pieces) £4,000-4,500
RBB

Berlin Porcelain Cabaret Set of
Exhibition Quality. £650-700
RBB

A Coalport part Dessert Service,
the maroon borders with gilt
gadroon rims; 15 pieces. £460-520
LC

An early 19th C. Copeland
Indian tree pattern part Dinner
Service, comprising of 52 pieces
£1,950-2,100   WW

A 34 piece Davenport part tea
service, dark green seaweed
design, picked out in gilding,
gilt-edged rims and handles,
plus cake plate: 9½"; 24 cm.,
printed Davenport and anchor
mark, pattern number 952
painted in gilding, 1840's; and six
matching Spode Side Plates, 6½";
16.7 cm., printed Spode Bone
China England, 20th century.
£150-250 SBel

A Meissen 'Onion Pattern' part
dinner service, comprising:- 11
Dinner Plates, 5 Side Plates, 5
Soup Plates, 2 oval Vegetable
Dishes, 3 oval Covers and one
circular Cover, and eleven other
pieces, 9¾", 24.8 cm., crossed
swords in underglaze-blue, late
19th C. **£800-900** SBel

A 38 piece Davenport part tea
and coffee service, with orange-
ground panels on a pink-scale
border, (five items damaged).
saucer: 5½" 14 cm., printed
Davenport and Rd. mark for
1849. **£630-660** SBel

A Meissen outside decorated Tete-
A-Tete, tray: 10½", 26.5 cm.,
19th century. **£230-280** SBel

A 20 piece Crown Derby dessert
service, each piece signed H. S.
Hancock and marked with crown,
crossed batons and D flanked by
initials SH in puce. **£1,850-2,200**
LC

A Japanese 56 piece dinner
service, marked Made by Hichozan
Shimpo, 19th century, **£780-
900** LC

A fine Crown Derby Porcelain tea
and coffee service of 'Dublin'
shape, decorated with Imari
pattern, No. 2451, printed mark
to bases with date codes, c1924
£450-500 KC

A Satsuma tea service, well
painted and gilt, 22 pieces, two
character mark. **£75-125** LC

A Paris (Faubourg Saint-Denis)
20 piece coffee service painted
'en camaieu' with named portrait
busts, the jug, bowl and saucers
marked Schoelcher in black script.
£115-130 LC

Victorian porcelain breakfast set
with butterfly handles, raised
decoration dated 6th March 1871
£52-60 WW

A Staffordshire tea service of
wrythen fluted baluster shape,
comprising 30 pieces, **£300-
350** HKC

A 30 piece Worcester tea and
coffee service, richly decorated
in blue, red and gold with a
Japan pattern, the lids of the tea
pot and sugar basin marked
Chamberlains Worcester War-
ranted in service, with buildings
and flowers in Chinese taste,
Worcester in red script. **£270-
290** LC

A Carl Thieme, Potschappel part
solitaire, 4 pieces, crossed lines
and T in blue, late 19th C. **£150-
200** SBel

A Royal Worcester part dessert
service comprising 9 pieces, by
G.H. Evans, printed mark in puce
for 1933. **£180-200** LC

A Royal Worcester part dessert
service painted by Richard Seb-
right and Frank Roberts, 1912-14,
16 pieces, **£1,300-1,500** OL

A Berlin coffee can, with geese
in panel, on royal-blue ground,
with gilt rim, marked, c. 1800
£95-120 AA

A Bow blue and white cup and saucer, with the Chinese Fisherman pattern, c. 1753, £150-190 KK

A Bow coffee cup. c. 1755, £36-40 MW

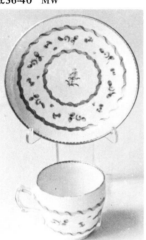

A Bristol coffee cup and saucer, c. 1780, blue cross mark, £150-180 RD

A Caughley teabowl and saucer, 'fruit and wreath' pattern. 'S' mark, c. 1775 £60-80 MW

Set of six Cauldon china coloured floral decorated coffee cups and saucers, £35-40 WW

A Chantilly teacup and saucer, with Japanese Kakiemon design, Mid-18th century £750-850 JEV

A Chelsea double-handed chocolate cup, painted with English garden birds and insects, on reverse with large dragonfly, red anchor mark, c. 1754, £150-180 HA

A Chelsea gold anchor coffee cup and saucer, with pineapple moulding, c. 1765 £200-230 MW

A Chelsea octagonal teabowl and saucer, printed with Aesops Fables in colours by J. H. O.Neale, raised anchor period, c. 1751 £900-1,000 HA

An acanthus moulded white teabowl, triangle marked, c. 1745, 1¾'', £340-400 HA

A Chelsea-Derby teabowl and saucer, c. 1775, £50-60 KK

A Derby cup and saucer, puce, marked Derby, c. 1785, £26-28 MW

A Derby cup and saucer, c. 1800 £24-28 ET

A set of six Dresden tea cups and saucers, crossed swords mark in underglaze-blue; and tea pot and cover, 4¼'', 11 cm., £180-220 LC

A Liverpool teabowl and saucer, Chaffers pattern, c. 1760, tiny chip, **£55-65** MW

A Crown Derby teacup and saucer with pink ground, the cup painted by George Robertson with a frigate flying the Red Ensign, the saucer with other shipping of the Royal Navy, in gilt-framed square panels, puce mark crown, crossed batons and D and pattern no. 447 **£1,350-1,500** LC

A Liverpool coffee cup, late Christian, early Pennington period, c. 1778, **£40-50** MW

A Woolfe's Liverpool teabowl and saucer, with typical Chinoiserie pink decoration, c. 1780, **£50-60** KK

A Doccia coffee cup and saucer with Kakiemon decoration, a typical Italian shape handle (particular to Capo di Monte), c. 1760, **£240-250** HA

An Oude Loosdrecht cup and saucer, marked M.O.L. c. 1775 **£200-280** KK

A Frankenthal coffee can painted in colours, green, puce and gold trellis border, blue crowned C.T. mark, c. 1765, **£85-110** HA

A Lowestoft blue and white painted feeding cup, c. 1768 **£320-400** HA

A Lowestoft coffee cup and saucer, c. 1772, **£45-55** MW

A Liverpool Chaffers blue and white teabowl and saucer, with the 'Jumping Boy' pattern, c. 1758, **£165-185** HA

A Lowestoft fluted teabowl and saucer, with typical flower decoration, c. 1770, **£70-80** KK

95

A Ludwigsburg cup, with chocolate rim marked, c. 1760, £50-70 AA

A Meissen Cabinet cup and saucer, saucer 5¾″, 14.3 cm. underglaze-blue crossed swords, late 19th C. £230-260 SBel

A pair of Meissen teacups and saucers, blue crossed swords marks Pressnummer 17 and 63, c.1745. £1,100-1,200 CStJ

A pair of Meissen coffee-cups and saucers, blue crossed swords marks Pressnummer 63, c.1745. £800-860 CStJ

A pair of Meissen teabowls and saucers painted en camaieu rose, blue crossed swords marks, C.1745 £900-950 CStJ

A Meissen tall beaker and saucer, minor rim repair, blue crossed swords and Gilder's mark 15, c.1735. £800-880 CStJ

A Meissen coffee-cup and saucer, chipped, blue crossed swords mark, c.1745. £170-190 CStJ

A Meissen coffee-cup and saucer, crack to handle, blue crossed swords and gilder's mark X, c.1745. £350-400 CStJ

A pair of Meissen 'Schnee-Ballen' cups and covers, 5″, 12.5 cm., crossed swords in under glaze-blue, late 19th C. £290-320 SBel

A pair of Meissen cups and saucers, saucer 6⅛″, 15.3 cm., underglaze-blue crossed swords, early 19th C. £250-280 SBel

A pair of Meissen custard cups,
6″, 15 cm., underglaze-blue
crossed swords, late 19th C.
£110-140 SBel

A Meissen tall cup and saucer,
painted in colours, with Watteau
Scenes by B.G. Hauer, with gilt
lace borders, c. 1743, crossed
swords mark. **£350-400** HA

A pair of Meissen small cups and
saucers, with ochre Kakiemon
decoration, c. 1740 **£1,170-1,300**
JEV

A Minton coffee cup and saucer
decorated in blue and gilt, pattern
no. 499, c. 1800, **£32-35** ET

A Newhall coffee can, with a
dark-blue ground, pattern 533
(rare), c. 1798, 2½″, 6.5 cm.,
£25-30 MW

A Meissen cup and saucer, Haus-
maler decorated, with Quaker
farming scenes, c. 1745-50
marked, **£450-500** AA

A Newhall trio, pattern no. 206,
rare shape, c. 1790, **£42-48** MW

A Nantgarw cup and saucer,
London decorated, with typical
handle, c. 1815 **£200-250** KK

A Meissen Bleu-de-Roi Cabinet
Cup and Saucer well painted in
muted colours with reserved
panels of galleons, 5½″, 14.2 cm.,
crossed swords, star and 4 in
underglaze-blue, second quarter
of the 19th century. **£380-450**
SBel

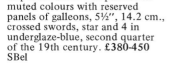

A Newhall coffee cup with gilt
rim, c. 1782, **£29-35** MW

A Chinese export teabowl and
saucer,.c. 1765, cracked, **£10-15**
DW

A Famille Rose Chinese cup and saucer, **£35-40** HHA

A Ridgway cup and saucer, c. 1800, **£25-30** ET

6 Sevres tall coffee-cups and saucers, blue interlaced L marks enclosing date letters, 1770-1775. **£400-430** CStJ

A Paris Charles Potter cup and saucer, from the Rue de Gusson, with butterfly decoration in colours, c. 1785-90 **£60-85** KK

Samson Chinese-style tea cup and saucer, puce scale borders and sprigs of flowers, **£15-20** WW

6 Sevres custard-cups and covers, repaired, blue interlaced L marks, 1770, Painter's marks, 3¼", 8 cm. **£380-420** CStJ

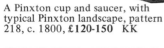

A Pinxton cup and saucer, with typical Pinxton landscape, pattern 218, c. 1800, **£120-150** KK

A highly decorative cup and saucer, possibly by Ridgway , c. 1840, **£30-35** ET

A St. Cloud soft paste cup and saucer, with pine cone moulding, c. 1725, **£100-130** KK

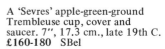

A 'Sevres' bleu-celeste-ground cabinet cup and saucer, painted interlaced L's, late 19th C. **£180-200** SBel

A 'Sevres' apple-green-ground Trembleuse cup, cover and saucer. 7", 17.3 cm., late 19th C. **£160-180** SBel

A 'Sevres' cabinet cup and saucer, 5¾", 14.7 cm., painted interlaced L's, late 19th C. **£210-230** SBel

Sevres coffee cup and saucer painted with panels of birds on a green ground interlaced L's mark, 1767, painters mark C.P. **£170-200** RD

A Sevres soft-paste cabinet cup and saucer, painted summer flowers on a pink ground with blue oeil-de-perdrix, 8", 20 cm., painted interlaced L's, incised 41, mid-19th century, **£80-120** SBel

A pair of Sevres bleu-celeste ground soft-paste cups, later painted within gilt foliate borders, the rim, base and twin loop handles gilt, 4³/₈", 11.2 cm., painted interlaced L's, 18th and mid-19th century, **£240-300** SBel

A miniature porcelain cabinet cup and saucer in the Sevres taste, the pink and gilt enriched ground relieved with panels of birds, **£22-30** RB

A Spode stoneware cup and saucer (interesting mark), c. 1830, **£20-25** ET

A 'Sevres' soft-paste 'jewelled' cup and saucer, on a bleu-de-roi ground, saucer 5", 12.7 cm. interlaced L's, mid 19th C. **£190-210** SBel

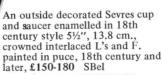

Spode Roses pattern cup and saucer, c. 1835, **£27-30** RA

An outside decorated Sevres cup and saucer enamelled in 18th century style 5½", 13.8 cm., crowned interlaced L's and F. painted in puce, 18th century and later, **£150-180** SBel

Vienna porcelain chocolate cup and cover with stand, each piece painted with scenes of classical figures in colour on a royal blue and gilt ground, **£100-130** RB

99

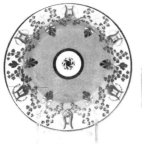

A Vienna coffee can and saucer 10⅛", 15.3 cm. shield in underglaze-blue, 1830-40. £600-700 SBel

A Worcester trio, Sunflower pattern, c. 1765, crescent mark, teabowl and saucer, £100-120 MW

Worcester blue and white tea bowl and saucer printed with 'fruit' pattern. c. 1775, crescent mark, £54-60   RD

A Wallendorf Thuringian cup and saucer, cafe au lait and blue decoration, the pattern and ribbing typical of this factory, marked in underglaze-blue c. 1765, £80-100   KK

Worcester blue and white tea bowl and saucer – printed fruit pattern, c. 1770 crescent mark, £65-75   RD

A Worcester teacup and saucer marked F.B.B., c. 1810, £20-25 ET

Worcester blue and white tea bowl and saucer, printed with Chinese figures, c. 1770, crescent mark, £58-70   RD

A Chamberlain Worcester cup and saucer, in gilt with a pictorial view on the saucer, c. 1815, £30-35 ET

A Wedgwood three-colour Jasper-Dip cup and saucer, decorated with lilac-ground classical Medallions, with trophies, ribbons and floral borders, saucer discoloured, saucer: 5¾", 13.8 cm., impressed Wedgwood and date code for 1869 £400-500   SBel

Worcester blue and white teacup and saucer – printed with pattern of flowers, c. 1770, crescent mark, £58-65   RD

A pair of Chamberläin Worcester gilt and white cups and saucers, c. 1800 £45-50 pair,   HHA

A Worcester blue scale coffee cup and saucer, c. 1770, £160-180   MW

A trio of teacup, coffee cup and saucer, possibly Worcester, c. 1815-20 **£30-35** ET

Chamberlains Worcester two cups and saucer, c. 1820, **£35-40** ET

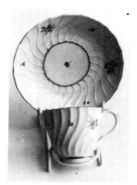

A marked Barr Worcester cup and saucer, c. 1800, incised B mark, **£20-23** ET

An eggshell porcelain Worcester teabowl and saucer, painted in colours after the Chinese, c. 1755 **£260-300** HA

Worcester blue and white tea bowl and saucer, printed with sprays of flowers c. 1775, **£43-50** RD

Worcester blue and white coffee cup and saucer, printed with the 'fence' pattern. c. 1775 crescent mark, **£54-60** RD

A rare Frankenthal coffee pot and cover, 10¼", 26 cm. Mark in underglaze – blue of Palatinate Lion. c.1760. **£1,050-1,200** GP

19th century Germain Mother Hubbard novelty coffee pot, 11½"; 29 cm., **£26-30** WW

A Limbach coffee pot and cover, decorated in puce, circa 1783, marked, 12½"; 32 cm., **£170-190** AA

A Liverpool blue and white coffee pot and cover, from the Pennington factory, circa 1775 8½"; 21.5 cm., **£120-140** MW

A Meissen coffee-pot and cover, painted by G.B. Hauer, chip to cover, blue crossed swords mark, Gilder's mark 50, c.1730, 8", 20 cm. **£1,600-1,700** CStJ

A Meissen pear-shaped coffee-pot and domed cover, cover repaired, incised N mark, c.1745, 9½", 24 cm. **£750-810** CStJ

101

Rare Saltglazed Stoneware Coffee Pot and Cover. Crabstock handle and dragon spout. Moulded in Polychrome. Enamelled figures with robes of iron-red and yellow trousers, 15 cm., 6″ (knop SR) £800-1,200 PL

A Meissen Coffee Pot and Cover painted with figures strolling or gaming, gilt spout and borders, bud-knopped cover, 22.4 cm., 10¾″, cancelled crossed swords in underglaze-blue, late 19th century. £100-150 SBel

A Worcester Coffee pot and lid, 23.5 cm., high; 9¼″ £660-720 KC

A Berlin teapot (without cover), with puce scale pattern and mask spout, circa 1770, 3½″, marked, 9 cm., £180-240 AA

An early 19th century Wedgwood Creamware veilleuse, with pierced breather holes, basin liner and teapot, tea cup burner, impressed mark in capitals, 30 cm., 12″ high £145-165 OL

Coffee pot, chocolate ground, gilt and floral decorated (spout repaired) £22-30 WW

A Lowestoft teapot, in the 'Doll's House' pattern, circa 1785 £80-120 KK

A Worcester blue and white feather moulded coffee pot and cover. circa 1760, lid restored, 8¾″; 22 cm., £140-160 MW

A Yabu Meizan Sake Pot and Cover, the ovoid body delicately enamelled and gilt, 12 cm., 4¾″, gilt Yabu Meizan, circa 1900 £150-200 SBel

An 18th century Lowestoft teapot and cover decorated in polychrome with the 'two bird pattern' 15 cm., 6″ high. £230 OL

Lowestoft Teapot and Cover of rare barrel shape. Open flower finial, painted in colour in Chinese style. Reverse with a Chinaman on an island. Red loop and dot border, 12 cm., 4¾" £480-530 PL

Victorian Coalport porcelain teapot, decorated with gilt-enhanced blue borders. £8-15 RB

A rare Woolfe's Liverpool Teapot and Cover, with a pink transfer print and panel painted border. circa 1798 £80-120 KK

A Lowestoft teapot with coloured floral decoration attributed to the tulip painter. Restored. £32-45 WW

A Meissen globular teapot and cover, minor chips, blue crossed swords mark, c.1745, 8", 20 cm. £550-600 CStJ

A Pennington Liverpool Teapot and cover, with flower decorations and a 'wet' blue border, circa 1780. £80-105 KK

A Meissen teapot and cover, circa 1740 7¼", wide; 18.5 cm., marked, £2,200-2,400 JEV

An early Meissen Hausmalerei teapot and cover, painted in Schwarzlot in the manner of Preissler, chip to rim, c.1725, 6¼", 16 cm. £900-1,000 CStJ

An early Meissen teapot and cover, cracked, blue crossed swords mark, Gilder's mark H, c.1725, 6", 15 cm. £850-920 CStJ

Chinese export porcelain teapot, blue and white, mid 19th century £68-80 LBA

A very rare Plymouth teapot, circa 1769 £260-290 KK

A shaped Victorian Minton teapot and cover, decorated with birds in flight in underglaze-blue. £19-25 RB

A Newhall teapot and cover, pattern No. 273, circa 1785. £65-75 MW

An I-Hsing cylindrical teapot and cover of aubergine colour, the cover chipped, 5¾'', 14.5 cm., the base with an impressed square seal mark of a dragon. £200-240 CStJ

A Sevres teapot with a band of scrolls and flowers on a green ground, and gilded, blue painted monogram F.R. mark, 1792-1804 £170-230 HKC

A Newhall teapot and cover, pattern No. 421, (spout restored) circa, 1785, 5½''; 14 cm., £58-68 MW

Staffordshire Teapot circa 1820 6¾''; 17 cm., Pattern No. 750 £55-65 RD

An I-Hsing globular teapot and cover of aubergine colour, chipped, 6½'' long, 16 cm., impressed double-gourd mark. £95-110 CStJ

A Whieldon tortoise-shell in a mottled manganese glaze, highlighted in places in green and yellow, 8¾'' wide; 22 cm., £410-460 CStJ

Caughley blue and white tankard printed with the 'parrot pecking fruit' pattern, c. 1775, 3¼", 8.0 cm., C mark, **£110-130** RD

A Dresden gilt-metal-mounted tankard, moulded with a medieval, brightly coloured battle scene, the hinged cover with feathered knop, scrolling dog-head term handles, 9⅞", 25 cm., painted R, late 19th century, **£160-210** SBel

A Mettlach tankard, modelled in the form of a tapering turret, incised and painted colours, 9½", 24 cm., impressed mark Mettlach, 2382 **£130-160** LC

A Meissen tankard and cover, blue crossed swords mark, Pressnummer 20, c.1765, 6¼", 16 cm. **£750-800** CStJ

A Volkstedt 'Doccia' tankard and cover, robustly moulded with Silenus' drunken parade, scrolling lion's head handle, in fleshy tones and strong colours, 12¼", 31.2 cm., underglaze blue crown and AVP monogram, c. 1910, **£100-120** SBel

A Martin Bros. large tankard of tapering cylindrical form signed R.W. Martin and incised A20, October, 1874, 6¾", 17 cm., **£360-400** KC

A Mettlach stoneware stein, after M. Hein, signature, metal-mounted cover, 7¾", 19.5 cm., impressed castle mark, Mettlach and numerals, incised VB, c. 1900 **£180-240** SBel

A Mettlach stoneware stein moulded with an inn scene, hinged pewter-mounted cover with a warrior bust thumb-piece, 10¼", 26 cm., impressed castle mark, Mettlach and numerals, incised VB, c. 1900 **£210-250** SBel

Minton tankard, c. 1840, 3¼", 8.0 cm., £45-50 RD

A Worcester tankard, 3½", 9.0 cm., £775-850 JEV

A Mettlach stoneware stein, the handle as a branch, 7¼", 18.5 cm., impressed castle mark, Mettlach and numerals incised VB, c. 1900 £50-70 SBel

A 1st period Worcester mazzarine blue-ground tankard, painted with European flowers, gilt rim, crescent mark, c. 1768, 5½", 14.0 cm., £280-320 RD

A Vienna tankard, 6¼", 16 cm., underglaze-blue shield, late 19th C. £260-300 SBel

A Mettlach Tankard decorated after H Schlitt, impressed signature, metal-mounted-lid, 8⅛", 20.5 cm., impressed Mettlach and tower mark, c. 1910, £300-340 SBel

Worcester tankard, deep-blue scale ground, two panels framed with rococo scroll gold and painted with butterflies, insects and birds, 6", 15 cm., square mark, 1st period £850-950 PK

An enamelled Milchglas tankard, tones of pink and green, 4¾", 12 cm., Bohemian, c.1770. £260-290 SBS

Two Worcester blue and white tankards printed with Le Promenade Chinois' and the 'Plantation' patterns, c. 1765, 4¾", 12.0 cm., £150-170 each, MW

A Worcester bell shaped tankard, painted in underglaze-blue, 5¾", 14.5 cm., c. 1765, £120-140 DW

A rare jewelled and coloured Biscuit Goblet, probably Sevres, 6½", 16.6 cm., 1860's. **£210-240** SBel

A Chelsea Teaplant beaker in brilliant condition, in bright enamel colours and applied decoration, with apple sprig and insects inside, with brown-edged rim. c. 1745 3", 7.5 cm., Triangle period, **£1,000-1,200** HA

A fine Cologne stoneware copper-gilt mounted Bellarmine of rich brown colour, the waist girdled by an inscription, the copper-gilt cover embossed with acanthus and with floret finial. 10¾", 27.0 cm., 16th century, **£950-1,200** NN

A celadon glazed wine cup and stand, the glaze of olive-green tone, 4", 10 cm., overall, Korean, Koryo Dynasty, 13th century, **£900-1,100** KC

Ashstead blue pottery mug designed by Percy Metcalfe, the head of Stanley Baldwin, No. 76 of a limited edition of 1,000 **£21-30** RB

A small Bow coffee mug, painted in colours, with 'Chinese Peony' pattern, green trellis and floral border, c. 1758, **£80-90** HA

A gilt and white Derby mug, c. 1782-1825, marked, 3¾", 9.5 cm., **£85-95** HHA

A Longton Hall mug, with 'pecking parrot' decoration, decorated by Littler in this typical Westpans manner. **£450-500** KK

A rare Minton beer mug (Society of Arts Prize — silver medal winner 1846), **£56-70**

A Worcester straight-sided mug, with honeycomb transfer printed border and 'parrot pecking fruit' design, crescent mark to base, c. 1770, 5¼", 13 cm., **£140-180** KC

A Rare Worcester Blue and White Inscribed and Dated Cylindrical Mug, extensively cracked, 4⅝", 11.5 cm. high, 1776. **£300-340** CStJ

A Worcester Blue and White Cylindrical Mug, 3⅜", 8.5 cm. painter's mark, c.1758. **£550-600** CStJ

107

A Bow leaf sauceboat, leaves in green and yellow with puce ribbing. Stem handle in white 'boung' puce. Foot rim edged with puce scrolls. 17.5 cm., 7". £380-450 PL

A Champion's Bristol Sauceboat. Marked with crossed swords circa 1770-5. £150-180 KK

Worcester Double-lipped Sauce-boat, scroll handles and button thumb rests. Painted in under-glaze-blue with a central Oriental landscape. 16.5 cm., 6½", painters mark, circa 1760 £230-270 PL

A Chantilly double handled sauce-boat, painted in colours with Kakiemon plants and red hunting horn mark, circa 1735 8" long; 20 cm. £420-500 HA

Pair of blue and white Worcester sauce boats, circa 1765, 8" crescent mark; 20 cm., £230-280 RD

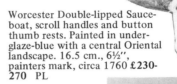

A pair of Ch'ien Lung famille rose oval soup tureens, with rare George III silver Covers, 14", 35.5 cm. by John Lloyd, Dublin, c.1770. 14 oz. £3,000-3,600 SIre

A Mason's ironstone sauce tureen, cover and stand, painted in red, blue, green and gold, with im-pressed mark Patent Ironstone China, £230-300 LC

A pair of 8"; 20 cm., Meissen Sauce Boats decorated with apple-green and gilt banding, puce figures and scroll entwined handles, splayed feet. £190-210 VC

A Pennington's Liverpool blue and white sauceboat, with Acanthus moulding, circa 1783. £50-70 KK

An 18th century Meissen gravy boat of Kakiemon design, with mask lips, 10" wide; 25.5 cm., £400-450 AA

A pair of Sevres shaped oval sauce-boats, minor repairs, blue interlaced L marks, 1789, Painter's mark Mereaud, Gilder's mark Chauveaux, 9¼", 23.5 cm. £370-420 CStJ

A small enamelled and gilt Mil-chglas tureen and cover, in puce, orange and green, 4¾", 12 cm., Bohemian, c.1760. £150-180 SBS

A large Luneville tureen with cauliflower finial to cover, 11″ dia; 28 cm., £140-160   WW

An early Spode Tureen and lid of fine quality, marked SPODE in red, circa 1800, 6¾″ wide; 17 cm., £70-80   HHA

A Berlin Porcelain Tureen and cover 13″; 33 cm., printed sceptre in underglaze-blue, last quarter of 19th century. £240-280   SBel

Crown Derby vegetable dish with cover, circa 1800 £65-75 GA

A pair of blue and white Meissen soup tureens, with flowers and insects, circa 1742, marked, 9½″ wide; 24 cm., £775-850 pair   AA

A Spode 19th century two-handled soup tureen with scenic transfers in blue and white. £55-60   AB

Late 19th century Stoneware German punch tureen, 12″; 30.5 cm., across handles. £48-55 WW

A rare blue and white Derby chestnut basket, applied flowers outside and chinoiserie scene inside, circa 1758. £290-350 KK

A Famille Rose Porcelain Tureen and Cover, painted with coats-of-arms and the motto above "Nec Fluctu Nec Flatu", 37 cm., 14½″ wide, Ch'ien Lung. £1,400-1,800   KC

A Helene Wolfsohn Ecuelle, Cover and stand, the cover with a canary knop and applied with nuts and twigs, saucer; 21.2 cm., 8¾″ crowned D in underglaze-blue, late 19th century. £120-180 SBel

A French Faience Rhinoceros Tureen and Cover, covered over-all in a thick, turquoise glaze glaze, 42 cm., 16½″ incised 1211, late 19th century. £100-150 SBel

A pair of two-handled Sevres-style tureens and covers, decorated with flowers in panels on a magenta and gilt ground. (slight damage) £190-250   RB

109

A Worcester Oval Sauce Tureen,
cover and stand, painted in
Japanese style, the tureen 7¼",
18.5 cm., overall, tureen, stand
and cover with seal mark in underglaze-blue. Flight period. £300-
350 LC

A Victorian China soup tureen
with Oriental pattern and entwined handles, 15" over; 38 cm.,
£38-45 WW

A Worcester tureen, cover and
stand enamelled with flowers,
the cover with a moulded fig
finial, impressed mark, 1865-80
£160-180 HKC

A 19th century beige ground
Stilton cheese dish on stand.
scene, (slight chip to base) 12"
dia; 30.5 cm., £50-60 AB

A pair of Dresden Candelabra,
19¾", 50 cm., crossed swords
mark in underglaze-blue. £580-
640 LC

A pair of Bow porcelain candlesticks circa 1760, 9¾" high;
24.5 cm., £1,200-1,500

A Dresden centrepiece, 16¼",
41 cm., crossed swords in underglaze blue, late 19th C. £150-170
SBel

A pair of Dresden candelabra,
each for three lights, 8½"; 21.5
cm., 19th century. £240-280
SBel

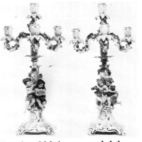

A pair of Meissen candelabra,
19¾", 50 cm. underglaze-blue
crossed swords, late 19th C.
£800-900 SBel

A Plaue-on-Havel Centre Piece,
detachable pierced bowl, the
whole in pastel shades, 43.2 cm.,
17¼", crossed parallel lines in
underglaze-blue, impressed 454,
late 19th century. £300-400
SBel

A Pair of Meissen Porcelain and
Ormolu Candelabra, symbolic
of Spring and Autumn. £410-500
SBel

A pair of Sitzendorf Candelabra,
19″, 48 cm., underglaze-blue,
crossed parallel lines, late 19th C.
£150-180 SBel

A Rockingham Pale-Blue Ground
Centrepiece, crack to bowl,
some chips, 14⅛″, 36 cm. high,
c.1835. £1,100-1,200 CStJ

A Plaue-on-Havel centrepiece,
12¼″, 31 cm., underglaze-blue
double crossed parallel lines,
late 19th C. £210-240 SBel

Pair of Porcelain Candlesticks
blue glazed and gilt decorated
with gilt metal nozzles and
drip trays. 11½″; 29 cm., £220-
260 WW

A Volkstedt centrepiece, 14½″,
37 cm. underglaze-blue sunburst
mark, late 19th C. £150-180
SBel

A Pair of Worcester Comport
Stands after a model by Charles
Toft, moulded signature, in
'Raphaelesque' colours, circular
rings with pierced rims, restored,
15″; 38 cm., impressed crowned
circle, circa 1865. Est. £150-220
SBel

French ormolu mounted stamp
box. £25-30 TJC

A Well-Painted 'Meissen' Box and
Cover, gilt-metal hinged cover,
18.5 cm., 7¼″, crossed swords
in blue, mid 19th century. £300-
400 SBel

A Battersea enamel box, 4″ wide.
10 cm., £1,000-1,200 JEV

A Meissen silver-gilt mounted
snuff-box painted en camaieu
rose, c.1760. £650-720 CStJ

A Meissen scroll-moulded snuff box painted in colours with castle of Saxony, circa 1750, 2¾" wide; 7 cm., £1,900-2,400 HA

A Meissen shaped box with lid, decorated in puce, circa 1745, 4½" marked; 11.5 cm., £450-550 AA

A Meissen sugar box and cover, with the Kakiemon 'Bee Pattern' decoration, and an unusual rabbit finial, c. 1740 crossed swords mark, 5" wide, 12.5 cm., £1,000-1,200 HA

Moorcroft pin box, signed, with inscription 'Potter to H.M. the Queen' inside lid. £16-20 TJC

A blue and white circular box and cover, K'ang Hsi, 4", 10 cm. diam., £240-270 CStJ

A Satsuma cosmetic box, the cover decorated in gold and soft colours, within a red and gilt demi-lune border, the base with butterflies, 3"; 7.6 cm., £65-75 LC

Satsuma cosmetic box and cover, oblong with re-entrant corners, gilt and painted within a red gilt demi-lune border, the base with butterflies, 2⅞"; 7.3 cm., £100-120 LC

A 'Sevres' box by F. Ambtet, 12¾", 32.3 cm., painted M. Imple, de Sevres, late 19th C. £480-560 SBel

A 'Sevres' bleu-de-roi ground casket, by Ault, signed, 8", 20 cm., overall, painted interlaced L's, late 19th C. £360-420 SBel

A 'Sevres' gilt-metal-mounted casket, by Poitevin, 10⅞", 27.5 cm. late 19th C. working key. £1,000-1,200 SBel

A 'Sevres' gilt-metal-mounted box and cover, on a bleu-celeste ground, 4⅜", 11 cm., late 19th C. £190-210 SBel

A Vienna purple-lustre-ground casket and cover, 31.2 cm., 12¼", late 19th C. £420-500 SBel

A Dresden clock case with two-train movement, brightly coloured with gilt details, 18¼", 46.5 cm., cross and dot in underglaze-blue, c.1880. £500-600 SBel

A Meissen rococo clock-case and shaped oval stand, painted in colours, chips, blue crossed swords mark, c.1750, 15¼", 39 cm. **£2,800-3,000** CStJ

A Meissen clock case, 21⅝", 5.5 cm., cancelled underglaze-blue crossed swords, late 19th C. **£1,200-1,400** SBel

A Meissen clock-case, with two-train movement, in underglaze-blue and white, 9½", 24 cm., underglaze-blue crossed swords, late 19th C. key. **£540-620** SBel

A 'Sevres' Ormolu-Mounted biscuit clock case, by Chaudelair, signed, 11¼", 28.6 cm., c.1900. key and pendulum. **£360-400** SBel

A Meissen oval frame, now converted to a dressing-table clock, signed J.W. Benson, 25 Old Bond Street, 13", 33.2 cm., crossed swords in underglaze-blue, late 18th C. **£480-540** SBel

Victorian 3-piece pottery clock set with blue/gilt decoration. **£20-30** RB

A rare commemorative mug, made on the occasion of the coronation of Queen Victoria, transfer-printed in pink. (minor chips) 3½"; 9 cm., **£520-600** SBel

A Doulton 1897 commemorative beaker and an Edward VII similar. (hair cracks) **£15-20** RB

A Victorian Commemorative bowl made by Goss for the Diamond Jubilee of Queen Victoria. **£20-25** F

A Booths china mug depicting the allied soldiers at the outbreak of the First World War. **£18-25** WW

A jug published by Goodwin, Bridgwood and Harris to commemorate the death of George IV in 1831 7½", 19 cm., **£200-250** JJM

A Jackfield Commemorative jug, 1897. 6½" high, 16.5 cm., **£20-25** RB

A small plate published to commemorate Victoria and Albert's wedding. 5¼", 13 cm., **£120-140** JJM

A small plate published to commemorate the coronation of Victoria, 5½", 14 cm., **£230-270** JJM

A small plate of Queen Victoria 5¼", 13.cm., **£120-140** JJM

Victorian plate 1896. 8", 20 cm., **£15-20** F

A rare Staffordshire pottery mug with two portraits of George III and Queen Charlotte. Cartouche inscribed "A King Rever'd and a Queen Beloved" King and Constitution, 4¾", 12 cm., **£220-280** LE

A Staffordshire Jug published for the coronation of William IV, with slight restoration. 8", 20 cm., **£170-190** JJM

A jug published by Read and Clemenston of Hanley, Staffordshire for the proclamation of Victoria. 1837. 7½", 19 cm., **£400-450** JJM

A William IV Coronation Jug, Staffordshire, 1831 8½", 21.5 cm., **£90-100** DW

A first period Worcester mug marking the fame of 'Grunby the Brave' c1760 6", 15.0 cm., **£750-900** JJM

A Worcester King of Prussia Mug, black on white transfer print dated 1759, signed R.H. Worcester, c1760. **£200-280** KK

Worcester plate, Coronation of George V, (marked) 10½", 26.5 cm., **£15-20** F

A jug to commemorate the first visit of Jenny Lind to England in 1847. 8", 20 cm., **£70-90** JJM

A jug to commemorate the raising of Rifle Volunteers in 1860. 8¼", 21 cm., **£45-50** JJM

King George V milk jug signed Russell & Son. **£10-15** F

A Sunderland Earthenware Jug, transfer-printed Masonic verse, a ship and view of the Iron Bridge with mottled pink lustre. 9", 22.8 cm., c1840 £85-110 SBel

A Sunderland Lustre Jug, with transfer-printed boats and poem within painted garlands with pink lustre. 7¼", 18.7 cm., c1840 £100-150 SBel

A salt glaze gin flask of William IVth, published by Oldfield of Chesterfield, Derby c1830, 9¾", 24.5 cm., £230-270 JJM

A Liverpool bowl published in 1793 to commemorate the Duke of York leading the English to join the Combined Armies under the Prince of Coburg. 10", 25.5 cm., £350-400 JJM

A Chinese export bowl commemorating the Jacobite Rebellion in 1745, damaged, 10" diam. 25;5 cm., £2,000-2,500 JJM

A Sunderland Creamware jug, published c1806 with this previously unrecorded print of the Victory. £300-330 JJM

A Liverpool creamware mug published for Trafalgar. Note the Masonic Emblem on Nelson's Nile Medal, a very rare print, only three examples recorded 4¾", 12.0 cm., £230-270 JJM

'The Great Performer of the Adelphi' Plate, published in 1824 to mark the opening of the play 'The Elephant of Siam', Swansea pottery, 6½", 16.5 cm., £230-280 JJM

A Sunderland tankard, published to promote the cause of the Hon. T. Liddel at the General Election of 1826. 5¼", 13 cm., £120-150 JJM

A plate published on the death of Prince Albert. 9¼", 23.5 cm., £140-180 JJM

'Admiral Keppel for Ever' plate, a Lambeth Delft plate published in 1779 in Admiral Keppel's support at the time of his most unjust court martial. 9", 23.0 cm., £370-420 JJM

A Crimean war jug, published by Ridgway and Arington, in 1854 (slightly damaged) £40-50 JJM

An Isaac van Amburgh mug, published for the American Animal Trainer. Queen Victoria visited him six times at Drury Lane in 1839. £150-200 JJM

A jug published to commemorate the death of Peel. 7", 17.5 cm., £70-90 JJM

King George V cream jug £5-10 F

George V Coronation Beaker. £10-15 F

A Prince of Wales and Princess Alexandra Jug, 8¾", 22 cm., £75-85 JJM

1914 Allies plate, gilt rim. 8¾", 22 cm., £15-20 F

A jug regretting the death of Queen Caroline in 1821. The verse is very unusual. (repaired chip) 6", 15.0 cm., £180-220 JJM

A creamware jug published c1804 at the time of the threatened Napoleonic invasions. 7½", 19 cm., £400-500 JJM

Octagonal Commemorative Plate of 1887. 10", 25.5 cm., £20-25 F

Silver Jubilee George V Plate 6", 15 cm., £5-10 F

A 'Peace Jug' for the 'Brave Soldiers and Sailors of the Crimea, 8½", 21.5 cm., £70-80 JJM

A Duke of Cambridge Plate 8½", 21.5 cm., £200-250 JJM

Small Silver Jubilee Plate, 1910-1935, 5", 12.5 cm., £5-10 BF

A blue and white small plate of Queen Caroline, 5½", 14.0 cm., £150-180 JJM

A plate to commemorate the Great Exhibition at Crystal Palace in 1851. 7", 17.5 cm., £40-50 JJM

A mug published to commemorate the Battle of the Saints in 1782 when Lord Rodney defeated the French. 3¾", 9.5 cm., £240-280 JJM

116

A William IV and Queen Adelaide coronation mug, transfer-printed in sepia. (slight wear) 5″, 12.7 cm., c1831 **£170-200** SBel

A mug to commemorate the 'Illustrious Prince Ferdinand of Brunswick' who was the English Commander in Chief at the Battle of Minden, 1750. 3¾″, 9.5 cm., **£640-700** JJM

George V Coronation Mug **£10-15** F

George V porcelain Coronation Mug. **£10-15** F

A rare commemorative cup and saucer made after the death of Princess Charlotte, printed in black. (slight wear,) saucer: 5½″, 14 cm., c1817 **£60-100** SBel

Silver Jubilee Mug George V. **£10-15** F

A Duke of Waterloo black transfer Mug, 4″ High, 10.0 cm., **£150-200** JJM

A mug to commemorate the famous boxing clash between Humphries and Mendoza, c1790. 4″, 10.0 cm., **£350-400** JJM

George V Silver Jubilee Mug. **£10-15** F

A mug commemorating the Battle of Alma, 1854, showing the Clan Campbell rallying the troops. 3″, 7.5 cm., **£120-140** JJM

King Edward VII Coronation Mug. **£10-15** F

Edward VIII Coronation cup & saucer. **£10-15** F

A mug marking the election of Kinloch in the Reform Parliament of 1832, for the city of Dundee. 3½″, 9.0 cm., **£120-150** JJM

A meat-paste jar bearing a print of the 'Landing of the British Army at the Crimea' (Clarke 73) **£180-210** SBel

C.S. Parnell, W. E. Gladstone and a group Symbolic of Peace, issued to commemorate the Kilmainham Treaty of 1882, £230-270   SBel

A salt glaze Stone ware flask made to regret the death of the Duke of York in 1827. 8″, 20.0 cm., £280-320   JJM

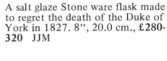

A bowl to commemorate the visit of George IV to Scotland in 1822, 5½″ wide, 14.0 cm., £300-400   JJM

A vase published in 1820 as part of a series regretting the death of George III, 4½″, 11.5 cm., £145-165   JJM

A Frog loving cup commemorating actions in the Crimea, on one side the Light Cavalry Charge at Balaclava and on the other the Sebastopol attack and capture of the Malakhoff by the French, 1855 £200-250   JJM

A Berlin Plaque painted with the figure of Gretchen after John Baptiste Bertrand, the girl in brown bodice and blue skirt, 9½″ x 6⅜″; 24 cm., x 16.2 cm., impressed sceptre and KPM and incised dimensions in inches, 1870-1875, carved wood Grecian temple frame. £450-520   SBel

A Fine Berlin Porcelain Painted Plaque of Ruth in the Cornfield, after Landelle, frame titled and signed G.G. Olse, impressed K.P.M. and sceptre and Nos. 330 and 200, plaque 33.4 cm., x 20.3 cm., 13¼″ x 8″. £780-860 KC

A Berlin oval plaque of St. Jerome, 10¾″, 26.8 cm., impressed KPM and sceptre, late 19th C. £260-290   SBel

A Berlin rectangular plaque painted by Wagner, signed, 6″ by 8″, 15 by 20 cm., impressed KPM and sceptre, late 19th C. **£620-700** SBel

A fine Castelli plaque, 13″ by 15″, 33 by 38 cm., **£1,150-1,300** LC

A Minton Porcelain Plaque, in a black frame decorated with gilt impressed Minton and 16 and 18, circa 1870, plaque 37 cm., x 20 cm., 14½″ x 8″, **£190-250** KC

A Berlin rectangular plaque, signed, Emil Ens, 7¾″ x 10″, 19.3 cm. by 25.4 cm., impressed KPM and sceptre, 1854, **£320-360** SBel

A Pair of Copeland Plaques, by W. Yale, signed, 14″ x 10″, 35.5 cm., x 25.5 cm., painted titles and impressed Copeland, circa 1885. **£250-280** SBel

A Mettlach Plaque after a design by J. Stahl, impressed signature, decorated in low white relief on a blue-grey ground with a scene of Jason and the Argonauts, 46 cm., 18″, impressed castle mark, 2442, circa 1900. **£390-450** SBel

A Berlin rectangular plaque painted by Maltz, signed, 8″ by 6″, 20 by 15.2 cm., impressed KPM and sceptre, late 19th C. **£200-230** SBel

Unusual 18th century Delft ware 'pillslab' wall plaque. Verso having a cheque work design, 8″, square; 20 cm., **£280-340** LE

A large French earthenware rectangular plaque, 32⅜″, by 22¾″, 82 by 57.2 cm., signed, late 19th C. **£120-140** SBel

A Set of Six Bing and Grondahl Biscuit Plaques after Thorvaldsen, the subjects including 'Night' and 'Day' 5¾″, 14.4 cm., impressed B & G or Bing and Grondahl, Eneret, impressed or incised M, late 19th century, **£120-160** SBel

A Meissen Plaque 'La Chocolatiere' after Liotard, 28 cm., x 18. 7 cm., 11″ x 7¼″, crossed swords in underglaze-blue, late 19th century, carved giltwood frame. **£550-620** SBel

A Minton circular plaque, painted by J.E. Dean, signed, 9⅜″, 23.8 cm. late 19 th C. **£200-230** LC

A Pair of 8", dia; 20 cm., Portuguese green moss and reptile plaques. £10-15 AB

A 'Vienna' wall plate, 16½", 41.9 cm., shield in underglaze-blue, late 19th C. £360-400 SBel

A Pair of Plaques, painted by C. Austin, signed and dated 1900, 13¾" x 10", 35 cm., x 25.5 cm., 1900, framed. £200-240 SBel

A Prattware Plaque printed with 'The Last In' (Clarke 412) 11¼"; 28.5 cm., printed title after W. Mulready, R.A., framed £200-300 SBel

A 'Vienna' rectangular plaque painted by B. Rudolf, 5¾" by 8¼", 14.4 by 21.2 cm., late 19th C. carved giltwood frame. £780-880 SBel

An early 19th century Delft 6"; 15 cm., square tile; monochrome with harbour scene. £12-15 AB

A Pair of Famille-Rose Plaques painted with a landscape, within diaper and scroll borders, 37.5 cm., x 24.5 cm., 14¾" x 9¾", early 20th century, framed. £360-420 SBel

Wedgwood Fairyland Lustre Plaque decorated in well-controlled lustre colours and within a wide midnight-blue border gilt with dots, 26 cm., x 18 cm., 10¼" x 7", gilt Portland Vase mark and number Z5288 in black, in wood frame. £1,700-1,900 PL

Three early Dutch tiles £27-35 LBA

A Pair of 19th century Vienna Plaques, with inset silver-plated medallions impressed P.J. Urlich, Himmelpfortg, 22, Wien, 16½", 41.9 cm., dia. £200-270 KC

An English Porcelain Plaque, 1883, 12¼" x 10", 31.1 cm., x 25.4 cm., gilt frame. Label inscribed 'A Summer Walk by H.B. Hill. Principal artist at the Royal Factory Worcester.' £260-290 LC

A Tile picture inscribed J. R. 1760, 20", 50.8 cm. square. £660-720 LC

A Rare Wedgwood & Bentley White Jasper Medallion with a portrait of Hesiod, 2⅛"; 5.5 cm., Hęsiod (sic) and Wedgwood & Bentley impressed, 1770-1780. £180-210 SBel

A 19th century Sitzendorf posy basket, 6", 15.0 cm., £50-70 RA

Pair of posy vases supported by cupid figures, 4¼", 10.5 cm., £30-35 WW

A pair of Parian ware posy holders in the form of doves, £25-30 WW

A pair of 9", 23.0 cm., Royal Worcester figure posy vases, with boy banjoist and a dancing girl, £90-110 AB

Wedgwood & Bentley. A black jasper-dip Cameo sprigged in white relief with a 'Sacrifice to Hygea' 1¼"; 3 cm., Wedgwood & Bentley impressed, 1775-80. £210-270 SBel

An early 19th century tile of puce colour, an interior scene in ebonised frame. £15-25 AB

A Garniture of Three Derby Bombe Bough-Pots and Pierced Covers, restored, from 8¾", 22 cm. to 7¼", 18.5 cm. wide, Crown, crossed batons and D marks in iron-red, c.1820. £850-930 CStJ

A Pair of Chamberlain's Worcester Yellow-Ground D-Shaped Bough-Pots and Pierced Covers, painted in sepia, covers restored, 8", 20 cm. wide, c.1805. £620-690 CStJ

A Grey Pottery Brick of rectangular form pierced with an oval aperture in the centre, the front moulded in high relief with a prancing tiger, 9¾", 24.5 cm., Han Dynasty. £1,000-1,200 SBel

A Meissen parasol handle of pale complexion, with pink coloured scarf, 4.3 cm., 1¾", crossed swords in underglaze blue, late 19th century, £60-80 SBel

A Meissen parasol handle, as the head of a negro, 1¾", 4.4 cm., crossed swords in underglaze-blue, late 19th century, £70-90 SBel

Meissen parasol handle, of rosy colour, and with blue scarf, 4.3 cm., crossed swords in underglaze blue, late 19th century, £60-80 SBel

A Rockingham Rectangular
Pen-Tray, 11″, 28 cm. long, puce
griffin mark, c.1835. £160-180
CStJ

A pair of Paris green apple-green
ground ice-pails, covers and liners
with gilt scroll handles. 26 cm.,
high; 10¼″. £845-945 CSTJ

A pair of Chinese barrel-shape
garden seats, decorated in famille-
rose enamels, 20″, 51 cm., £820-
1,000 LC

A Flight and Barr Worcester inkstand, underglaze painted mark.
5½″ wide, 12.5 cm., £200-260
HKC

Lambeth Doulton water filter
£150-170 TJC

A Meissen desk set and pen tray,
coloured iron-red, green, pink
and underglaze-blue, 7 pieces,
10⁷/₈″, 27.4 cm., crossed
swords, late 19th C. £100-120
SBel

A Fine Pair of Worcester (Flight,
Barr & Barr) Two-Handled Cam-
pana-Shaped Ice-Pails, Covers
and Liners, minor chips to rims,
10½″, 26.5 cm. high, impressed
and script marks, c.1820. £1,500-
1,650 CStJ

19th century Doulton cask complete with brass tap marked
'Doultons Patent Lambeth' £50-
60

A Derby Mazarin-Blue-Ground
Desk-Set, the ink-well restored,
8½″, 21.5 cm. wide, c.1768/70.
£280-310 CStJ

A Rockingham Pastille-Burner,
chip to rim, 3½″, 9 cm. high,
puce griffin mark and CI. 3 in
gold, c.1835. £160-180 CStJ

A large Delft blue and white two-
handled milk pan 16″ dia. 40.5
cm., decorated with flowers and
figure scenes. £135-155 AB

122

A Pair of Worcester Blue and White Finger-Bowl Stands, with The Coronation pattern, 5⅞", 15 cm. diam, painter's marks, c.1755/8. **£400-450** CStJ

A Sevres Bordalou, decorated by Charles Buteaux, marked interlaced L's with D, 1756. **£300-400** KK

A pair of Berlin salts, 5", 12.4 cm. sceptre in underglaze-blue, impressed F, late 19th C. **£200-240** SBel

A Meissen Osier-Moulded Ecuelle, cover and stand, 9¼", 23.5 cm., crossed swords in underglaze-blue, late 19th C. **£340-400** SBel

A Worcester (Flight & Barr) Turquoise-Ground Garniture, 9½". 24 cm. wide, 6¼", 16 cm. high, with incised B mark, c.1800. **£1,000-1,150** CStJ

A Nove Faience Oval Verriere, lobed, with shaped and moulded border, 14½", 36.8 cm., star mark. **£150-200** SBel

A Paris grey-ground oil lamp and stand, with an ormolu base, 16", 40.5 cm. c.1870. **£200-240** SBel

A Rockingham Primrose-Leaf Moulded Square Comport, slight crack to centre, 10¼", 26 cm. wide, c.1835. **£220-240** CStJ

FURNITURE

Each year difference types of furniture will be discussed with points to look out for and to beware of:-

- **Bureau** – one of the main features of this piece is its width, a bureau under 3 ft. is a good find, under 2 ft. 9 in. worth a good deal more and under 2 ft. 6 in. extremely valuable. This has led to the abuse of cutting down a 4 ft. bureau to 2 ft. 6 in. and similarly reducing the depth. One other feature which adds to the value is original brass handles and escutcheons. It pays to remember that old brass had a slightly higher copper content which tends to a greenish sheen.

- **Wall Mirrors** – again with mirrors one of the main indications of high price is originality. The carved wood frame, glass and gilding are all of prime importance. Earl mirrors were blown and hence any mirror over about 3 ft. 6 in. had to be blown in several pieces. To check that the frame is carved wood try the 'pin' trick – a pin sticks in wood but not in plaster. All early mirrors have a pine frame.

- **Sideboards** – width again plays an important role in the estimation of price as any sideboard of original width under 4 ft. is extremely valuable. Inlay satinwood and crossbanding also tend to add to the value. All original 18th century sideboards had six legs and the tops were made from one piece of wood. All legs were made from one piece of wood – watch for inlay hinding joins.

A pale oak centre table, late 17th C., Flemish, 86½", 218.5 cm. wide, **£1,600-1,800** CStJ

An ebonised and scarlet boulle centre table. 51", 130 cm wide, mid-19th C. **£660-730** CStJ

A George III Mahogany Drum Table, the oval top crossbanded with rosewood and fruitwood, four drawers divided by false drawers, 42¾", 108.5 cm. wide. **£850-900** CStJ

A Dutch walnut and marquetry centre table. 37½", 95 cm wide. Early 18th C. **£1,600-1,800** CStJ

An Early Victorian Mahogany Drum Table. Four real and four dummy drawers, on a turned pillar, 4', 120 cm. diameter, includes cabinet maker's labels Robert Strahan and Co., Dublin, stamped 21443. **£440-500** KC

A French oval Kingwood & bronze centre table. 34", 86 cm. x 28", 71 cm. **£900-1,050** MH

A Thuyawood and Sycamore Centre Table, inlaid with a waved banding with a giltmetal border, carved frieze enclosing a drawer at each end, 29½" by 51½", 75 cm. by 131 cm., c.1880. **£580-680** SBel

An Oak 'Gothic' Centre Table. Slate top above a carved frieze. Outset legs with a composite capital and 'X' stretcher, with traces of gilding and red paint, 55" by 32", 139.5 cm. by 81 cm., 1860's. £1,000-1,500 SBel

A George III Mahogany Drum-Top Rent Table of unusual form, the revolving leather-lined top with a central well with hinged lid, and containing eight drawers each with an inlaid ivory number above it, 2'6½" high by 4'1" diameter, 77 cm. by 124 cm. £1,950-2,500 SBS

An early 17th C. oak credence table, circular top folding in half, 42", 106" cm. wide, x 35", 89 cm. high. £1,650-1,900 B

An Italian Marquetry Centre Table inlaid with ivory and various woods on a walnut ground with leafage carved edges, one frieze drawer and square tapering legs, 3'9", 114 cm. £1,100-1,400 LC

A James I oak credence table on bobbin-turned legs, 32", 81 cm. wide, £1,050-1,200 CStJ

An Unusual XVII Century Oak Credence Table, the folded octagonal top upon a trapezoid shaped base, inlaid with chequer-work of bog oak and holly and with a central frieze drawer, 35" wide, 89 cm. £1,250-1,500 B

An Italian high renaissance walnut centre table, some restoration, 53" by 25", 135 cm by 63 cm. £560-600 LC

A Mahogany Centre Table, with a writing surface, the frieze with a single drawer. Spun brass cup feet, 30" by 51", 76 cm. by 130 cm. c.1900. £160-200 SBel

A Green and Gold Lacquer Centre Table, 33", 84 cm. wide, early 18th C. Possibly Dutch. £480-520 CStJ

An Italian walnut marquetry centre table, the top inlaid fitted with one drawer. 50½", 128 cm. x 26½", 67 cm., 19th C. £550-620 LC

A Victorian walnut centre table, 46" wide, 116 cm. £480-530 HKC

An oak centre table, 17th C., 68½", 174 cm. wide, £680-750 CStJ

A good Victorian walnut table, the shaped oval top crossbanded with kingwood. 4'2", 127 cm. x 3'0", 92 cm. £460-500 LC

An Octagonal Table, with veneered
top, painted and parcel gilt pillar
supports, with castors on gilt
bun feet, 42", 106 cm. wide.
£560-600 KC

A Burr-Walnut and Ebonised
Centre Table, inset with porcelain
plaques and giltmetal mounts,
40½", 103 cm. wide, 1880's.
£320-380 SBel

A Victorian Walnut Circular
Occasional Table, extensively
decorated with marquetry designs.
Vase shaped pedestal and raised
circular base with carved supports,
32", diameter, 81 cm. **£950-1,100**
KC

A Marquetry Centre Table, with
a drawer at either end. Gilt-
metal bandings throughout,
51" by 28", 129.5 cm. by 71 cm.
wide and deep, 1860's. **£1,350-
1,600** SBel

A Good Marquetry Oak Centre
Table, on eight legs with gothic
arches, central plinth carved with
pineapple finial, 29" by 71", 73.5
cm. by 180.5 cm., c.1865. **£1,200-
1,800** SBel

Rare Walnut Veneered oblong
centre table, the top quartered
and cross-banded with moulded
edges, one long drawer, English,
c.1690. **£3,000-4,000** RB

A Circular Centre Table, Chinese
export lacquer top, gilt square
legs with blind fret carved decoration and pierced brackets, joined
by pierced stretchers, 3'1" dia.,
93.5 cm. **£200-250** HKC

A Mid 19th Century Walnut
and Rosewood Centre Table,
with parquetry top and pierced
trestle end support. **£320-400**
KC

An Oval Centre Table, on
tapering legs with stretcher rails
centred by an oval undertier,
3'9½" by 2'2', 115 cm. by 66 cm.
£500-600 KC

An Unusual Mahogany Centre
Table, in the Regency style,
upon massive addorsed Assyrian
sphinxes, 59" by 37¼", 150 cm.
by 94.5 cm. wide and deep, 1880.
£1,500-1,800 SBel

An ebonised fruitwood Centre table, the frieze enclosing two drawers. 30", 76 cm. x 37", 94 cm. c.1900. £200-300 SBel

A North Italian bone-inlaid ebony Table, the frieze with a drawer on baluster legs. 52¼", 133 cm. wide, 19th C. £750-850 CStJ

An amboyna and parcel gilt porcelain mounted table. 19th C. 3'5", 104 cm. £500-590 LC

A marquetry centre table, the frieze with a drawer, gilt-metal dog and rams' head mounts, 27½", 70 cm. by 32¼", 82 cm. 1870's. £300-350 SBel

A Victorian circular marquetry table, veneered in various woods on a walnut ground. 56", 142 cm. diam. £750-830 LC

A 19th Century Red Tortoise-shell and Marquetry Ebonised Centre Table, with ivory inlay and chequered border, fitted a frieze drawer, 3'6", 106 cm. wide. £500-600 KC

An ebonised centre table with a frieze drawer and gilt-metal masks and mounts. 51", 130 cm. wide, 1870's. £230-290 SBel

A green and gold lacquer centre Table, on fluted baluster legs and shaped cross-stretchers. 33", 84 cm. wide, early 18th C. possibly Dutch. £480-560 CStJ

A mahogany drum table, the top inset with a leather surface, with four real and four dummy drawers. 31½", 80 cm. by 53¼", 135 cm. diam. Top modern, base c.1840. £500-800 SBel

A parquetry centre table banded in ebony and mahogany inlay, on walnut legs. 29", 74 cm. x 45" 114 cm. c.1900. £300-450 SBel

A walnut centre table on cabriole legs with gilt-metal foliate mounts. 28½", 72.5 cm. x 49", 125 cm. possibly German, 1860's. £300-380 SBel

A burr-walnut centre table, with one long drawer, inlaid through-out with beechwood foliage, 42", 107 cm. wide. c.1870. £220-250 SBel

A mahogany centre table, the top with hinged 'D'-shaped ends inset with a leather surface. 28½", 72.5 cm. by 51½", 131 cm. mid-19th C. £580-640 SBel

An English walnut and parcel-gilt three-tier centre table, with burr-walnut cross-banding. 2'10", 86.5 cm. wide, c.1850. £300-400 SBel

DRAWERS — GUIDE TO DATING

- early 17th C. drawers were nailed together, with side runners which fitted into deep side grooves
- bottom runners, usually made of oak, appeared c.1680
- no 18th C. drawer completely fitted the space between front and back — a space left for ventilation
- good quality drawers had sides of oak, with rounded top edges
- up to 1770 grain in bottom boards of drawers ran from front to back, from 1770 the grain ran from side to side
- 18th C. cabinet makers made the bottom boards from 2 or 3 pieces of the same wood; the Victorians used one piece which was usually screwed
- corner mouldings were a Sheraton innovation, hence give a date of after 1799

A Boulle Side Table, banded with brass above a frieze drawer on cabriole legs mounted with gilt-metal herms, 31½" by 42", 80 cm. by 107 cm., 1840's. £800-900 SBel

A Louis XV Oak Side Table with a panelled top, each side with a drawer, 2'6½" high by 5'10" wide, 77 cm. by 177 cm., c.1770. £450-550 SBS

A Pair of George III Elliptical Side Tables, with a painted top and a giltwood underframe, 2'10" high by 4'5½" wide, 87 cm. by 136 cm., c.1770. tops re-painted. £950-1,100 SBS

A Late George II Mahogany Side Table with two short and one long drawer, 2'5" high by 2'8" wide, 74 cm. by 81 cm., c.1760. £380-450 SBS

A rosewood side table with carved winged lion legs. 34½", 88 cm. x 66", 168 cm. mid-19th C. £200-260 SBel

An Italian Giltwood Side Table, 36", 91.5 cm. wide, late 18th C. £380-410 CStJ

A George I Walnut Side Table with a rectangular top, one long and three short drawers in the shaped frieze and leaf-carved cabriole legs, 2'5" high by 2'6" wide, 74 cm. by 76 cm., c.1715. £2,900-3,400 SBS

A North Italian Painted and Gilt-wood Side Table, with a simulated breccia marble top, above a carved frieze, on fluted turned legs carved with leaves and beading, 3'1" high by 4'9" wide, 94 cm. by 145 cm., 18th century, probably Piedmont. £650-750 SBS

A pair of George III giltwood side tables with satinwood tops cross-banded with tulipwood, 47", 119.5 cm wide. **£8,500-9,000** CStJ

A Dutch oak side table on turned-baluster legs and stretchers, 17th C., 46", 117 cm. wide, **£600-680** CStJ

An oak side table on turned baluster legs and square stretchers, first half of 17th C., 62½", 159 cm. wide, **£700-800** CStJ

A 17th Century Oak Side-Table. Cupboard enclosed by a pair of panel doors flanking a central panel with initials and date, 3'10¾", 118 cm. wide. **£2,000-2,500** KC

A walnut side table, 17th C., 37½", 95 cm wide. **£720-840** CStJ

A Venetian blue and grey-painted side-table, 53", 135 cm wide, partly 18th C. **£650-730** CStJ

A Portuguese rosewood side Table with crossbanded top and ebonised and spirally-turned legs. 46", 117 cm. wide, early 18th C. **£620-700** CStJ

A George III mahogany serving table with drawer each side and dummy drawers in front, 73", 105.5 cm wide. **£1,900-2,000** CStJ

129

A Dutch Satinwood Side Table with a shaped frieze, square tapering legs inlaid to simulate fluting, 2'6" high by 2'4" wide, 76 cm. by 71 cm., c.1790. **£450-550** SBS

A Fine Regency Period Small Faded Rosewood Library Table banded in bleached mahogany with line inlay, the ends with frieze drawers, 19" by 3'1", 45 cm. by 91 cm. **£1,900-2,200** WW

A Small Oak Side Table 2' high by 1'7½" wide, 61 cm. by 50 cm. 17th C. **£400-450** SBS

A Mid-Georgian Mahogany Side Table with breccia marble top and coved carved frieze, 37½" wide, 95 cm. **£950-1,100** CStJ

A German Walnut Side Table with moulded frieze and pierced spiral legs joined by waved moulded stretchers centred by a pierced spiral finial, 2'5" high by 3' wide, 74 cm. by 91 cm., late 17th century. **£1,250-1,500** SBS

A Charles II oak side table, 27" wide, 68.5 cm. **£420-470** HKC

A Georgian oak side table, 30" wide, 76 cm., **£320-360** CStJ

A William and Mary Oak Side Table, 2'3½" high by 2'8" wide 70 cm. by 81 cm. c.1685. **£1,150-1,300** SBS

A Dutch marquetry side table, brass knob feet, late 18th C., 30½", 77.5 cm. **£310-340** LC

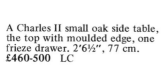

A Charles II small oak side table, the top with moulded edge, one frieze drawer. 2'6½", 77 cm. **£460-500** LC

A William and Mary walnut side table. 31" wide, 79 cm. **£750-830** CStJ

A Pair of Rosewood Tea Tables with a hinged top on a fluted stem, the base with bun feet, 30¾" by 37½", 78 cm. by 95 cm. c.1840. **£600-680** SBel

A Dutch Marquetry Table inlaid on mahogany tray top, frieze drawer and cabriole legs, 2'5" high by 2'7" wide, 74 cm. by 80 cm., c.1740. **£700-900** SBS

A Queen Anne red walnut tea-table with semi-circular hinged double flat top, 27", 68.5 cm wide. **£820-900** CStJ

A pair of Victorian rosewood Tea Tables with rounded rectangular fold-over swivel tops, each 37½", 95 cm. **£750-850** LC

A 17th Century Italian Walnut Marquetry and Ivory Inlaid Table, the top depicting a hunting scene. Caryatid supports united by stretchers, 48", 122 cm. wide. **£500-600** KC

A Dutch Table, the oyster-veneered olivewood top with central oval of marquetry partly in green-stained ivory, 2'5½" high by 3'3" wide, 74 cm. by 99 cm., late 17th century. **£750-850**

A Chinese Lacquer Tray with gilt flowers on black, everted trellised bamboo rim, 2'10" wide, 86 cm., c.1820, now on four bamboo cluster column legs as a table. **£700-800** SBS

An Early George II Mahogany Drop-Leaf Table with moulded oval top, cabriole legs, hoof feet, 3'1" wide, 94 cm., c.1730. **£900-1,100** SBS

A Rare George II Brass-Inlaid Mahogany Table attributed to John Channon, the Kingwood-crossbanded top with a central lobed panel outlined with brass strapwork. Legs inlaid at the knees and on the pad feet, 2'5½" high by 2'9½" wide by 1'11" deep, 75 cm. by 85 cm. by 58 cm. c.1740. **£14,000-16,000** SBS

A Victorian walnut oval two-lap table, the top inlaid with narrow bands of amboyna. 3'2", 96 cm. x 4'3", 130 cm. **£500-600** LC

An oak hutch table on block feet, late 16th C., 37¾", 96 cm. wide, **£2,800-3,000** CStJ

A North Italian Bone-Inlaid Ebony Table, 52¼", 133 cm. wide, 19th C. **£750-820** CStJ

A Chinese Hexagonal Bamboo Stand with caned top, fretwork frieze and six columnar legs, 1'8" high by 1'1½" wide, 51 cm. by 34 cm., c.1820. £700-800 SBS

A Regency Painted "Bamboo" Table with two frieze drawers, "bamboo" legs joined by a concave-fronted platform, 2'6½" high by 3'2½" wide, 77 cm. by 98 cm., c.1810, now painted with flowers. £600-700 SBS

A 'Louis XVI' Provincial Walnut Parquetry Occasional Table, the frieze enclosing a single drawer, 28¼" x 18¼"; 72 cm. x 46.5 cm., circa 1900. £90-120 SBel

A Pair of George IV Amboyna Occasional Tables, tilt tops raised on swelling octagonal columns, 1'5¾", 45 cm. wide. £600-800 BON

Georgian mahogany Duncan Phyffe table. £300-350 JWB

A figured walnut table. 19", 48.5 cm wide, mid-18th C. German or Swiss. £1,500-1,700 CStJ

A Mid-19th Century Walnut and Kingswood Crossbanded Shaped-Top Occasional Table in the Louis Quinze Style, 2'6¾", 78 cm. wide. £450-500 KC

A George III Giltwood Occasional Table in the manner of Robert Adam, painted on paper to resemble wood and marble. Beaded legs headed by goat's heads hoof feet, 2'4" high by 1'7¼" wide, 71 cm. by 49 cm., c.1780. £2,800-3,400 SBS

An early 18th century table, with veneered walnut top, gateleg supporting triangular flap. 29" square x 28" high; 73.5 cm x 71 cm. £400-480 DHBN

A nest of 4 Regency mahogany quartetto tables. 26" to 20" wide, 66 cm to 51 cm wide. £1,150-1,250 CStJ

An Unusual Walnut Occasional Table, top and scrolling apron supported on a baluster column on a winged lion, 28", 71 cm., Italian, late 19th century. £200-300 SBel

An oval satinwood occasional table of 18th C. design on mahogany ground, with ebony stringing and rosewood crossbanding. 34" wide, 86 cm. £290-330 HKC

An oval mahogany occasional table of Sheraton design, 21" wide, 53.5 cm. £180-200 HKC

A George III Mahogany Serpentine Occasional Table, with spindle turned gallery to the revolving top, on a baluster turned pillar and tripod supports, 26¾", 68 cm. wide. £1,000-1,300 KC

A Rosewood Occasional Table with pierced frieze, shaped legs joined by a lower tier, 28" x 28"; 71 cm. x 71 cm., 20th century. £150-200 SBel

An Ebonised Wood and Kingwood Parquetry Occasional Table, three-quarter gilt-metal gallery and single frieze drawer, 31½"; 80 cm., c.1880. £170-200 SBel

A Victorian walnut circular top occasional table on a spiral twist stem to three carved cabriole legs 17½", 44.5 cm. (wormed) £54-68 WW

A George III Mahogany Reading-Table with easel top fitted with a drawer and candle-slide each side. 25¼"; 64 cm. wide. £600-700 CStJ

A George II Mahogany Tripod Table. Revolving top carved around the edge with flower-heads. Birdcage support and spiral-fluted baluster, 2'5" high by 2'7" wide, 73 cm. by 79 cm., c.1750. £2,800-3,500 SBS

A Chinese lacquer Tripod Table, hinged top, bamboo gallery, on birdcage support and simple stem, 2'6" high by 2'5" diam. 76 cm. by 74 cm., c.1800. **£1,000-1,200** SBS

A George II Brass-Inlaid Ebonised Supper Table attributed to Abraham Roentgen, 2'3" high by 2'5" wide, 69 cm. by 74 cm., c.1735. **£1,200-1,500** SBS

A George III mahogany tripod table, 38¼", 72 cm diam. **£840-940** CStJ

A George II Mahogany Tripod Stand. Carved baluster stem and leaf-carved cabriole legs, 1'9½" high by 11" diameter, 55 cm. by 28 cm., c.1735, with a later piecrust top. **£1,400-1,600** SBS

A George II Mahogany Tripod Table, hinged top with waved border, and fluted stem with leaf-carved base, 2'3" high by 2'3" high by 2'1" wide, 68 cm. by 62 cm., c.1750. **£1,800-2,000** SBS

A George III mahogany tripod table, 28", 71 cm wide. **£1,700-1,800** CStJ

A Georgian oak tripod table. **£150-190** JWB

A fine late 18th C. mahogany circular table, 36" diam., 91 cm. **£650-750** HKC

A Rare George II Yew-Wood Tripod Table of fine colouring, turned column and pad feet, 2'10" diameter, 86.5 cm., mid-18th C. **£480-560** SBS

A walnut Games Table, the detachable top enclosing a chess and backgammon board, 23", 58.5 cm. x 23¼", 59 cm. mid-19th C. £230-300 SBel

A Pair of George III Amboyna Work Tables, with mahogany cross-banded hinged tops enclosing velvet-lined interiors above an apron drawer. 16", 40 cm. wide. £280-340 KC

A Mahogany Work Table with a recessed top above two frieze drawers. 30 by 19¼"; 76 by 49 cm., German, mid 19th century. £200-300 SBel

A Victorian walnut work table with pierced three-quarter gallery, fitted drawer and pull-out silk covered work drawer. 1'9"; 53 cm. £280-360 LC

Sheraton work table, c.1800. £1,000-1,250

A Regency rosewood and line inlaid two-flap work-table. 35¼", 89.5 cm. (one caster missing). £500-560 GCH

A Rosewood and Marquetry Work Table, opening to reveal work container. Twist-turned legs, on trestle feet. 30½ by 21¾"; 77.5 by 55 cm., work bag added, mid 19th century. £170-200 SBel

A Georgian work table in burr elm veneers, c.1790. £850-950 LKL

A Regency mahogany drop flap work table of fine colour, c.1820. £950-1,050 LKL

Victorian walnut, boxwood line inlaid work table with fitted interior above a bag. 21", 52.5 cm. £310-350 WW

19th C. mahogany work table, with pull-out silk covered bag (restored) 22", 55 cm. £80-90 WW

A William IV rosewood work table, 21", 52.5 cm. £420-500 WW

135

A Walnut combined Games and Work Table. Hinged top enclosing cribbage, backgammon and chess boards. Frieze drawer with a work bag below. 28½ by 21¾"; 72 by 55 cm., c.1870. **£340-400** SBS

A Shoolbred & Co. Rosewood Games and Work table opening to reveal backgammon and chess boards. Single fitted drawer and four small drawers. Stamped Js Shoolbred & Co. 3888, 27½ by 27" by 27"; 70 by 69cm., late century. **£280-360** SBel

A Regency Rosewood Drop-leaf Games and Work Table. Sliding reversible top with chessboard inlay, and a pleated well. 20¾", 52 cm. wide. **£780-880** KC

An English walnut combined games and work table with swivelling baize-lined top; 30", 76 cm wide, mid-19th C. **£190-290** S Bel

A walnut games or work table, the quarter-veneered top opening to reveal backgammon and chess boards, 28¾", 73 cm. x 22", 56 cm., c.1860. **£370-420** SBel

A Regency period mahogany games table crossbanded and inlaid with brass stringing. 22½"; 56.5 cm., **£550-600** LE

A Late Regency Rosewood Work and Games Table with a fitted frieze drawer and pull-out work bag. 21½"; 56 cm., **£320-390** LC

Moresque inlaid games table with interior fitted for cards and backgammon. 29", 73.5 cm. **£210-230** WW

A Late George III Mahogany Games Table crossbanded with ringwood, with a sliding chess-board panel above a drawer. 2'4½" high by 2'5" wide; 72 cm. by 74 cm. c.1810. **£800-900** SBS

A Victorian walnut foldover top Games Table with chess inlaid interior. **£220-240** RB

A Regency rosewood work and games table with adjustable reading slope. c.1820. **£1,250-1,400** LKL

A Chinese export black and gilt lacquer Games Table, with a chessboard and enclosing a backgammon board, 30½", 76 cm. x 35", 89 cm. c.1850. **£490-580** SBel

A Rosewood Card Table with a hinged top and carved frieze. 29½ by 36"; 75 by 92 cm., 1840's. **£220-280** SBS

A George III mahogany card table with fold-over top, 33", 83.5 cm. **£350-400** LC

A George III Satinwood Card Table, the rectangular top with rounded inset corners and with a broad Purplehead banding. 2'6" high by 2'11½" wide; 76 cm. by 92.5 cm., c.1790. **£320-390** SBS

A Regency rosewood Card Table, 36"; 91 cm., **£340-400** OL

A Burr-Walnut Card Table with folding top, 29 by 35"; 73 by 89 cm., 1860's. **£280-360** SBS

A pair of Regency coromandel card tables. **£2,500-2,700** pair. JWB

A George III Burr Yew and Satinwood Card Table, the serpentine top crossbanded in kingwood, on toupe feet, 3' wide 91.5 cm. c.1800. **£480-560** BON

A Walnut Card Table, the top inlaid with stringing and foliage. 28½ by 35"; 72 by 89 cm., 1860's. **£220-250** SBel

A Rosewood Card Table on a square double-baluster column and concave-sided base, with paw feet. 29 by 35½"; 74 by 90 cm., c.1840. **£220-260** SBel

A George II Giltwood Console Tea Table with a serpentine marble top, the frieze carved with flowers and leaf-scrolls and on three S-scroll legs, 5'1" wide, 185 cm., mid-18th century. **£600-1,000** SBS

An 18th century mahogany fold over top cardtable, baize lined interior, the frieze fluted and carved with pendent, pierced corner brackets, 2'10½" wide; 87.5 cm., **£490-550** PWC

A Regency Padoukwood Card Table, reeded top with rounded corners, legs headed by leafy capitals, 2'5½" high by 3' wide, 75 cm. by 91 cm., c.1820. £650-750 SBS

A Dutch Marquetry Triangular Card Table with baize lined fold-over top. 3'3½"; 100 cm. square. £420-490 LC

A Pair of Card Tables. Inlaid border to the folding top. White painted pillars with gilt trellis decoration. 39"; 98.5 cm. wide. £450-500 KC

A Walnut Card Table in the Louis XV style. 39"; 99 cm., 19th century. £480-540 LC

A Late Regency mahogany card table with wide crossbanded foldover top. 3'; 91 cm. £300-390 LC

Italian late 17th C. carved and gilded console table with striated marble top. 32", 81 cm. wide. £600-700 LJ

A Pair of Red Boulle Card Tables. Green baize-lined interior, shaped frieze with a cartouche and the whole mounted with gilt-metal, 30¼ by 35"; 77 by 89 cm., c.1870. £950-1,100 SBel

A Pair of George III Semi-circular Card Tables, the baize-lined tops inlaid with segmental burr yew-wood veneer. 2'8" wide; 81 cm., c.1785. £3,500-4,000 SBS

A Louis Phillipe Rosewood and Floral Marquetry Card Table, mounted with gilt-metal enrichments. 35" wide; 88.5 cm., £620-700 KC

A Pair of Gilt Side Tables in George I style, 2'11" by 1'5" by 3'2" tall, 89 cm. by 43 cm. by 96.5 cm. £1,050-1,200 BON

A Rosewood Card Table, the hinged top enclosing a baize-lined playing surface, above a shallow well. 28¾" by 36½"; 73 by 92 cm., c.1840. £200-240 SBel

An ebonised and scarlet boulle card-table. 36¼", 92 cm wide. mid-19th C. **£500-560** CStJ

A George III mahogany inlaid card table, D-shaped fold-over top. 3', 91.5 cm. **£280-360** LC

A Dutch walnut and marquetry card-table with lobed serpentine baize-lined folding top. 28¾", 73 cm. wide. **£1,450-1,600** CStJ

A pair of Regency rosewood card-tables. 35½", 90 cm wide. **£2,700-2,900** CStJ

A Dutch Walnut and Marquetry Card-Table on cabriole legs and claw-and-ball feet, 28¾", 73 cm. wide. **£1,450-1,600** CStJ

A Regency rosewood card table, the fold-over top crossbanded. 36", 91 cm. **£450-500** LC

A William IV swivel top card table. 3'91 cm. **£195-250** WW

A George II card table veneered to simulate walnut, the fold-over top with candle and counter wells on a concertina action. 2'11", 89 cm. **£350-400** LC

An Italian Marquetry Card-Table in the Maggiolini style, 34½", 82.5 cm. wide, late 18th C. **£1,700-1,800** CStJ

A Regency mahogany card table with fold top, canted ends, frieze with inlaid brass decoration, on unusual 'U' and circular support. 36", 91 cm. wide. **£1,100-1,300** LJ

A 33", 83.5 cm. William IV fold-top mahogany card-table. **£200-240** RB

A 17th Century Italian Walnut Writing Table, with fringed top and fall front revealing small drawers, 54", 137 cm., wide. **£1,700-2,000** KC

A Rosewood Writing Table, with letter compartment, each side with hinged flap, inlaid throughout with boxwood stringing and scrolls, 32" x 24"; 81 cm x 61 cm., circa 1900. **£260-300** SBel

A faded mahogany table a ecrire in Louis XVI style, 26¼", 67 cm wide, late 18th C, possibly Swedish. **£420-460** CStJ

A giltmetal-mounted figured walnut writing-table with serpentine-sided oval top 54", 137 cm. wide, mid-19th C. **£700-800** CStJ

A Satinwood 'Plum Pudding' Writing Table, 4'5" wide, 134.5 cm. **£500-800** BON

A general purpose table for an artist, or a writing table, Sheraton, c.1800-1810. **£1,500-1,600**

A Walnut Writing Table, the quarter-veneered top inlaid with stringing and scrolling foliage, single drawer, on cabriole legs with gilt-metal mounts, 28" by 46" 71 cm. by 117 cm., early 20th century. **£360-400** SBel

A George III Mahogany Chart-room Table, the top rising upon double ratchets to eye level height, the two top drawers fitted with writing slides and an ink well drawer. 47"; 119 cm. wide **£700-800** B

A Burr Chestnut Marquetry Writing Table, the top inlaid on an ebony ground, the frieze with a drawer, and with gilt-metal mounts to the legs. 30¾" by 40¼", 77 cm. by 102.3 cm., c.1870. **£1,200-1,500** SBel

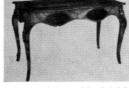

A 17th Century Italian Walnut Writing Table, fall front frieze revealing pigeon-holes and three small drawers above two apron drawers, 54-3/8" 138 cm., wide. **£680-780** KC

A walnut writing table, inlaid with stringing and mahogany panels. 19th C. 47½", 121 cm. **£680-760** LC

A George II artist's mahogany table with green baize covered top, side candle and instrument slide, 35½", 105 cm. wide. **£480-560** PK

A George III mahogany architects table, 42" wide, 106 cm. **£115-135** HKC

A George III mahogany architect's table with gilt-brass inkwell and pounce pot, 36", 91.5 cm wide. **£1,300-1,400** CStJ

A William IV Rosewood Sofa Table, having bobbin turned decoration and square pillar support, the base with scroll feet and castors, 34¾", 88 cm. wide. **£340-400** KC

A William IV Mahogany Sofa Table, with floral strapwork banding and inlaid satinwood panels, fitted two frieze drawers, 3', 92 cm. wide. **£540-640** KC

A Regency Mahogany Sofa Table, the front with two drawers with ebony stringing, on a spiral twist pillar and reeded sabre legs, 36½" by 60" extended, 93 cm. by 152 cm. **£420-500** LC

SOFA TABLES

- popular from late 1790's
- basically an elongated Pembroke table
- often made in satinwood with contrasting banding
- Sheraton in 1803 said it should be 5-6' long, 22-24" wide and 28" high
- a genuine 18th C. sofa table is very rare; each flap should have 2 fly rails and 3 hinges
- many fakes made from cheval mirrors
- in early 19th C. many veneered in amboyna or zebra

A Regency Rosewood Sofa Table, the top inlaid with a broad satinwood band on lyre end supports, 3'1" wide 5' extended, 91 cm. by 152 cm. **£1,400-1,700** BON

Regency sofa table. **£1,700-1,800** JWB

141

George III Rosewood sofa-table /games table, with backgammon well and chequer board. 4'11½''; 151 cm. wide opened. £3,900-4,400 HKC

A Regency amboyna sofa table, 59½'', 151 cm wide, £2,600-2,800 CStJ

A late Georgian mahogany sofa table, crossbanded and inlaid with stringing. 38'', 97 cm. sun bleached. £720-820 LC

A Regency rosewood sofa table, 64'', 164 cm wide, open. £800-900 CStJ

An 18th C. rosewood sofa table, the top with satinwood crossbanding, 59'', 150 cm. wide. £900-1,100 LJ

A Regency mahogany sofa table, top inlaid with stringing, drawers with rosewood facings and kingwood crossbanding. Brass edging. 58½''; 149 cm extended. £900-1,000 LC

PEMBROKE TABLES

- named after Countess of Pembroke, said to be the first to order one
- dates from 1750's
- often used as a breakfast table
- from 1770's often satinwood with marquetry or inlay
- Sheraton said height should not exceed 2'4''

- very popular in 1780's, also then made in mahogany
- Edwardians frequently painted earlier pieces
- oval and serpentine-shaped tops more valuable than square top
- shaped tops should have bow-fronted drawer ends

A George III Yew-Wood Pembroke Table, on bobbin and ring-turned legs, 2'1½'' wide, by 2'4'' high, 63.5 cm. by 71 cm., c.1800. £450-550 SBS

A Sheraton period satinwood Pembroke table, crossbanded oval top inlaid with boxwood and ebony stringing. 28¼'', 81.5 cm. £680-750 DHBN

A George III oval mahogany Pembroke table with one frieze drawer. 2'6'', 76 cm. x 3'1¼'', 94.5 cm. £535-600 LC

A late Georgian mahogany Pembroke table, one frieze drawer, turned pillar, reeded sabre legs, 33", 84 cm. **£440-500** LC

A good George III oval mahogany Pembroke table with kingwood crossbandings, 30½" by 40", 77 cm by 102 cm. **£1,000-1,100** LC

A late 18th C. mahogany Pembroke table, with boxwood inlay, two drawers in under frame. Top 37½", 95 cm. **£580-660** DN

A Queen Anne small circular oak gateleg Table. 3'5", 104 cm. diam. **£500-600** LC

A Mid-Seventeenth Century Carved Oak Gateleg Table, the oval top carved with a centre panel of dolphins, 72", 183 cm. wide open, the table mid-17th century, the carving mid-19th century. **£320-400** SBel

An unusual solid yew gateleg-table with oval twin-flap top on baluster legs and stretchers, late 17th C., 44¾", 114 cm. wide, **£550-600** CStJ

A rare XVII century oak sledge foot gateleg table, with a single drawer beneath the top with applied mould and running almost the full length of the top on a single central slide. Opening to 46" x 37", 117 cm. x 94 cm. **£850-950** B

A William and Mary oak gateleg Table. 48", 122 cm. x 55½", 141 cm. extended. **£680-780** LC

A William and Mary Walnut Gateleg Table with a rectangular top and flap, a drawer on one side, 2'5" high by 2'9" wide, 74 cm. by 84 cm., c.1690. **£1,250-1,500** SBS

A fine English walnut gate-leg Table with oval top, 46", 116 cm. by 42", 106 cm. on bobbin turned legs, c.1700. **£700-800** GSP

Early 18th C. oak gateleg Table, with four turned supports, in walnut, with an external gate on each side. Extending to 65" x 55", 165 cm. x 139 cm. **£1,400-1,700** B

A 17th C. oak gateleg table, fitted one drawer. Top 59", 150 cm. maximum. **£590-690** DHBN

A Rare Charles II Walnut Gateleg Table, 2'1½" high by 2' long by 2'5½" open, 64 cm. by 61 cm. by 75 cm. c.1675. **£640-700** SBS

A large oak gateleg table. 62" wide, 157.5 cm., open, 17th C., (restorations). **£1,150-1,300** CStJ

A William and Mary Oak Side or Gateleg Table, 2'2" high by 1'11½" wide, 66 cm. by 59 cm. c.1690. **£1,550-1,700** SBS

A good George III rectangular mahogany and crossbanded drop leaf spider gateleg table. **£700-900** PK

A 17th C. oak gateleg table, 30" wide, 76 cm. **£500-560** HKC

An oak gateleg table, late 17th C., 45" by 64", 114 cm by 137 cm. **£480-520** LC

A William IV circular rosewood Breakfast Table with lobed bun feet. 54", 137 cm. diam. **£380-460** LC

A mahogany octagonal Breakfast Table, inlaid with stained beechwood star motifs, c.1880. **£140-160** SBel

A walnut Breakfast Table, inlaid with burr-walnut and boxwood. 45¾", 160 cm. diam., c.1870. **£380-440** SBel

A George IV Amboyna and pollarded oak veneered circular snap top Breakfast Table in the manner of Thomas Holland. 4'2", 127 cm. **£550-600** WW

An early Victorian oval rosewood Breakfast Table, 54", 137 cm. **£400-500** OL

A fine Regency mahogany breakfast Table with well figured top with cut brass inlay, 50", 127 cm. diam. **£1,700-1,900** GSP

A Walnut Breakfast Table. Quarter-veneered oval top inlaid with box-wood stringing, on four turned supports, 29" by 53½", 47 cm. by 136 cm., c.1860. **£260-290**   SBel

A Rosewood Breakfast Table, octagonal baluster column, with foliate base, 51", 130 cm. diameter, 1840's. **£300-500**   SBel

A George III mahogany Breakfast Table, 35", 89 cm. x 48", 123 cm. **£450-500**   LC

A William IV Rosewood Table, having a chamfered pillar support and triform base, on carved claw feet castors, 4'3¼", 130 cm. diameter. **£300-350**   KC

A George III design mahogany circular breakfast table, with walnut crossbanding. 63" dia. 159.5 cm. **£470-520**   HKC

A Good Early Victorian Rosewood Breakfast Table, the hectofoil top veneered with a radial pattern of cross-cuttings, 4'3" diam. 129.5 cm. **£550-600**   BON

A Regency rosewood breakfast table. 61½", 156 wide. **£700-780**   CStJ

A George III figured mahogany oval snap-top Breakfast Table. 5'6", 168 cm. x 4'7¼", 140 cm. **£2,000-2,200**   PL

A Victorian octagonal rosewood Breakfast Table, on flattened bun feet. 56", 142 cm. **£380-480**   LC

A Late George III Mahogany Breakfast Table, the top with fluted edge and rounded corners, 4' by 3'11", 122 cm. by 119 cm. **£420-500**   LC

A Fine George IV Two Pillar Mahogany Dining Table with three extra leaves, 46" by 117" extended, 117 cm. by 298 cm. **£2,400-3,000** LC

Georgian square top dining table in rosewood, pedestal base. **£485-565** MP

A Fine XVII Century Oak Ten-Seater Double Gate Dining Table, the circular top with two drop leaves, 62" circular, 157 cm. **£1,850-2,000** B

An 18th C. mahogany fall flap dining table, the cabriole legs headed by carved scrolls, 3'11", 119.5 cm. x 3'3", 98.5 cm. **£390-450** PWC

A mahogany oval dining Table. 53½", 136 cm. wide, c.1840. **£260-290** SBel

A George III mahogany Break-fast Table, with fluted sabre legs. 54", 137 cm. x 48", 122 cm. **£480-540** LC

A 17th C. twelve seater oak double gate Dining Table, Opening to 6'4" x 5'4", 193 cm. **£2,800-3,100** B

A fine late Regency mahogany dining Table, with crossbanded and triple ebony strung border. 5'0", 152 cm. **£1,000-1,300** PJ

Good quality George III mahogany double "D" end Dining Table with two central leaves. Length 72", 183 cm. c.1800. Width 46", 117 cm. Height 30", 76 cm. **£330-400** WB

A Dutch oak draw-leaf table on cup-and-cover baluster legs, 17th C., 78", 198 cm. wide, open, £1,700-1,900 CStJ

An Extremely Fine Charles I Oak Draw-Leaf Refectory Table, with carved frieze and carved turned bulbous supports, 33" by 6'6", 84 cm. by 198 cm., extending to 12'2", 370 cm. £3,800-4,500 KC

An early 17th C. oak Refectory Dining Table, plank top with cleated ends, 6'8", 203 cm. long. £1,100-1,300 B

Late 17th Century Oak and Elm Serving Table, carved frieze inscribed with the initials 'M.G.' and the date 1686, 9'5½" by 2'5½, 288 cm. by 75 cm. £3,800-4.000 KC

A 17th C. oak Long Bench with single plank top. 87", 221 cm. long. £500-560 B

A Henry VIII Altar Table, the plank top upon a base with carved frieze to the front and two sides, 73" long by 28" wide, 185 cm. by 71 cm. £540-650 B

Elizabethan Oak Drawleaf Refectory Table, 3'4" wide and extending to 15'11" long, 102 cm. by 484 cm. £10,500-12,000 RBB

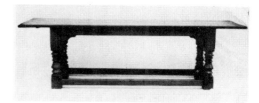

French oak Refectory Table, 105", 267 cm. long x 34", 86 cm. wide. £1,000-1,200 B

A James II Oak Refectory Table, with strapwork carved frieze and columnar supports united by stretchers, 2'8½" by 6'4", 82 cm. by 192 cm. £980-1,100 KC

An oak refectory table, of fine colour, 17th C., 80", 203 cm. wide, £1,200-1,400 CStJ

17th C. Dutch oak Refectory Table, plank top connected by pegs to the base. 70", 178 cm. x 30", 76 cm. **£1,900-2,100** B

A 17th C. Dutch oak drawleaf Refectory Table, opening to 82", 208 cm. **£1,000-1,200** B

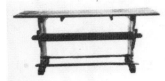

A fine 16th C. oak Refectory Table, the two plank top raised upon slab ends, 6', 183 cm. long x 31", 78 cm. high. **£2,500-3,000** B

A 16th C. Henri II walnut Refectory Table, on nine column supports with ionic capitals. 55", 140 cm. wide x 35", 89 cm. x 32", 81 cm. high. **£1,400-1,600** B

53 Oak Refectory Table, 6', 183 cm. x 2'8", 81 cm. **£125-150** W

A 17th C. Dutch oak drawleaf table, on a deep frieze and four bulbous turned supports. Opening to 7'3", 221 cm. **£560-620** B

A good ash and elm cricket table, 18th C., 24", 61 cm. **£370-400** LC

A Mahogany Display Table with glazed top and sides on leaf-carved legs joined by a lower tier, 28¼" by 24"; 71.5 cm. by 61 cm., 1890's. **£190-250** SBel

A Rosewood and Marble Specimen Table, the circular top inlaid with a radiating design of coloured marbles, 28½" by 31", 73 cm. by 79 cm; 1830's. **£750-850** SBel

A Mother-of-Pearl Inlaid Papier Mache Dressing Table, with single frieze drawer, and double serpentine drawer, 59" by 28", 150 cm. by 71 cm. mid-19th C. **£1,600-1,800** SBel

An Oak Table Chair with tip-up top, panel seat and four turned supports joined by base stretchers, late 17th/early 18th century, 27½" by 48½", 70 cm. by 123 cm., **£440-500** LC

A cricket table with yew wood top and ash legs, late 18th/19th C., 19½", 49.5 cm diam. **£290-320** LC

Victorian kidney-shaped kneehole writing desk. Top inlet with leather, original brass gallery. £810-950 RB

An 18th century mahogany silver table, gallery sides pierced with quatrefoils, chamfered legs with pierced corner brackets 2'8½" wide; 82.5 cm. £400-480 PWC

Walnut Kneehole Desk with Centre Cupboard and Six Drawers 30" wide; 76 cm. with repairs (once the property of Sir Winston Churchill at Chartwell). £1,400-1,600 W

An Oak Writing Desk, the fallfront enclosing a fitted interior flanked by ebonised inlay, 43" x 46"; 110 cm. x 117 cm. 1890. £180-250 SBel

A fine Queen Anne walnut kneehole desk, with superb patination and original brasses, c.1710. £4,500-5,000 LKL

A George III kingwood and marquetry dressing table, after Pierre Langlois. 24¾", 63 cm wide. £2,300-2,500 CStJ

A Late Georgian Mahogany Partner's Desk, The pedestals each with three drawers and a cupboard, on a plinth base, 163 cm. wide. 5'4" £680-780 KC

Mahogany partner's desk. £1,500-1,600 JWB

A Mahogany child's desk, later decorated in lacquer. 21"; 52.5 cm. £210-250 WW

A Victorian 30". 76 cm. Walnut desk with slope top, stationery compartments, £130-180 RB

A Georgian kneehole desk. £300-350 JWB

A George III Mahogany Writing Desk enclosed by a domed tambour, with pigeon holes, drawers, and candle slides, writing surface with a central ratchet supported book slope. The whole with tulipwood crossbanding. 3'1" wide 94 cm. £4,000-4,800 HKC

A Mahogany Pedestal Desk, each pedestal containing four graduated drawers locked by a hinged flap, 30" x 50"; 76 cm. x 127 cm. c.1880. £250-300 SBel

An 18th C. Mahogany kneehole writing desk, with recessed cupboard brass 'H' hinges, keyhole plate and handles, 2'6" wide; 76 cm. £285-325 PWC

A Late George II/Early George III Mahogany Writing Cabinet 72" x 44", 183 cm. x 112 cm., c.1890. £550-650 SBel

A Carved Oak Writing Desk with leather inset top, on gadrooned legs, 51½"; 131 cm. wide, c.1880. £260-300 SBel

An Italian ebonised ladies writing bureau with fitted interior, inlaid in ivory and mother-of-pearl. 32" wide, 81 cm. £390-450 HKC

A Mahogany Pedestal Cylinder Desk, tambour front, 44½" x 54½" x 36"; 113 x 138 cm. x 92 cm., bearing the label Maple & Co., early 20th C. £600-700 SBel

A Walnut Kneehole Desk in well-figured wood, drawers, divided by corbels, 31" x 54" x 24½"; 79 cm. x 137 cm. x 63 cm., 1860's £340-390 SatHH

A Mahogany Pedestal Desk. Moulded top with leather writing surface. 152.5 cm. x 89 cm., 5'0" x 2'11¼", late 19th C. £600-700 SBel

A Walnut Pedestal Desk in well-figured wood, 43¼" x 48"; 110 cm. x 122 cm. c.1898. £390-450 SBel

A South German Mahogany Secretaire, the writing surface enclosing a fitted interior with three drawers below, 69" x 39"; 175 cm. x 99 cm. 1840's. £380-460 SBel

Early 18th C. Dutch Parquetry Walnut Kneehole Desk. The interior with writing surface and ink wells. 43" wide; 109 cm. £950-1,100 B

A Late George III Tambour Mahogany Desk Bookcase with fitted interior. 2'5" x 5'10"; 73.5 cm. x 178 cm. high. £440-500 LC

A mahogany bureau-plat in the style of J H Riesener, 41¾", 106 cm. wide. £700-780 CStJ

French Rosewood and Tulip-wood Bureau-Plat, with fitted three drawers, leather top, ormolu mounts. 50½" by 27", 128 cm. by 68.5 cm., £850-950 KC

A 'Louis XV' Rosewood and Tulipwood Bureau-Plat, top inset with a tooled leather writing surface, with gilt-metal mounts throughout, 30" by 54", 76 cm. by 137 cm., 1870's. £850-950 SBel

A figured walnut and marquetry bureau plat with serpentine leather-lined top, cabriole legs headed by giltmetal angles. 43" wide, 109 cm., mid-19th C., £900-1,000 CStJ

A Walnut, Ivory and Mother-of-Pearl Bureau-Plat with a central reserve of a dog attacking a deer, the frieze with three drawers. 31½" by 56", 77.5 cm. by 142 cm., possibly German, c.1870. £1,550-1,700 SBel

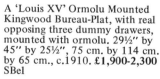

A Rosewood Bureau-Plat, with a tooled leather writing surface. Three frieze drawers opposing three false drawers. Gilt-metal mounts throughout, 29¼" by 54", 75 cm. by 137 cm., early 20th century. £800-900 SBel

A 'Louis XV' Ormolu Mounted Kingwood Bureau-Plat, with real opposing three dummy drawers, mounted with ormolu. 29½" by 45" by 25½", 75 cm. by 114 cm. by 65 cm., c.1910. £1,900-2,300 SBel

A 'Louis XVI' Mahogany Bureau-Plat, the brass-banded top inset with a leather writing surface, each side with a pull-out brushing slide. 28½" by 51½" 72 cm. by 131 cm., early 20th century. £380-440 SBel

An 18th C. style miniature lowboy in satinwood decorated with ebony stringing and rosewood crossbanding, 20" wide, 50.5 cm. £680-740 HKC

A Small Queen Anne Oak Lowboy. £410-460 B

A William and Mary Walnut Lowboy, with featherbanding and quarter-veneered top, 2'6" wide, 76 cm. £300-350 KC

An 18th C. Dutch marquetry and mahogany serpentine-fronted lowboy, 33″, wide, 84 cm. £580-680 KC

An Ebonised and Ivory Bonheur-Du-Jour, with a central cupboard door inscribed 5me Entree de Charles VIII a Naples, en 1494, d'apres une miniature de XV. 61¼″ x 61″; 155.5 cm x 155 cm., c.1870. £1,750-2,200 SBel

A satinwood bonheur-du-jour of George III design, crossbanded with rosewood and inlaid with ebonised lines, 18″, 46 cm wide. £1,100-1,200 CStJ

William and Mary walnut lowboy, c.1690. £5,000-5,200 VM

BONHEUR DU JOUR

- popular in France in 1760's
- originally a Louis XVIth writing table
- essentially a decorative 'ladies' piece and hence frequently of satinwood with marquetry
- watch out for imitiation Louis XV style (often with rococo mounts) — frequently Victorian
- Victorians often added small mirrors to act as a firescreen
- in 1860's frequently painted panels

A Kingwood and Gilt Metal Mounted Bonheur-Du-Jour inlaid on stained panels and outlined with stringing. 19th century, 3′4″ x 4′3½″; 102 cm x 130 cm., £580-680 LC

A Kingwood and Tulipwood Marquetry Bonheur-du-Jour, Two inlaid serpentine doors. Hinged inlaid writing surface, enclosing two small drawers above a single frieze drawer. Gilt-metal mounts throughout, 54″ x 33½″, 137 cm x 85 cm., c 1880 £2,100-2,400 SBel

A Rosewood Bonheur Du Jour, fitted interior, a frieze drawer above a sliding work compartment, 44¼″ x 24″; 112 cm x 61 cm., c 1900. £330-400 SBel

A Red Boulle Bonheur-Du-Jour. Two doors above two short drawers, the lower part with a frieze drawer containing a writing surface, 57″ x 32″; 145 cm x 81 cm., 1880's. £620-700 SBel

Sheraton period mahogany and inlaid bonheur-du-jour, circa 1790. £1,000-1,200

George III satinwood bonheur-du-jour, with mirrored doors. Drawer fitted with writing slope and pen and ink compartments. 2′ wide; 61 cm., £5,700-6,700 HKC

A Victorian Burr Walnut Piano Top Davenport, the pull-out writing slide with rising leather inset surface and pen and ink compartments, drawer with secret button activating a pop-up gallery with drawers and pigeon holes. 21" wide by 36" high; 53 cm. by 91 cm., **£770-870** B

A Late Regency Walnut Davenport, the sliding section with lined writing slope and pierced gallery, having small drawers to the interior and hinged pen tray 2'0"; stamped Johnstone and Jeanes, New Bond Street, **£750-850** KC

A Victorian Rosewood 'Piano top' davenport, with satin walnut veneered interior, the lift-up top encloses drawers and leather lined sliding adjustable writing surface, having four side drawers, on lightly carved scrolled supports, 25" wide; 63.5 cm. **£650-750** GC

A Walnut Davenport, opening to reveal a letter compartment, each side with four real opposing four dummy drawers, 85 cm., 2'9¾", late 19th century, **£370-420** SBel

A Rosewood Davenport, with an inset writing surface and three small drawers, four graduated drawers, four dummy drawers, 36½" x 26½"; 93 cm. x 67 cm., mid 19th century. **£200-280** SBel

A Walnut Harlequin Davenport, with a sprung superstructure operated by releasing a lever concealed within the right-hand drawer, 38" by 23" 97 cm. by 59 cm., 1860's **£750-950** SBel

A Good Walnut Harlequin Davenport, with letter compartments, sliding writing surface, two small drawers, one false, one real cupboard door enclosing four drawers, 36" x 33½"; 91.5 cm. x 70 cm., 1860's **£640-750** SBel

A Victorian Walnut Davenport with piano shape front on scroll supports. 1'11"; 58 cm., **£680-780** LC

An Oak Davenport, the writing surface enclosing a fitted interior, four real and four dummy drawers, 37" x 24"; 94 cm x 61 cm., 1880's **£240-280** SBel

A Burr-Walnut Davenport with four columns applied with Wedgwood' plaques, ebonised bandings, distressed, 36"; 91.5 cm., c 1860. **£320-380** SBel

A Walnut Davenport, the writing slope sliding forward, fitted interior, with a slide each side, pen drawer, three further drawers, mid-19th century, 1'8½"; 52 cm., **£760-860** LC

153

A Victorian walnut davenport with brass gallery, 21″, 53 cm. **£390-430** LC

A Walnut Davenport, the lower part with a hinged writing slope enclosing a well and four dummy drawers, the sides with four real opposing four dummy drawers 37½″; 95 cm., c 1860 **£300-400** SBel

A Victorian Rosewood Davenport, the lined writing slope on carved cabriole supports, fitted four real and four opposing dummy drawers, on bun feet and castors, 53 cm., wide; 1′9¼″. **£440-540** KC

A Walnut Davenport with a leather-lined writing slope, the side with a pen drawer above four short drawers, opposing four dummy drawers, with moulded serpentine legs, foot lacking, 24″; 61 cm wide, 1870's **£320-400** SBel

A George I Walnut Bureau, 36″; 91 cm. **£1,250-1,500** OL

Georgian Mahogany bureau. 3′1¼″ wide x 1′9¼″ deep; 94 cm. x 53 cm. **£740-840** JWB

A George II oak bureau, interior with cupboard, pigeon holes, drawers and well, minor repairs, 36″, 91.5 cm. **£600-660** ,LC

A pair of painted satinwood child's bureaux with ivory handles, 15¾″ and 15″, 40 cm and 38 cm wide. **£1,150-1,250** CStJ

A giltmetal-mounted kingwood bureau de dame with shaped sloping flap with centrally-mounted Sevres-pattern plaque, leather-lined fitted interior. 26¼″ wide, 67 cm., mid-19th C. **£1,000-1,200** CStJ

A Spanish Vargueno, engraved bone and parcel gilt and turned spiral columns, 2'2" high by 3'6" wide; 66 cm. by 107 cm., on walnut stand. **£2,000-2,500** SBS

A Dutch marquetry Bureau, with mahogany ground, 3'6" high by 3'9" wide by 1'10" deep, 107 cm by 114 cm by 56 cm, mid-18th C. **£2,800-3,200** SBS

An eighteenth century Dutch marquetry bombe bureau, the cylinder fall and slide enclosing drawers, pigeon-holes and secret compartments. 44" wide; 11 cm. **£2,300-2.800** LJ

An 18th century German Walnut Serpentine-Fronted Bureau Cabinet, decorated with cross-banding and geometric inlay. The fall revealing a leather lined interior, 90 cm. wide; 2'11½". **£4,200-5,000** KC

George III Mahogany bureau, the fall flap reveals a fitted interior above four graduated oak-lined drawers with brass swan neck handles on bracket feet. 3'1"; 93.5 cm. **£860-960** WW

A North Italian Walnut Bureau, with an interior of short drawers flanking a recess, three bow-fronted drawers below, cross-banded and inlaid, 3'7" wide; 109 cm., c.1730. **£1,550-1,800** SBS

A Dutch walnut and marquetry bureau with fitted interior. 45", 114 cm wide. **£3,000-3,300** CStJ

An Italian Walnut Bureau, interior of drawers and pigeon holes, the serpentine front with two drawers carved with shaped panels. 4' wide 122 cm., c.1770. **£3,800-4,200** SBS

A giltmetal-mounted kingwood and marquetry bureau a cylindre. 32" wide, 81 cm., late 19th C., **£800-900** CStJ

A Queen Anne walnut bureau, later bracket feet, 38", 96.5 cm wide. **£1,750-1,850** CStJ

A mid-Georgian oak bureau, 34" wide, 86 cm. **£340-380** HKC

A Dutch Marquetry Bureau with scrolled lid on claw-and-ball feet, 52½" wide; 133 cm., mid-18th century. £3,400-4,000 CStJ

A Dutch Walnut and Marquetry Bureau, the bombe front between chamfered angles on claw-and-ball feet, 47" wide x 44½" high, 119.5 cm. x 113 cm. £3,400-4,000 CStJ

A nineteenth century lady's walnut bureau, gallery with Porcelain de Paris panels in gilded cartouches, ormolu masks to knees, 42" wide; 106 cm. £850-1,000 LJ

A fine 18th century Dutch walnut and marquetry bombe front bureau, with fitted interior and well. 3'8½"; 112.5 cm. £2,750-3,200 PJ

A rare Queen Anne laburnum bureau, veneered in oyster pieces, the fall front enclosing a later fitted interior with small drawers, pillar drawers, cabinet and pigeon holes. 3'2½"; 97.5 cm. £1,100-1,400 PWC

A 17th century-Design Yew-Wood and Crossbanded Bureau, having oyster veneers. Stepped and fitted interior with well. 78 cm. wide; 2'6¾". £1,180-1,400 KC

A 19th century Dutch Mahogany Bureau of 18th century design with fitted interior. 108 cm., maximum width; 3'6¾". £760-960 PJ

An oak Bureau, the Mahogany cross-banded fall flap enclosing stationery compartments and maple faced drawers. 3' wide x 1'8" deep, 43" high; 91 cm. x 50 cm. x 108.5 cm. £400-480 VC

A Late 18th century Dutch Mahogany and Marquetry Bombe Cylinder – Top Bureau. Ornate stepped and fitted interior of concave design with tambour cupboard. 114 cm. wide; 3'9¼". £2,000-2,400 KC

A Rare Small William & Mary Oak Bureau, the interior of small drawers flanking convex recesses and secret drawers. On separate base of two short and two long drawers, 34½" wide; 87 cm., £1,200-1,500 B

An 18th century Dutch Marquetry Walnut Bureau. The fall revealing a stepped interior with small drawers, secret drawers, pigeon-holes, a cupboard and a well. 106 cm. wide; 3'6". £3,350-3,700 KC

An 18th century German Walnut and Marquetry Bureau. Fall flap enclosing four short drawers with three long serpentine-fronted drawers to base. 53" wide; 134.5 cm. £2,200-2,500 KC

A Mid-19th Century Continental Mahogany and Painted Cylinder Bureau. Three-quarter pierced brass gallery to the top. The cylinder revealing a lined writing slide, small drawers, pigeon-holes and a cupboard. 97 cm. wide; 3'2¼''. £1,100-1,500 KC

18th century Dutch Marquetry Bureau. Interior of fall fitted with drawers, pigeon holes and well, four long graduated drawers to base. All-over floral marquetry. 35½'' wide; 90 cm. £2,600-3,000 KC

A Georgian Walnut Bureau, with featherbanding and crossbanding. Fitted interior above two short and two long graduated drawers, 98 cm. wide; 3'2¾''. £1,400-1,600 KC

A Dutch Walnut and Marquetry Bureau, 47'', 119.5 cm. wide, 44½'', 113 cm. high. £3,400-3,700 CStJ

A Mahogany Inlaid Bureau, kingwood crossbanding throughout. Well fitted interior with pigeon holes, drawers and central cupboard. One drawer fitted with inkwells and pen tray and the whole sliding forward to reveal hidden recess. 42''; 107 cm. First half 19th century. £1,150-1,500 LC

A Late 18th century Dutch Marquetry Bureau. Fitted interior with drawers, pigeon-holes and well. Two short and two long drawers, 94 cm. wide; 3'1¼''. £2,300-2,800 KC

A Queen Anne Walnut Bureau, having crossbanding and featherbanding. The fall revealing a stepped and fitted interior with well. 91 cm. wide; 3'0''. £700-800 KC

A Late 18th century Finely Figured Mahogany Bureau cross banded with ebony stringing decoration. 33¾''; 85.5 cm., £775-875 LE

An 18th century Burr Elm Bureau, with fitted interior above four long graduated drawers. 86 cm. wide; 2'10''. £920-1,000 KC

A Dutch Marquetry Bureau, 52½'', 133 cm. wide, mid-18th C. £3,400-3,700 CStJ

157

18th century Dutch cylinder bureau. £1,550-1,700 JWB

A French giltmetal-mounted kingwood cylinder bureau. 29½", 75 cm wide, late 19th C. £1,000-1,100 CStJ

A Dutch walnut and marquetry cylinder bureau. 38½", 98 cm wide, 50½", 128 cm high, c.1830. £2,100-2,300 CStJ

A Dutch marquetry cylinder front bureau, with fitted interior, late 18th/early 19th C., 42½", 108 cm, £1,050-1,100 LC

A Cylinder Bureau with a tambour front enclosing drawers and pigeonholes, and a slide above two tambour cupboards, 3'3" high by 2'2" wide; 99 cm. by 66 cm., c.1800, possibly German. £800-900 SBS

A 32" wide lady's Regency rosewood bureau, the top enclosed by mirrored doors, the bureau with cylinder roll top, inlaid with brass stringing. 32" wide; 81 cm. £1,800-2,100 LJ

A late 18th century Dutch walnut marquetry cylinder bureau with a curved interior with an arrangement of stepped drawers flanking pigeon holes and a cupboard. 3'9" wide; 113.5 cm. £2,200-2,500 HKC

A Rosewood and Kingwood Marquetry Bureau a Cylindre, with a breccia marble top. 42" x 35½", 107 cm. x 90 cm. c.1880 £1,600-1,900 SBel

A Louis Quinze-Design Kingwood and Crossbanded Bureau A Cylindre, with marble top. Pull-out lined writing inset, pigeonholes and drawers. Chevron parquetry apron drawer, 77 cm. wide; 2'6¼". £700-800 KC

A George III Mahogany Cylinder Bureau, the upper part with gothic arcaded frieze and two gothic-pattern glazed doors between reeded angles, 37½"; 95 cm. wide. £1,700-2,000 CStJ

A Queen Anne-style walnut bureau bookcase. Fall revealing a stepped interior with drawers, pigeon-holes and a cupboard. 3'0", 91 cm. wide. £1,900-2,100 KC

A William and Mary oak Bureau-bookcase, fitted with pigeon holes, drawers, candle trays and a secret compartment; size 80" 203 cm. high x 42", 106 cm. wide. £3,900-4,500 MH

A fine George III mahogany bureau bookcase. Interior fitted with drawers, pigeon-holes and central cupboards. 39", 100 cm. wide. £1,800-2,000 KC

A good oak bureau bookcase in the 18th C. style, crossbanded in mahogany. 19th C. 3'2½", 98 cm. x 6'10½", 210 cm. high. £1,300-1,600 LC

A George III mahogany bureau bookcase. Flap revealing cross-banded small drawers, pigeon-holes and a mirror door cupboard, 3'9½", 115 cm. wide. £2,900-3,400 KC

A fine Queen Anne Walnut Bureau Bookcase, having mirror doors, candle slides, recessed well, stepped short drawers and pigeon holes. 7'9", 236.5 cm. high x 3'5", 103.5 cm. wide. £8,750-9,750 PK

A 19th C. Continental Queen Anne style walnut pier bureau bookcase with etched mirror door of later date. £880-980 LJ

A Mid-19th century Continental Mahogany Cylinder Bureau. Raised back with a pair of tambour doors. Cylinder revealing a writing slide and fitted interior. 120 cm. wide. 3'11½". £290-340 KC

A Mahogany Inlaid Bureau Bookcase with glazed doors enclosing adjustable shelves, the bureau with fall-front and fitted interior. 42"; 107 cm., 19th century. £1,500-1,800   LC

A Mid-18th C. mahogany bureau bookcase. Flap enclosing an interior fitted with drawers, pigeon-holes and central cupboard. 39¼", 100 cm. wide. £2,900-3,200   KC

A mahogany bureau bookcase. Leather-lined fall-front with six burr-maple veneered drawers. Crossbanded throughout in satinwood, 1900's. £980-1,100 SBel

A Georgian mahogany bureau bookcase. £850-950 JWB

A George II mahogany bureau bookcase with carved cornice, c.1770. £5,000-6,000   LJ

An 18th C. German walnut bureau bookcase. Fall front with crossbanding and parquetry panels, 86", 218 cm. high x 43", 109 cm. wide. £3,400-4,200 B

A late 18th C. Dutch oak and marquetry Bureau Bookcase, 3'9½", 15 cm. wide. £3,800-4,300 PL

An 18th C. South German oak and marquetry bureau bookcase; heavy brass side carrying handles, 3'0", 113.5 cm. wide. £2,040-2,300 PWC

A Georgian oak bureau bookcase. The lower part with an interior of drawers and pigeon holes, 3'4", 101 cm. wide. £1,450-1,600 B

A fine 18th C. South German cross-banded figured walnut 3-tier bureau Cabinet with brass loop handles; 4'4", 132 cm. height overall 6'3½", 191 cm. £5,200-6,000 GSP

A George I small walnut bureau-cabinet, 27", 68.5 cm wide, 76" 193 cm high. £4,000-4,300 CStJ

A Dutch Bureau Bookcase, the upper part with a leaf-carved cresting, the whole inlaid with floral marquetry on a mahogany ground, 8'4" by 4'9" wide; 254 cm. by 145 cm., late 18th/ early 19th century. £6,000-7,000 SBS

An 18th C. German walnut bureau cabinet, all inlaid and chequered in walnut. 44", 111 cm wide x 80", 203 cm. high. £3,000-4,000 B

A Queen Anne walnut double-domed bureau-cabinet, 42", 107 cm wide. £7,500-8,200 CStJ

A Victorian carved oak bureau bookcase. Astragal doors above the fall, with fitted interior. 37", 93.5 cm. wide. £700-900 KC

A Fine 18th century South German Walnut Bureau Cabinet, decorated with stringing and cross-banding, on ebonised bun feet, 117 cm. wide; 3'10¼". £2,000-2,500 KC

An 18th C. Dutch walnut and floral marquetry decorated bureau bookcase, £3,800-4,800 LJ

An Early Georgian Mahogany Bureau Bookcase, with fall-front to a bureau with a well fitted stepped interior. 39" wide; 99 cm. £800-900 B

161

An early eighteenth century walnut fall front bureau, crossbanded and herringbone inlaid. 41" wide; 103.5 cm. **£1,400-1,700** LJ

Regency mahogany secretaire bookcase. **£950-1,100** JWB

A 19th C. French amboyna, ebonised and ormolu secretaire-cabinet, pull-out writing drawer with sliding secretaire flanked by small drawers. 48", 122 cm. wide x 59", 149.5 cm. high x 22", 55 cm. deep. **£2,800-3,200** MH

A Regency mahogany breakfront secretaire/bookcase. **£3,700-4,000** JWB

A giltmetal-mounted mahogany and marquetry secretaire a abattant of Louis XV design with three-quarter galleried marble top and concave frieze. 31½" wide, 80 cm. **£1,050-1,200** CStJ

A Dutch Walnut and Marquetry Inlaid Secretaire A Abattant, decorated in numerous woods and ivory inlay, having pierced gallery above frieze drawer. 3'2" wide, 1'7" deep; 4'7" tall; 96 cm. by 47.5 cm. by 139 cm., c.1800. **£1,700-1,900** BON

18th C. mahogany kneehole secretaire bookcase, 3'11" wide, 1'10" deep, 8'3" high., 118.5 cm. x 55 cm. x 252 cm. **£2,500-3,000** PWC

Early 19th century beidemeyer secretaire-abettant veneered in mahogany, the interior comprising drawers, pigeon-holes and secret drawers. **£900-1,500**

A Kingwood Parquetry Secretaire. Fall-front inset with a leather writing surface, two short drawers and a well. Gilt-metal foliate mounts throughout, 64¼" x 34½"; 163 cm. x 87.5 cm. c.1880. **£1,000-1,400** SBel

A good Dutch mahogany secretaire a abattant with fitted interior, early 19th C., 39" by 56", 99 cm by 142 cm. **£660-740** LC

An early 18th C. colonial walnut escritoire cabinet. 51″ by 68½″, 130 cm by 174 cm. **£1,050-1,100** LC

A William and Mary walnut escritoire with original brasses. c.1690. **£5,000-5,500** LKL

A mid-19th century Empire style mahogany escritoire, fitted secretaire compartment and three drawers. 40¾″ wide x 79″ high. 103 cm. x 200.5 cm. **£380-480** DHBN

An 18th C. Dutch Marquetry Escritoire, interior of small drawers and stationery compartments, 33″ wide; 83.5 cm. **£1,500-2,000** MH

'Sheraton' mahogany secretaire bookcase. **£700-800** JWB

A Georgian mahogany Secretaire-Bookcase, 3′4″, 101 cm. wide 20″, 50 cm. deep, 88″, 223 cm. high. **£1,500-1,800** VC

A George III satinwood Secretaire cabinet, the lower part with a fitted secretaire drawer with pigeon holes and drawers and three drawers beneath. 3′4″, 101.5 cm. x 6′5″, 196 cm. high. **£950-1,050** LC

An early Victorian figured mahogany break-front secretaire bookcase, 7′6½″, 230 cm. wide. **£1,800-2,000** KC

A Federal Secretaire Cabinet, 8′2″ high by 4′ wide, 249 cm by 122 cm, American, c.1800. **£1,500-2,500** SBS

A George III Sheraton-style mahogany secretaire bookcase; inlaid with satinwood, the lower well with indexed filing boxes, c.1810. 54″, 137 cm. **£2,400-2,800** RB

An Ivory Inlaid Ebony Veneered
Secretaire with a fitted interior,
53″ x 26½″; 135 cm. x 67.3 cm.
French or Italian, 1870's. £200-
350 SBel

Peter Waals. An Important
Solid Walnut Secretaire,
the front with raised and
strapped panel, interior of two
cupboards, three nests of
pigeon holes and ten drawers.
The base having seven drawers,
44¾″ wide, 50″ high, 17″
deep; 111 cm. by 127 cm. by
47.5 cm. £2,100-2,500 WW

Regency Period Small Faded
Rosewood Secretaire in the
manner of John McClean, brass
gallery, brass inlaid ebony banding and brass handles. Fitted
interior with cedar lined drawers
and pigeon holes, silk panel
doors. 34″ wide 16½″ deep by
4′1½″ high; 86 cm. by 42 cm.
by 126 cm. £4,700-5,000 WW

A Mahogany Secretaire Cabinet
the cupboard doors enclosing a
mirror-lined interior. 57″ x 39″;
145 cm. x 99 cm., French, 1830's
£140-180 SBel

A French Giltmetal-Mounted
Tulipwood Secretaire, 24½″,
62 cm. wide, mid 19th C. bearing
the label of 'Carlhian & Corbiere,
Paris'. £680-740 CStJ

An Empire Style Marquetry
Secretaire A Abattant with a
frieze drawer above a fall-front
and two drawers, 41″; 104 cm.,
19th century. £800-900 LC

A pair of Chinese black lacquer
Cabinets, with engraved brass
lock-plates and hinges, 3′1″, 94
cm. wide; 5′2″, 157.5 cm. high.
19th C. £3,200-3,600 CStJ

Italian mahogany Cabinet inlaid
with various woods with ivory
finials, Arundel prints to upper
cupboards. £300-380 W

An 18th C. Scandinavian painted
Cabinet. 4′9″, 145 cm. wide x
4′6″, 137 cm. high. £600-700 B

A Damascus Ivory and Brass-Inlaid Hardwood Cabinet, 2′6″ by 1′4″, 75 cm by 40 cm, c.1900. **£250-300** SBel

A 17th C. Italian ebonised Cabinet, on Stand, veneered and inlaid with tortoiseshell and mother-of-pearl, 4′4″ wide, 132 cm. incorporating a later organ mechanism with single rank of pipes. **£1,800-2,000** LJ

A Mid-19th C. ormolu mounted walnut and parquetry Display Cabinet on writing Stand in the Louis Seize style. 5′0½″, 153 cm. wide. **£900-1,100** KC

A mahogany and marquetry Side Cabinet with kidney-shaped mirror and single cupboard. 4′9¼″, 145.5 cm. by 2′7″, 79 cm. c.1900. **£300-380** SBel

An XVIII Century Dutch Marquetry Walnut Vitrine Chest, Floral marquetry in various woods, with bombe front to the drawers. 35″ wide x 72″ high; 89 cm. x 183 cm. **£1,900-2,100** B

A pair of 19th C. Sheraton style satinwood demi-lune china display cabinets, crossbanded and inlaid with kingwood. 32″ wide, 81 cm. **£1,750-1,950** HKC

A French Marquetry and Gilded Bronze Vitrine, 6′10″ wide by 8′2″ high, 208 cm by 249 cm. **£3,800-4,200** MH

A mid 17th C. Ebony Cabinet on Stand, height 4′7″, width 2′4½″, 140 cm by 72 cm, probably German. **£1,000-1,500** SBS

A Liberty & Co. oak side Cabinet, 5′6½″, 169 cm. by 2′2″, 66 cm. with label Liberty & Co. Ltd., London, c.1920. **£250-300** SBel

A George IV mahogany Corner Cabinet. 3′8″, 111 cm. wide. **£1,600-1,900** HKC

An art nouveau satinwood cabinet, 60" by 79", 152 cm by 201 cm high. **£640-690** LC

A mother-of-pearl inlaid carved lacquer Display Cabinet on a painted red ground, 5'8", 173 cm. by 3'2", 97 cm. late 19th C. **£450-530** SBel

A mahogany Vitrine with gilt-metal mounts, 4'7¾", 141.5 cm. x 2'3", 69 cm. early 20th C. **£400-480** SBel

A fine Japanese Cabinet in carved blackwood and lacquer work with 15 gold lacquer Shibayama panels; 6 carved ivory figure mounts and finials. 4'7", 138 cm. wide. 8'0", 240 cm. high. **£4,200-5,000** GSP

An Unusual Display Cabinet, designed by Clement Heaton, 62½" by 48", 159 cm by 122 cm, c.1880. **£1,900-2,200** SBel

A kingwood and ormolu-mounted serpentine-fronted Vitrine. Lower section with a bombe panel painted in the Vernet Martin style. 2'6", 76 cm. wide. **£1,200-1,400** KC

A brass inlaid rosewood Cabinet, the double glazed doors enclosing 3 shelves, 3'5", 103.5 cm. wide. 1'0", 30.5 cm. 5'7", 170.5 cm. high. **£290-350** VC

A 17th C. Portugese Hardwood and Ebonised Standing Cabinet, 46" wide by 73" high, 117 cm by 186 cm. **£850-950** B

A Dutch walnut and marquetry small display cabinet. 37", 94 cm wide, 76", 193 cm high. **£2,200-2,400** CStJ

A Satinwood and Marquetry Display Cabinet, 72½" by 60½", 184 cm by 154 cm, c.1880. **£2,450-2,700** SBel

A mahogany and Vernis Martin Vitrine 4'6½", 138 cm. x 2'2½", 67.5 cm. early 20th C. **£460-500** SBel

A 19th C. French kingwood and cube parquetry ormolu mounted Vitrine, 4'5½", 136 cm. wide. **£3,000-3,300** KC

A pair of giltwood Display Cabinets. 4'7", 140 cm. x 1'11½", 60 cm., early 20th C. **£600-700** SBel

A porcelain mounted ebonised and amboyna Cabinet, 3'11½", 120 cm. x 4'9", 145 cm. high. **£900-1,100** LC

Fine Chinese hardwood Display Cabinet. **£2,500-3,000** RBB

A mahogany Display Cabinet, glazed doors with applied astragals enclosing shelves, 5'5½", 166.4 cm. by 3'3¼", 100 cm. 1880-1900. **£280-340** SBel

A fine Mid-19th C. ebonised break-fronted Side Cabinet, decorated with ornate stringing, mounted with gilt-metal enrichments and turned columns, 5'6", 198 cm. wide. **£700-800** KC

A French rosewood and marquetry Vitrine of neo-classic influence. 19th C. 3'3", 99 cm. x 6'6", 198 cm. high. **£540-640** LC

An Art Nouveau style mahogany display cabinet, 54" wide, 137 cm. **£460-540** OL

A Dutch walnut Cabinet, the bombe base with two short and two long drawers. 6'0", 183 cm. x 7'6", 229 cm. high. 18th C. **£2,800-3,200** LC

A late 19th C. mahogany and inlaid bow-front Display Cabinet on Stand in the Sheraton style. 3'1½", 95 cm. wide. **£600-700** KC

An 18th C. Dutch oak Vitrine Kast, 5'6", 168 cm. wide x 6'5", 196 cm. high. **£1,550-1,750** B

A 18th C. French walnut Encoignure-Cartonier, **£1,800-1,900** B

An early Louis XVI Cauchoise oak buffet vitrine, 58" wide, 147 cm. **£1,700-1,900** HKC

A Vernis Martin serpentine Vitrine, 4'7½", 141 cm. x 2'2½", 67 cm. c.1900. **£800-900** SBel

An unusual kingwood and walnut Display Cabinet, 3'6", 107 cm. c.1870. **£410-460** SBel

A Dutch oak and marquetry Display Cabinet 4'10", 147.5 cm. wide, 7'5", 226 cm. high; 1'4", 41 cm. deep, 18th C. **£4,600-5,000** C

A Vernis Martin kingwood Vitrine, Gilt-metal mounts throughout, 6'5¼", 196.2 cm., x 4'0", 122 cm. c.1900. **£2,600-2,800** SBel

A chromium-plated and ebonised Display Cabinet. 3'5", 104 cm. x 2'1¼", 64 cm. Late 1920's. **£150-170** SBel

An extremely fine French kingwood and mahogany breakfronted Vitrine, with crossbanding and parquetry panels. 6'4", 193 cm. wide. **£1,550-1,750** KC

A pair of late 19th C. satinwood bow-front Display Cabinets. 3'1½" wide, 95 cm. wide. £850-950 KC

A Victorian ebonised satinwood and painted side cabinet in the manner of T.E. Collcutt, 43" wide, 108.5 cm. £180-220 HKC

A rosewood and tulip-wood vitrine of Louis XV design, 34" wide, 86 cm., 57" high, 144.5 cm. £820-910 HKC

A pair of tulipwood and walnut Croner Cabinets, crossbanded in figured wood. c.1870. £1,000-1,200 SBel

A Victorian mahogany side cabinet, 48" wide, 122 cm. £170-190 HKC

A Rosewood and Marquetry Side Cabinet, 91½" by 50¼", 232.5 cm by 138 cm, c.1900. £340-400 SBel

A Vernis Martin mahogany Vitrine, with marble top, gilt-metal mounts. 4'11¾", 152 cm. by 2'0¾", 63 cm., c.1900. £200-400 SBel

A 19th C. French kingwood vitrine with gilt metal mounts. 66" high, 168 cm. £650-720 HKC

A satinwood and porcelain mounted Display Cabinet, 6'1", 185.5 cm. by 2'6", 76 cm. 1870's. £600-700 SBel

A late Victorian satinwood Display Cabinet in the Sheraton manner. 3'10", 116 cm. **£1,350-1,550** LE

A George III mahogany cabinet-on-stand, 21½", 54.5 cm wide. **£2,200-2,350** CStJ

A Chinese polychrome lacquer cabinet on giltwood stand with 12 drawers, early 18th C., 33", 84 cm wide. **£2,200-2,300** CStJ

A good 18th C. German cabinet upon stand, in a parquetry of oak, sycamore, boxwood, walnut and purple heart, with original pewtered locks and hinges. 3'8" wide, 111 cm. x 3'4" high, 101 cm. **£680-780** B

An ebonised cabinet-on-stand. 43½", 110.5 cm wide. **£1,250-1,500** CStJ

A fine early George III mahogany cabinet-on-stand with 10 drawers, 40", 102 cm wide, 65", 165 cm high, **£3,800-3,900** CStJ

A 17th C. style credence cupboard on stand in oak and walnut, 38" wide, 96 cm., 72" high, 183 cm. **£1,200-1,400** HKC

A Walnut cabinet constructed from panels of late 16th century South German marquetry. Top set with three small views of buildings the front enclosed by a pair of doors. Three panels in the apron and a shelf set with three architectural views. Ebony surround with ivory stars and other motifs. 3'5" wide; 103.5 cm., **£950-1,100** HKC

A Fine James I Oak Livery Cupboard, the plank top with moulded edge above a lunette carved frieze and two moulded panelled doors flanking a moulded central panel and raised upon cup and cover turned front supports united by a moulded front stretcher with silhouette carving. 50" wide by 42" high; 127 cm. by 107 cms. **£1,700-1,900** B

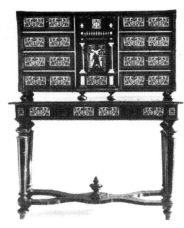

A fine 17th C. ebony and bone marquetry Antwerp Cabinet, central cupboard with bone and ebony pillars and turned ivory gallery. 3'7", 109 cm. wide. **£950-1,100** B

A black lacquered Cabinet on carved and gilt Stand, with pierced and engraved gilt metal clasps and lock plate. 3'4½", 102 cm. x 5'9½", 176 cm. high. 18th C. **£800-900** LC

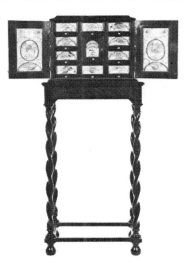

A Flemish ebonised and tortoise-shell table cabinet. 20¾", 52.5 cm wide. 17th C. **£600-680** CStJ

A 'Queen Anne' burr-walnut chest on stand. 6'5¼", 196 cm. by 3'8¼", 112 cm. The upper part re-veneered from 18th century wood, c.1920. **£750-850** SBel

HANDLES — GUIDE TO DATING

- until 1660 – wooden knobs
- 1660-1710 – brass drops
- 1690's – brass loop handles with sold backplates
- c.1710 – pierced backplate
- c.1735 – swan-neck backplate
- 1780's – stamped circular or oval brass backplates
- 1800's – turned wooden knob
- 1880's – return to brass handles of various styles – different colour brass to earlier examples

A porcelain panelled and lacquer Cabinet on Stand. 2'5½" high, 75 cm. x 4'5⅝" overall, 136 cm. Japanese, late 19th C. **£975-1,075** LC

A Mid-18th C. Oriental Cabinet on Stand, with black lacquer and gilt decoration. 2'9½" wide, 85 cm. **£560-620** KC

A rare 17th C. Antwerp ebony and Stumpwork Cabinet, exterior in veneered panels flanked by applied moulded ebony. 2'8", 81 cm. **£1,000-1,200** B

A French antique ornate carved Cabinet on Stand. 4'0" wide, 122 cm. **£850-980** KC

A Dutch Kingwood Cabinet on Stand, 4'11" high by 4' wide, 150 cm by 122 cm, late 17th C. **£3,200-3,500** SBS

A Pair of Ormolu-Mounted Figured Walnut Cabinets, 28", 71 cm. wide, mid-19th C. **£7,000-7,800** CStJ

A 17th C. Spanish walnut Vargueno, the fall front in fine iron work and traces of original gilt decoration, interior of eighteen drawers. **£1,400-1,600** B

A Simulated Rosewood and Parcel-Gilt Cabinet-On-Stand, 44", 112 cm., wide, 18th C. Flemish or North German. **£3,400-3,800** CStJ

A Late Victorian Rosewood and Marquetry Vitrine 6'7" high, 40½" wide, 21½" deep, 200.5 cm by 101 cm by 54 cm. **£660-740** WW

An antique walnut Cabinet on Stand of William and Mary design, on barley sugar twist supports, bun feet. 3'8", 111 cm. wide. **£1,600-1,800** KC

A late 17th C. Dutch colonial silver mounted Cabinet on Stand. 1'6¾" wide, 47 cm. **£1,800-2,100** KC

An Ebony and Marquetry Cabinet, inlaid throughout with floral marquetry with mother-of-pearl, on William IV stand, 60", 151.5 cm. wide, 17th C. probably Dutch. **£6,000-6,700** CStJ

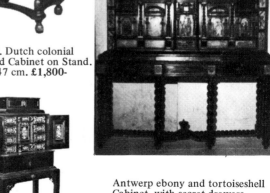

A Flemish Ebonised Cabinet, on a George III black and gold lacquer stand, 29", 73.5 cm. wide, the cabinet 17th C. **£1,150-1,300** CStJ

Antwerp ebony and tortoiseshell Cabinet, with secret drawers. 6'5", 196 cm. wide x 7'0", 213 cm. high. **£1,800-2,200** B

An unusual Regency mahogany bookcase with a canvas backed map covering the adjustable shelves, 5'6", 168 cm. x 7'2", 219 cm. high., some defects. **£1,000-1,200** LC

An early 19th C. Dutch mahogany bookcase. 51", 129.5 cm. wide. **£600-680** KC

Excellent quality late 19th C. Flemish style carved oak Bookcase/Cabinet Height 96", 244 cm. Width 56", 142 cm., greatest depth 24", 61 cm. **£850-950** WB

Georgian pine bookcase 9'1½", 279 cm. wide x 20", 51 cm. deep x 7'9¾", 239 cm. high. **£1,000-1,100** JWB

A Mid-19th C. mahogany break-front bookcase. Four astragal doors enclosing adjustable shelves, 7'2¾", 220 cm. wide. **£2,600-3,000** KC

A Regency bookcase. **£2,300-2,500** JWB

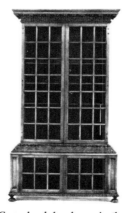

A Carved oak bookcase in the manner of the Samuel Pepys bookcases. 107", 272 cm. x 59", 150 cm. 1920's. **£700-800** SBel

Pair of mahogany inlaid open bookcases, with backs inlaid in neo-classical style in rosewood, satinwood, boxwood and harewood. Each 53", 135 cm. high x 39¾", 101 cm. and 41", 104 cm. wide, late 19th C. **£950-1,100** LC

Mahogany breakfront pedestal bookcase in the Chippendale style. **£2,300-2,500** RB

A Victorian carved oak cabinet bookcase, with Lion-mask decoration, 3'9¼", 114 cm. wide. **£390-480** KC

A George III mahogany break-front bookcase, 93½", 238 cm wide, 94", 239 cm high, 22", 56 cm deep. £5,400-5,700 CStJ

A George III mahogany break-front bookcase, 154", 392 cm wide, 110", 276 cm high. £2,600-2,750 CStJ

Dutch bookcase with cupboard under, carved with lion masks and nude figures. £800-900 W

A good quality Victorian walnut and marquetry bookcase, applied mouldings and decorated with marquetry and string lines, 4'0", 122 cm. wide. £780-880 PWC

An Oak Bookcase with central lower fall-front drawer, 97½" by 72", 248 cm by 183 cm, 1865-70. £780-880 SBel

A Viennese Satinwood Library Bookcase, the glazed doors faced with ebonised and parcel-gilt spears, flanked by turned pilasters headed by gilt finials. 7'2" high by 3'5" wide; 218 cm. by 104 cm., c.1820 £1,600-1,900 SBS

A 19th C. Mahogany Breakfront Library Bookcase, 12' wide, 3.65 m, £2,100-2,500 HKC

An early 19th C. mahogany book-case, with three ebonised astragal doors enclosing adjustable shelves, 6'2¼", 189 cm. wide. £1,850-2,000 KC

A Mahogany Bookcase, with two panelled glazed doors, flanked by stop-fluted columns, and two brushing slides above a pair of cupboard doors. 80" by 58½"; 203 cm. by 149 cm., c.1850. £820-920 SBel

A 17th C. German oak and walnut Cupboard on Chest, having scroll banding and carving with tapering pilaster terminals. 5'10¾", 180 cm. wide. £980-1,100 KC

A 17th C. Flemish carved oak Cupboard, with gadrooned and lion-mask frieze, fitted with drawer, 4'11", 150 cm. wide. £1,800-2,000 KC

Early 18th C. Spanish oak cupboard, doors inscribed 'Anno 1722 B.B.', with ring handles. 4'4", 132 cm. wide. £2,300-2,600 LJ

A Mid-19th C. carved oak Cupbaord in the French Renaissance style. 4'8¾", 145 cm. wide. £780-880 KC

An early 18th C. Dutch baroque rosewood Kas. Deep moulded cornice above a central cartouche 83", 211 cm. high x 68", 173 cm. wide. £1,050-1,200 B

16th C. Gothic oak Double Cupboard. Upper cupboard of two panelled doors with linenfold carved centres with Iron strap hinges, 51", 130 cm. high x 22", 56 cm. deep x 51", 130 cm. wide. £1,400-1,600 B

Queen Anne oak and yew livery cupboard. £2,250-2,500 JWB

1221

A fine antique oak linen-fold Cupboard, carved linen-fold panels, 69", 175.5 cm. wide. £1,400-1,600 KC

A 16th C. Continental oak Cupboard, with iron hinges, chip carved dentelling to cornice. 30½", 77.25 cm. wide. £2,300-2,600 LJ

A good 18th C. oak double Cabinet. 6'3", 190 cm. £800-900. B

A 20th C. Chinese black lacquered and carved Cupboard, 3'11" wide, 118.5 cm. £250-300 OL

A William and Mary Walnut
Chest on Stand, with featherbanding, 108 cm. wide; 3'6¾"
£600-680 KC

A pair of late 19th C. large
carved oak Cupboards on Chests.
5'8¾" wide, 175 cm. £280-360
KC

An Important Dutch Walnut
Cabinet on Chest, the interior with
row of pigeon holes above an
arrangement of twelve drawers
around a central pull-out cupboard, with many secret drawers
and compartments. 47½ by 71";
121 by 180 cm., high, 18th
century. £2,550-3,000 LC

A 19th C. ornate carved walnut
Cabinet in the French Renaissance
style. 2'8½" wide, 82 cm. £700-
800 KC

A Queen Anne Oak Chest on Stand,
the stand with one long drawer
on later bun feet, 42"; 107 cm.
£700-800 LC

An 18th C. Queen Anne-design
walnut and featherbanded fall-
front Cabinet on Chest. 3'8½",
112 cm. wide. £740-900 KC

A Fine William and Mary figured
walnut chest on stand, decorated
with featherbanding, on baluster
turned supports. 45" wide; 119
cm. £1,600-1,800 KC

A George III oak Cupboard on
Chest. 4'2¼", 128 cm. wide.
£550-620 KC

A good 16th C. French walnut
Cupboard, in two sections, the
lower part with a projecting shield,
£2,500-3,000 PL

A Queen Anne walnut Cabinet with two panel doors enclosing ten drawers, all with feather banding. 3'8", 111 cm. x 5'11", 180 cm. high. £1,250-1,500 LC

An 18th C. mahogany secretaire tallboy, with secretaire drawer fitted small drawers and pigeon holes, 3'9½" wide; 115 cm. £880-960 PWC

A Mid-19th C. Dutch Marquetry Tallboy, Pillars with brass cappings, 102 cm. wide; 3'4¼'" £880-980 KC

Georgian Mahogany Chest on Chest in Chinese Chippendale manner. Original brass drop handles and escutcheons of fine colouring. £600-700 W

A Chippendale mahogany tallboy. £650-750 JWB

A George IV Rosewood and Mahogany Clothes Press. Arcaded cornice with satinwood crossbanded panel doors enclosing hanging space. £780-880 KC

An 18th C. walnut Chest-upon-Chest, having graduated feather crossbanded drawers, 3'2" wide x 21" deep, x 70" high. 96 cm. x 52.5 cm. x 177.5 cm. £2.500-2,800 VC

A blue lacquer Bedroom Suite, comprising a Gentleman's Wardrobe, a Dressing Table, Bedside Table, cheval mirror, dressing table mirror, firescreen flanked by Koss'u embroidered panels, a wall mirror, and a pair of Side Chairs. c.1920. £580-640 SBel

A George III mahogany secretaire Tallboy inlaid with boxwood stringing, well-fitted secretaire drawer, 44½" height 73", 112.5 cm. 185;5 cm. £1,250-1,500 GSP

A George III mahogany gentlemans wardrobe, 45″ wide, 113.5 cm. £560-620 HKC

Large 18th C. oak cupboard £975-1,100 BA

A George III mahogany linen Press, with elaborate brass swan neck handles (feet missing). £330-370 WW

William Burges. A Rare Painted Wardrobe, taken directly from a design attributed to William Burges. 78″ by 53″; 197 cm. by 135 cm., 1870's, the doors painted, c.1890. £850-950 SBS

An 18th C. Continental carved oak bacon Cupboard on stand, with spindle turned pierced galleries and matching roundels. 6′6¾″, 200 cm. wide. £950-1,100 KC

An early George III mahogany clothes press, 50½″, 128 cm wide, 59″, 200.5 cm. £1,250-1,450 CStJ

A Flemish oak cupboard on massive turned feet, 17th C., 69¾″, 177 cm. wide. 75½″, 192 cm. high, £3,200-2.500 CStJ

Peter Waals. An important Solid Walnut Breakfront Wardrobe. Ebony and boxwood chequer stringing, and centre cupboard with doors. Raised escallop-grained panels and four oak lined drawers beneath, flanked by hanging cupboards with fielded panel doors. 7′11″ wide, 6′2½″ high; 27¼″ deep, (max.); 241 cm. by 189.5 cm. by 69 cm. £2,200-2,400 WW

A 17th C. Flemish Cupboard. Doors with inscribed name and date 1650, 4′11″, 150 cm. wide. £1,050-1,200 KC

A good 17th C. North German oak cupboard, the panel doors applied with contemporary iron escutcheons and undulating hinges. 5′1¼″, 155 cm. £3,600-4,000 PL

An oak Court Cupboard, 4'9", 145 cm. x 5'10", 178 cm. high. £625-725   LC

A Charles II oak press with moulded top and lunette carved frieze on carved baluster supports. 57¼" wide, 66½" high, 145.5 by 169 cm., £1,450-1,600   CStJ

An oak cupboard with moulded cornice carved with S-scrolls and the date 1672. 71¼" wide by 73" high, 181 by 185.5 cm., £2,300-2,600   CStJ

A breakfront walnut Side Cabinet the central door inlaid. 3'4½", 102.5 cm. by 4'10½", 147.5 cm. c.1860. £370-450   SBel

A Regency mahogany Side Cabinet. Top inset with a marble panel, fitted two drawers to frieze, 3'9¾", 114 cm. wide. £360-440   KC

An ebonised and burr walnut Side Cabinet. 3'6½", 108 cm. by 6'1", 185.5 cm. by 1'4¼", 41 cm. c.1870. £600-800   SBel

A Victorian Walnut Dwarf Cabinet of slightly breakfront form, 3'9" wide, 114.5 cm. £980-1,090   BON

An extremely fine pair of French kingwood and parquetry side Cabinets, with hoof feet. 1'10½" 56.5 cm. x 1'6", 45 cm. £3,000-4,000   KC

A walnut Side Cabinet. Frieze inlaid above a single-door similarly inlaid with Gilt-metal mounts, 3'9", 114 cm. x 4'8", 143 cm. 1860's. £680-780   SBel

A Victorian walnut breakfront side cabinet with rosewood cross-banding and boxwood stringing. 75" wide, 190.5 cm. £850-950 HKC

Pair fine ebonised Cabinets with ormolu decoration, relief decoration in ivory and coloured stones. £2,000-2,500   JHR

A fine Victorian ebonised Display Cabinet, decorated with satin-wood stringing, burr walnut cross-banding and ornate bands of brass; 2'5¼'', 74 cm. wide. **£450-550** KC

A burr-walnut and marquetry Display Cabinet with gilt-metal foliate mounts throughout, 3'8½'', 113 cm. by 4'0'', 122 cm. 1860's. **£750-850** SBel

A Dutch marquetry Corner Cupboard, 2'9'', 84 cm. x 2'11'', 89 cm. high. 19th C. **£450-520** LC

A Burr Maple and Porcelain Mounted Breakfront Side Cabinet, 48½'' by 73'' by 20'', 123 cm by 186 cm by 51 cm, c.1850. **£1,400-1,800** SBel

A red Boulle side cabinet of double serpentine form. Inlaid with cut-brass strapwork and gilt-metal mounts. 3'9'', 114 cm. by 4'6'', 213 cm. by 1'8'', 56 cm. c.1870. **£1,300-1,500** SBel

A Mid-19th C. ormolu mounted boulle Cabinet. Chamfered corners with caryatid surmounts and raised on a shaped plinth with River God mask, 3'9'', 113.5 cm. wide. **£520-620** KC

A hardstone-mounted Meuble D'Appui, in various coloured stones. Gilt-metal acanthus mounts throughout. 1'3¾'', 129 cm. x 5'10'', 178 cm. c.1870 **£1,400-1,600** SBel

An ormolu-mounted ebony pedestal cabinet with white marble top. 34'', 86.5 cm wide, mid 19th C. **£800-900** CStJ

A Giltmetal-Mounted Figured Walnut Meuble D'Appui, 49'', 124.5 cm. wide, mid-19th C. **£800-880** CStJ

A tulipwood and ormolu mounted Display Cabinet, rosewood cross-bandings and inlaid with stringing. 3'10'', 117 cm. x 3'6½'', 108 cm. **£1,050-1,250** LC

A porcelain mounted ebonised Side Cabinet. 4'10", 147 cm. 19th C. **£280-360** LC

A Victorian-period walnut and rosewood crossbanded bow-shaped Credenza, open end shelves. 7'0", 213 cm. wide. **£1,200-1,400** RB

A pair of ebonised and burr-walnut Side Cabinets. Gilt-metal mounts. 3'8", 112 cm. by 3'0", 92 cm. c.1880. **£440-500** SBel

A North Italian Walnut Side Cabinet, 3'6" high by 3'1" wide, 107 cm by 94 cm, late 16th C. **£850-950** SBS

A Dutch Side Cabinet, mahogany ground, 2'7" high by 2'6" wide, 79 cm by 76 cm, c.1780. **£550-650** SBS

A George III satinwood side cabinet with a rosewood cross-banded top and a slight inverse breakfront. 3'0", 91 cm. wide. **£3,900-4,500** HKC

A Dutch Mahogany Side Cabinet, 2'8½" high by 2'7½" wide, 82.5 cm by 80 cm, c.1785. **£400-600** SBS

A Dutch Side Cabinet in satinwood and lacquer, 3'1" high by 3'½" wide, 94 cm. by 93 cm, c.1785. **£1,150-1,300** SBS

An ebony veneered and marquetry Side Cabinet with gilt-metal banding. Fruitwood stringing throughout. 4'1", 124 cm. by 3'11", 120 cm. c.1880. **£1,250-1,500** SBel

A Mid-Victorian Amboyna Side Cabinet with breakfront top cross-banded, Sèvres-pattern plaques, 66", 168 cm wide. **£1,200-1,400** CStJ

A Victorian Walnut Breakfront Side Cabinet, 6', 183 cm. **£420-500** LC

A walnut and parquetry Side Cabinet, with a white marble top. Inlaid central cupboard door enclosing two shelves, with gilt-metal mounts. 3'8", 112 cm. by 3'7", 109 cm. c.1870. **£1,250-1,500** SBel

An ebonised mahogany Side Cabinet, with gilt-metal mounts throughout. 3'7¾", 111 cm. by 5'5", 165 cm. 1870's. **£170-190** SBel

A Late George III Rosewood Chiffonier in the manner of John McLean, pierced brass chinoiserie fretwork, 4'1" high by 2'8½" wide, 124 cm. by 82 cm., c.1815. **£2,900-3,300** SBS

Walnut 19th C. Credenza with ormolu mounts and boxwood and satinwood inlays. 6'0", 183 cm. wide. **£760-860** W

Early Victorian rosewood chiffonier. 3'6", 106 cm. **£100-130** WW

An amboyna wood Side Cabinet with blue-jasper plaques and ebonised husks and bandings. 3'5", 104 cm. by 2'10", 86.4 cm. c.1870. **£320-420** SBel

A George III satinwood cross-banded oriental lacquered semi-circular Cabinet. Gilt and rust-red decoration on a black ground, with plate glass top. 4'6", 137 cm. wide. **£4,800-5,200** KC

A Regency Rosewood Side Table Chiffonier, with a brass gallery, turned and fluted supports, with mirror back, 38½", 98 cm., **£520-600** LC

A Diehl ormolu and pietra dura mounted Meuble D'Appui. Look plate inscribed 'Madaille a L'Exposition, Universelle, 1855, manufacteur de meubles, Diehl, rue Michel le Comte, 19 Paris.' 5'3", 159 cm. by 3'8½", 103 cm. c.1855. **£2,200-2,400** SBel

A William IV Burr-Elm and Parcel-Gilt Chiffonier, the stepped upper part with a central cupboard door flanked by gilt-metal mounted columns, 62¼", 158 cm., wide. **£850-950** CStJ

An ebonised Side Cabinet. Brass bandings throughout and applied with giltmetal mounts. 4'2½", 128 cm. by 4'10½", 148.5 cm. c.1890. **£360-460** SBel

A Pair of Biedermeier Chiffoniers, 3'5" high by 1'7½" wide, 104 cm. by 50 cm. c.1840, each originally with another shelf. **£850-950** SBS

A satinwood Corner Cabinet. 3'3", 99 cm. by 3'2½", 98 cm. c.1900. £480-560 SBel

A Dutch Rosewood and Ebony Armoire. 8' high by 6' wide; 244 by 183 cm., mid-17th century. £3,600-4,000 SBS

A Louis XIII Oak Armoire with a stepped breakfront dentil cornice above a pair of fielded panelled doors, two drawers in the base with lozenge mouldings. 7'8½" high by 6'½" wide; 235 cm. by 184 cm., mid-17th century. £2,200-2,500 SBS

A Victorian burr walnut side-cabinet, 38" wide, 96 cm. £270-300 HKC

18th C. Flemish Baroque oak Armoire, with overhanging cornice and two panelled doors supported upon brass barrel hinges. 76", 193 cm. wide. x 100" 254 cm. high. £1,150-1,300 B

A Dutch Marquetry Armoire, 72½", 184 cm. wide. £2,000-2,200 CStJ

A Walnut Armoire with a Moulded cornice and geometric frieze supported on solomonic columns, 7'10" high by 4'9" wide; 239 cm. by 145 cm., c.1660, Portuguese or Spanish. £1,150-1,300 SBS

A Chippendale mahogany Cabinet with fitted brass carrying handles, 3'0¼" wide, 92 cm. £680-780 KC

A 17th C. French Armoire; Panelled doors with brass escutcheons and centre carved terminal, above a shaped apron. £500-560 KC

A fine and important 17th C. South German marquetry Armoire, the front decorated in a parquetry of numerous woods, 82", 208 cm. high, x 66", 168 cm. wide. £1,800-2,000 B

An 18th C. French walnut Provincial Armoire. Moulded cornice and a pair of arched fielded panel doors, with ornate brass escutcheons. 4'11", 150 cm. wide. **£680-780** KC

An 18th C. Burgundian walnut armoire. Diamond point panels in geometric patterns, 60", 152 cm. wide. **£320-380** B

A chestnut small armoire. 34", 86.5 cm wide, 18th C. Franco-Flemish. **£600-680** CStJ

An oak armoire inlaid with yew bands. 55¾"wide, 142 cm., early 18th C. **£850-930** CStJ

A 17th C. Dutch carved oak and walnut Armoire , 8'¾", 246 cm. high x 6'2¾", 190 cm. wide. **£2,400-2,600** KC

A 17th C. Swiss Armoire. Cornice with gouged battlement decoration. Central panelled door with blind fret carving and shaped pierced lockplate. 47", 119 cm. wide x 74", 188 cm. high. **£260-360** B

A Dutch walnut and marquetry corner cupboard. 38¼", 97 cm wide, late 18th C. **£1,300-1,500** CStJ

An 18th C. Dutch marquetry corner cabinet, 37" wide, 93.5 cm **£780-880** HKC

A mid 18th C. oak hanging corner cupboard, inlaid bog oak and holly floral decoration. 44" high, 111 cm. 27" wide, 68.5 cm. **£420-470** HKC

A mid-19th C. Georgian-design mahogany Standing Corner Cupboard. 3'7½", 110 cm. wide. **£680-780 KC**

A late 17th C. Scandinavian Standing Corner Cupboard, with initials and date 1791 panel door below. 2'2", 67 cm. wide. **£600-700 KC**

A George I Walnut Hanging Corner Cupboard, the bow front with two doors enclosing shaped shelves 2' high by 1'7½" wide; 61 cm. by 49 cm., c.1720. **£700-800 SBS**

17th C. cylindrical fronted double Corner Cupboard inlaid with detailed marquetry. 4'6", 137 cm. wide. **£2,800-3,000 W**

A bow fronted corner Cupboard. 1'11", 57.5 cm. **£400-460 WW**

An 18th C. German walnut and crossbanded strapwork-decorated Corner Cupboard. 4'8¾", 145 cm. wide. **£2,400-2,600 KC**

A late 18th C. mahogany corner cupboard inlaid with boxwood, satinwood and checkered stringings. 3'9", 113.5 cm. high. **£540-600 DHBN**

Georgian oak hanging Corner Cabinet. 2'3", 68.5 cm. wide. **£250-280 MP**

A walnut open Corner cupboard, 6'0", 183 cm. by 2'5", 84 cm. c.1860. **£340-370 SBel**

Queen Anne corner cabinet. **£500-560 VM**

An Oak Court Cupboard, 78" high by 55" wide; 198 cm., by 140 cm., mid 19th century. **£650-800 SBel**

A James II oak Court Cupboard. Projecting cornice above a pair of fielded panel doors. 4'8", 142 cm. wide. £1,000-1,300 KC

Early 17th C. North Country Oak Court Cupboard. 7'8", 233 cm. wide. £1,400-1,800 B

A bleached oak Court Cupboard. 65", 165 cm. by 57", 145 cm. c.1860. £400-500 SBel

An early 19th century walnut and fruitwood provincial buffet of Empire influence 5'3" wide; 159.5 cm. £1,050-1,200 HKC

A stained oak Court Cupboard. Angled sides carved and inscribed 'Caroits.I' and 'Gvlienvs III', made up in third quarter of 19th C. £700-900 SBel

An oak Court Cupboard on Stand, carved with battlements supported by a pair of herms, doors and drawer inlaid with a tulip. 62", 158 cm. x 24½", 62 cm. c.1900. £150-250 SBel

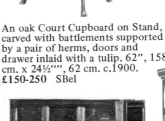

Mid 17th C. carved and panelled Oak Court Cupboard. £1,550-1,700 RBB

A massive walnut and oak press of 17th C. style with overhanging dentilled cornice, constructed from parts of a 17th C. press, 65", 165 cm. wide, 78½", 199 cm. high, £3,400-3,800 CStJ

A James II oak three-tier Court Cupboard, on columnar supports with square stem feet, 3'10", 117 cm. wide. £2,600-2,900 KC

A Welsh oak tridarn on block feet, 55½", 141 cm. wide, £2,100-2,300 CStJ

An antique carved oak Court Cupboard with projecting frieze. on stem feet. 4'2", 127 cm. wide. £600-750 KC

A 17th C. oak Tridarn, panel backed canopy with carved front frieze and reel turned supports, centre panel bearing initials and later date of 1736. £1,450-1,750 B

A fine late 17th C. oak Tridarn, canopied upper part with a frieze below of chequered inlay of bog oak and holly. 56", 142 cm. wide. c.1680-90. £1,450-1,700 B

An early George III oak Buffet. 4'6½", 138.5 cm. wide. £900-1,050 HKC

An Elizabethan carved oak Court Cupboard, with strapwork decoration and chequer inlay. 4'1", 124 cm. wide. £2,100-2,400 KC

A 17th C. oak Tridarn, Three frieze drawers and a pair of arched fielded panel doors below. 4'6", 137 cm. wide. £1,050-1,200 KC

An early 18th C. panelled oak tridarn, with lunette carved frieze initialled R.I. and dated 1714; length, 5'5", 164.5 cm. £800-900 PK

A 17th C. German ornate carved Cabinet. 5'4" wide, 162 cm. £480-560 KC

A Fine Early 18th C. Oak Tridarn, 1727, 54" wide, 137 cm. £1,000-1,200 B

An antique South German oak buffet cupboard, 49" wide, 124.5 cm. 82" high, 208 cm. £1,600-1,750 HKC

A 19th century Continental carved Sideboard, 73½", 187 cm., £540-640 OL

A good quality William IV Mahogany Pedestal Sideboard with arched panelled doors having free standing fluted turned pillars, enclosing sliding trays cellarette drawer, etc. 66" 168 cm., wide. **£150-200** PWC

A Sheraton mahogany sideboard, the doors and drawers with floral inlays and cross-banding. 5", 152 cm. **£620-720** LJ

A George III mahogany and satinwood banded bow-front sideboard, inlaid with fan medallions and having a brass rail back, 174 cm., 5'8½" wide. **£1.700-1,900** KC

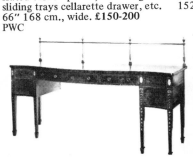

A George III Mahogany Serpentine inlaid Sideboard with brass rail back, with three frieze drawers by deep cellaret drawers, 84½" 215 cm. **£600-700** LC

A small oak sideboard, possibly by William Morris & Company, 53¼" by 36½", 135 by 93 cm. **£90-110** SBel

A George III Mahogany Sideboard with bowed side cupboards flanking a central drawer, inlaid with stringing, restored. 5'2" x 2'4½"; 157 cm. x 72 cm. deep. **£400-450** LC

A George III Mahogany Bow-Fronted Sideboard with a cross-banded top and with boxwood stringing throughout, 5'½" wide by 2'8¼" deep, 153 cm. by 82 cm., c.1785. **£900-1,200** SBS

A Mahogany Serpentine Front Sideboard with a central drawer above a tambour cupboard 68¼", 173.5 cm., first half 19th century, **£380-430** LC

Ornate 18th century Italian Sideboard with pink Carrara marble top. Pierced brass gallery. Cupboards decorated with brass work and monogram. Carved rope pillars and centre shelves, 5'3", 159.5 cm. wide. **£1,400-1,700** W

A George III Mahogany bow-front sideboard. **£440-500** HKC

An Oak Sideboard in the style of Bruce Talbert. Central mirror-backed recess flanked by two carved cupboard doors. Two central drawers and a pair of curved cupboard drawers below. 75" by 62½", 190 cm. by 159 cm., 1880's. **£300-600** SBel

A Late George III Mahogany Sideboard of breakfront outline inlaid with stringing outlining bands of rosewood. 7'8"; 234 cm., **£825-900** LC

A Louis XV Provincial Oak Sideboard. Centre section with three drawers applied with gilt-metal handles. 38" by 77" x 18¾"; 96.5 cm. by 196 cm. x 48 cm., third quarter of 19th century. **£800-900** SBel

An early XIX century Sheraton
Mahogany Sideboard, inlaid with
boxwood line. 81" 205 cm. wide.
£750-950 B

A Georgian satinwood and boxwood inlaid mahogany sideboard.
Centre plate and napery drawers,
cellaret draw ends, 84", 213 cm.,
£800-900 GSP

19th century pedestal sideboard.
£350-420 JWB

A Regency mahogany sideboard.
£450-520 JWB

A Rosewood Sideboard. Inlaid
throughout with boxwood
trophies and strapwork, 80" by
154¼"; 203 cm. by 138 cm.,
circa 1910. **£300-400 SBel**

CABINET MAKERS AND DESIGNERS

Adam, Robert
1728-1792
(influential from c.1765. Produced
'Works on Architecture' with
James Adam)

Chippendale, Thomas
1718-1779
(his main styles 1740-1760 'The
Gentleman and Cabinet Makers
Directory' pub. 1754)

Hepplewhite, George
died 1786
(mainly influential after death —
'Cabinet Maker and Upholsterer's
Guide' pub. 1788)

Sheraton, Thomas
1750-1806
('The Cabinet Maker and Upholsterer's Drawing Book' pub.
1791-1794 and 'The Cabinet
Dictionary' pub. 1803)

A Walnut Sideboard with a
crenellated and Vitruvian scroll
cornice and massive pierced brass
Gothic hinges 113½" by 57" by
24½"; 288 cm. by 145 cm. by 62
cm., German, 1870's. **£320-400**
SBel

An Italian small painted serpentine front commode, 31½";
80 cm. **£52-65 WW**

A Kingwood Bombe Commode of
Louis XV design, 57", 145 cm.
wide, **£1,000-1,100 CStJ**

A late 18th century North Italian
walnut commode, the drawer
fronts, angled sides and top all
crossbanded, 95 cm., 3'1½".
£1,150-1,300 PJ

189

Late 18th C. Milanese Walnut Commode, with marble top, three drawers to the frieze decorated with marquetry, surrounded by crossbanding and stringing, 49" wide; 124.5 cm. £3,000-3,500 KC

An Oak Commode, 50", 127 cm. wide, late 18th C. Flemish or North German. £850-930 CStJ

A South German Walnut Commode, each drawer with three quarter-banded panels. 3'½" high by 4'2½" wide, 93 cm. by 128 cm., c.1740. £1,350-1,600 SBS

A Milanese Kingwood and Marquetry Commode with a St. Anne Marble top, 2'11½" high by 4'3¼" wide, 91 cm. by 130 cm., c.1780, later handles. £1,350-1,550 SBS

A Walnut Parquetry Commode, marble top with chamfered corners, with two drawers and square tapering legs, 2'6" high by 2'7½" wide, 76 cm. by 80 cm., c.1790. German or Swiss. £1,650-1,800 SBS

A George III mahogany commode, 45", 114.5 cm wide. £2,900-3,100 CStJ

A Walnut Parquetry Commode with marble top, the serpentine front with drawers banded in olivewood, 4'4" wide, 132 cm., mid-18th century, probably German. £1,500-2,500 SBS

A pale walnut commode. 52½", 133 cm wide, mid-18th C. South German. £700-800 CStJ

A miniature serpentine fronted commode in satinwood of 18th C. design. 34" high, 86 cm., 21½" wide, 54.5 cm. £500-600 HKC

An Anglo-Indian Rosewood Veneered Commode, with marble top, 39" by 40"; 99 cm. by 102 cm., mid 19th century. £350-500 SBel

An Empire fruitwood commode, giltmetal handles. 50", 127 cm wide, German. £750-850 CStJ

A kingwood and marquetry commode of Regence design. 38", 97 cm wide. 19th C. £1,550-1,650 CStJ

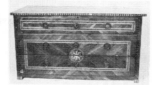

One of a pair of 18th C. Italian walnut feather veneered commodes with boxwood bandings, 4' wide; 122 cm. £1,700-1,900 HKC

An 18th C. South German walnut Commode, with a serpentine moulded top, fitted with two drawers, 71 cm. wide; 2'4". £1,300-1,500 PL

An 18th C. Continental walnut semi-bow fronted commode with cross-banded panel decoration, 48" wide; 122 cm. £1,500-1,700

A good mid-18th Century Dutch Mahogany Bombe Commode fitted with three drawers flanked by outset canted keel corners, 3' wide, 91 cm., £1,300-1,500 HKC

A Giltmetal-Mounted Kingwood Commode of Louis XV design, 53", 134.5 cm. wide. £1,050-1,200 CStJ

A Late George II Mahogany Commode in the manner of Vile and Cobb, the serpentine front with a shaped apron, cabriole legs and scroll feet, 2'9" high by 3'4" wide, 84 cm. by 102 cm., c.1760. £5,400-6,200 SBS

A Fine 18th C. German Walnut Commode, drawers with canted corners, decorated with inlaid stringing and crossbanding, ebonised turned feet, 52½" wide; 133.5 cm. £1,000-1,200 KC

A Late 18th C. North Italian Tulipwood and Harewood Cross-banded Petite Commode. 59 cm. wide. 1'11½". £680-780 KC

A late Georgian mahogany commode with ebony stringing, ornate pierced handles and escutcheons, carved in the revived rococo manner. £1,100-1,400 LE

An 18th C. French commode in rosewood and tulipwood, 42" wide; 106 cm., rouge marble top. £1,250-1,500 RB

A Louis XV style kingwood marquetry commode by Edwards and Roberts, with serpentine front, ormolu mounts and rouge-marble top, width 3'9"; 114 cm. £2,000-2,400 PK

A Louis XV Walnut Provincial Commode, serpentine front decorated with incised mouldings, 3'1½" high by 4'2" wide 95 cm. by 127 cm., c.1760. £950-1,100 SBS

An Oak and Walnut Coffer,
2'5" high by 4'9" wide, 74 cm.
by 145 cm. c.1665. £620-680
SBS

An oak coffer, the interior with
a side section with hinged flap and
small drawers, late 17th C., 58",
147 cm. wide, £1,200-1,400
CStJ

A mid 18th C. Chinese lacquer
coffer, with engraved brass lock
plate and corner pieces. 34" wide,
86 cm. £150-170   HKC

An oak coffer with quadripartite
panelled lid, late 17th C., 57½",
146 cm. wide, £550-610   CStJ

A Fine XVII C. Oak Coffer inlaid
in chequerwork in bog oak and
holly, 50" wide, 127 cm. £410-480
B

A Massive XVI C. German Oak
Muniments Chest, of plank construction with Wide stile
supports, decorated in iron bound
scroll and rosettes, 80" wide,
203 cm. £1,850-2,100   B

A Flemish oak coffer with
moulded hinged lid, 50" wide,
127 cm., late 15th C. £1,300-
1,500   CStJ

Early 19th C. brass-studded
leather chest. £250-275   BA

A pale oak small coffer, the
sides with iron carrying handles,
32½" wide, 82.5 cm., late 17th C.
Italian. £750-850   CStJ

An unusual kingwood and marquetry automaton case, the
back with detachable trellis
panel, 1'10", 56 cm. wide;
late 18th C., probably German.
£230-280   CStJ

A Scarlet Lacquered and Gilt-
Brass-Mounted Coffre Fort,
13¾", 35 cm. wide, probably
German, late 16th C. £700-770
CStJ

A 16th/17th C. oak dower
Chest. 44", 111 cm. height 31",
78.5 cm. depth 22½", 56.5 cm.
£1,150-1,300 GSP

A George I black and gold
lacquer coffer-on-stand, 60",
152.5 cm wide. **£4,600-4,800**
CStJ

A 17th C. carved oak Coffer,
with scroll frieze and triple
lozenge panel front, 4'7½",
140 cm. wide. **£260-300** KC

A 17th C. Italian Coffer, fitted
iron carrying handles. 5'9¼",
176 cm. wide. **£650-750** KC

A 17th C. carved oak Coffer.
3'11¼", 120 cm. wide. **£290-360**
KC

A very rare 13th/15th Century
oak Medieval dug out Tree Chest.
three rectangular lock plates.
55", 139 cm. wide x 15", 38 cm.
high x 16", 40 cm. deep. **£3,400-
4,000** B

A 17th C. carved oak Coffer on
stand. Decorated frieze drawer,
triple arched panels to the front,
4'6¾", 139 cm. wide. **£500-580**
KC

An oak food hutch on baluster
supports and square stretchers,
17th C., 40", 101.5 cm. wide.
£2,500-2,700 CStJ

A good 17th C. Italian Walnut Cassone, front with coat of arms 61", 155 cm. wide. £970-1,100 B

A 17th C. oak Coffer, 3'1", 93.5 cm. wide. £320-390 HKC

A 17th C. oak Coffer, 3'8", 111 cm. wide. £320-380 HKC

Elizabethan oak Chest, rising plank top. 59", 150 cm. wide. £620-700 B

Early 17th C. north Italian walnut Cassone, 55", 139 cm. wide. £700-900 B

Rare early 17th C. Italian cedarwood Chest, decorated in pokerwork and relief. 72", 183 cm. wide. £900-1,100 B

17th C. Alpine Cassone, painted in red, white, blue and simulated walnut panels, with the name 'Lucia' to the centre panel, and the initials LF and IP on either side. 67", 170 cm. long x 38", 96 cm. high. £1,400-1,600 B

A Jacobean oak Coffer, decorated with an ebony and ivory chevron border, 4'2", 127 cm. wide. £540-640 KC

XVI C. Continental Oak Chest, with original XVI lock mechanism, 60" wide, 152 cm. £550-650 B

A Small Oak Coffer of boarded construction, 39", 99 cm., 17th C. £190-240 LC

A Flemish Oak Chest, on bun feet, 2'7" high by 3'9" wide, 79 cm. by 114 cm., first half 17th C. figures possibly earlier. £650-750 SBS

An early 17th C. German oak
Chest, dated 1624 with initials
and writing with ball feet, 57",
144 cm. wide x 34", 86 cm. high.
£1,200-1,350 B

A 17th C. Italian walnut Cassone,
63", 160 cm. wide. **£620-700** B

A good 17th C. oak Coffer, **£410-
460** PWC

A 17th C. Italian walnut Cassone
5'6", 168 cm. wide. 1'10",
55 cm. deep. 2'0", 61 cm. high.
£900-1,200 PWC

A Charles I oak Coffer with
initials and date IB 1629, 3'10½",
118 cm. **£1,650-1,850** LC

A 16th C. French oak Gothic
Chest, side panels with linenfold
and Gothic decoration. 69",
175 cm. wide. **£1,400-1,600** B

15th/16th C. German oak Ark,
pegged construction to the back,
front and panelled sides. **£580-
680** B

A rare 16th C. Renaissance oak
Chest. 44", 111 cm. wide. **£300-
500** B

Stained walnut Cassone, 35½",
90 cm. by 81½", 207 cm.
Italian, c.1870. **£1,600-1,800**
SBel

A 16th C. Gothic oak linenfold
Chest, 48", 122 cm. wide. **£1,250-
1,500** B

An Oyster-veneered Walnut Chest with crossbanded inlaid top, two short and two long drawers, the lower part with a long drawer on bracket feet, 32½''; 82.5 cm., wide, basically late 17th century. **£2,300-2,600** CStJ

A Mahogany Wellington Chest, with a locking flap, 53''; 134.5 cm., c.1880. **£280-320** SBel

An early 18th century walnut chest, the top veneered in a geometrical design with feather bandings, later bracket feet, 3'3''· wide; 98.5 cm. **£480-560** PWC

Early 19th C. Dutch Marquetry Chest with floral marquetry decoration, surrounded by geometric banding, 42'' wide; 106 cm. **£900-1,000** KC

A late 17th century walnut chest of drawers, 3'1'' wide; 93.5 cm. **£540-600** HKC

A chest of drawers veneered in amboyna with coramandel edging, the drawers inset with flush brass handles, 38''; 97 cm., 19th C. **£810-900** LC

Pair of late 17th C. Carved Oak Chests. 34'' x 33½''; 81 cm x 80 cm., c.1690, with alterations, the carving mid-19th c. **£240-300** SBel

A William and Mary oystershell veneer chest, c.1690. **£3,000-3,500** LKL

18th century Chippendale period caddy-topped chest with brushing slide, in mahogany with original handles, 2'10'' wide. 86 cm. c.1760-65. **£1,400-1,700**

An 18th C. Italian Walnut and Ebonised Marquetry Chest. 145 cm. wide; 4'9¼''. **£1,550-2,000** KC

A Small XVIII Century Dutch Walnut Bombe Fronted Chest of Drawers, quartered top with multiple scroll shaped edge, 32'' wide; 81 cm. **£1,200-1,400** B

An early 18th C. oak apprentices chest with brass mounts on splayed ends, 8½'', 21.5 cm., **£50-70** WW

196

A 17th C. Oak Chest on Stand, shield and serpent motifs to the four drawers. Musk-carved drawer to base, 42" wide; 106 cm. £400-500 KC

A Restoration oak chest of drawers, 38" wide, 96 cm. £400-490 HKC

An antique Korean chest on chest. £170-190 JWB

A George II padoukwood chest, 33¼", 84.5 cm wide. £1,100-1,200 CStJ

A George III mahogany bow-fronted chest, 40", 101.5 cm wide. £1,000-1,150 CStJ

An Unusual George I Walnut Chest with a cross and feather-banded top and four similar long drawers, on bracket feet, 3'7" wide; 109 cm., by 99 cm., c.1720. £1,250-1,400 SBS

An oak rectangular chest, late 17th C., 36", 91.5 cm. wide, £580-630 CStJ

A mid-Georgian walnut chest, 32" wide, 81 cm. £290-320 HKC

A Mid-Georgian figured Mahogany Secretaire Chest of small proportions, the upper drawer having fall front revealing well fitted interior. 37¼"; 94 cm. £500-650 LE

George I burr walnut chest, later oak sides, 39" wide, 98.5 cm. £750-850 HKC

A Mahogany Secretaire Military Chest in Two Parts, 43½" by 45"; 110.5 cm. by 114 cm., mid 19th century. **£380-450** SBel

A George III mahogany serpentine chest with gilt-brass handles and lock-plates, 48½", 123 cm wide (cut down). **£1,200-1,300** CStJ

A Dutch Figured Walnut Bombe Chest, 36½", 93 cm. wide, mid-18th C. **£1,800-1,900** CStJ

A William and Mary Marquetry Chest of drawers inlaid with panels of stylized foliage and birds, on a walnut ground, 3'1" high by 3'1" wide; 94 cm. by 98 cm., c.1690, later feet. **£1,950-2,200** SBS

A Mahogany Wellington Chest, the two lockable panels enclosing seven graduated drawers, 46¾"; 119 cm. c.1900. **£260-290** SBel

A fine William & Mary walnut parquetry and ebony chest of drawers in two parts, with box-wood line, 37" wide; 94 cm. **£300-370** B

A 19th C. Hepplewhite-Design Mahogany Serpentine-fronted chest. Satinwood crossbanding and lined writing slide to the upper drawer, 100 cm. wide; 3'3½" **£780-860** KC

A mid Georgian mahogany bachelor chest, moulded edge, fitted brushing slide, with four graduating drawers **£800-900** LE

A Dutch Marquetry Chest with fluted canted corners, early 19th C. 3'1½", 95 cm. **£510-600** LC

Georgian Oak Chest. **£100-130** JWB

Georgian bow front mahogany chest with inlaid drawers. **£300-340** BA

A Chippendale mahogany and crossband serpentine fronted chest of drawers, the top drawer fitted with lidded compartments for toiletries. **£1,150-1,300** PK

A Jacobean walnut and oak chest of drawers. Applied moulding in geometric patterns, centered with boxwood and flanked by walnut. 35" wide; 89 cm. **£680-750   B**

Georgian Mahogany mule chest. **£335-380   JWB**

Late 17th or early 18th C. painted oak chest. **£500-600   BA**

A Queen Anne Walnut Chest, of two short drawers with cross-banded top and feather banding. 103 cm. wide; 3'4¾". **£420-500 KC**

A Mahogany Wellington Chest, 48½" x 22¾"; 123 cm. x 58 cm. 1870's. **£260-290   SBel**

An 18th C. Dutch Walnut Shaped-front Chest. Four long, featherbanded drawers and concave corners, 86 cm. wide; 2'10". **£650-720   KC**

An Unusual Small Tunbridge Ware and Walnut Wellington Chest, 21" x 14½; 53.5 x 37 cm., c.1870. **£135-170   SBel**

A Jacobean Oak Chest. Fronted by geometric moulded panels, 39½" wide; 100 cm. **£580-640 KC**

A Dutch Marquetry Tall Chest of drawers, early 19th C. 3'3" x 5' high, 99 cm. x 152.5 cm. **£800-900   LC**

A Pair of Mahogany Semaniers with marble tops, the cabriole legs ending in gilt-metal sabots. 54" x 15½"; 137 cm. x 39 cm., 20th C. **£400-600   SBel**

A Good Charles II Oak Cupboard, with a crude dentil cornice above a frieze drawer, cupboards below. 4' wide 3'8" high, 122 cm. by 111 cm. £900-1,000 BON

Rare 16th C. Renaissance oak Chest. 37", 94 cm. wide. £1,200-1,400 B

A Regency faded rosewood Cabinet with brass inlay. c.1820. £2,200-2,500 LKL

A 19th C. carved oak Cabinet in the French Gothic style, 2'8½" wide, 82 cm. £300-400 KC

A Charles II oak chest with rectangular top and frieze drawer above a deeper coffered drawer. 49" wide, 124.5 cm. £2,200-2,500 CStJ

An Oak and Walnut Chest, 53", 134.5 cm. wide, basically 17th C., possibly Spanish. £1,400-1,600 CStJ

An Interesting XVI Century Flemish Oak Vestment Cupboard, with drawer beneath with applied mouldings and raised upon a short stand of four turned bulbous supports united by a cross stretcher. 28" wide by 72" high; 71 cm. by 183 cm. £780-880 B

A Charles II oak chest with two long panelled drawers inlaid with bone and mother-of-pearl. 46½" wide, 118 cm. £1,200-1,400 CStJ

A 16th C. Henri II Renaissance oak Cabinet a Deux Corps, 5'2" wide, 157 cm. £1,600-1,800 B

19th C. walnut veneered cabinet approx. 18" high, 46 cm. £120-160 PG

A Charles II oak and walnut chest on block feet. 40½" wide, 103 cm. £800-900 CStJ

A George I Oak Yorkshire Dresser Base of good proportion, 6'2" long, 188 cm. £980-1,200 B

A Queen Anne oak low dresser, restored, 63", 160 cm. £620-680 LC

A Fine Cromwellian Oak Dresser, on baluster turned supports, 6'1¼", 186 cm. wide. £750-850 KC

A mid 18th C. oak buffet, 4'6" wide, 137 cm. £250-300 HKC

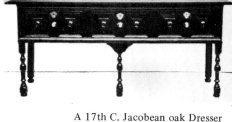

A 17th C. Jacobean oak Dresser Base; Two plank top with thumb nail edge, 73", 185 cm. wide. £2,600-2,900 B

A Late XVII C. Oak Dresser Base, the three frieze drawers with applied mouldings forming double panels, 78" wide, 198 cm. £1,250-1,500 B

An oak Dresser, 6'1", 185.5 cm. long, 1'6", 45 cm. deep, 2'11", 88.5 cm. high. £700-900 VC

An antique oak small dresser with moulded rim, 4'8½", 143.5 cm. x 1'6", 45 cm. £1,200-1,400 JSS & TF

A late Stuart low oak Dresser, 6'4", 193 cm. wide. £900-1,100 LC

A Georgian oak low dresser, lock-plates divided by split balusters on turned legs and moulded stretchers, 82¼", 209 cm. wide, £2,500-2,700 CStJ

An oak low dresser on turned legs, 17th C., 96", 218.5 cm. wide. £3,100-3,400 CStJ

A 17th C. Jacobean Oak Dresser base, 7'4", 223 cm. wide. £1,800-2,000 B

201

A 17th C. Carolean oak and walnut Dresser Base, with over-hanging top and deep walnut cross-grained moulded frieze. 72", 183 cm. long. £1,700-1,900 B

Early 18th C. oak Dresser base. 7'2", 218 cm. wide. £900-1,200 B

A small oak low Dresser with moulded rectangular top. Re-placed handles, early 18th C. 4'9" x 2'8", 145 cm. x 81 cm. high. £1,400-1,700 LC

An antique oak dresser, 7'1", 215.5 cm. x 1'7½", 49 cm. C. late 17th C. £1,550-1,700 JSS & TF

An antique oak Dresser, 7'9½", 238 cm. x 1'8¼", 50.5 cm. £1,400-1,500 JSS & TF

A Georgian oak low dresser, top cross-banded with mahogany, on cabriole legs and pad feet, 73", 185.5 cm. wide, £1,300-1,500 CStJ

GUIDE TO STYLES		
1714-1727	George I	Early Georgian
1727-1760	George II	Georgian
1760-1812	George III	Late Georgian
1812-1820	George III	Regency
1820-1830	George IV	Regency
1830-1837	William IV	William IV
1837-1860	Victoria	Early Victorian
1860-1901	Victoria	Late Victorian

A mid-Georgian oak Dresser. 5'7", 169.5 cm. wide. £900-1,200 HKC

A rare 17th C. English oak Canopy Dresser. 4'7", 140 cm. wide x 5'8", 168 cm. high. £2,800-3,000 B

An English oak Dresser with fielded panels, brass loop handles and knobs, 7'0", 213 cm. height, 6'5", 195.5 cm. overall. £1,700-1,900 GSP

An unusual 18th C. oak Dresser, with brass knob handles and key-hole plates, 6'0'', 183 cm. wide 1'8'', 50 cm. deep, 7'1'', 215.5 cm. high. **£1,050-1,300** PWC

A Louis XV French Provincial Dresser, basically 18th C. 7'10'' x 4'3'' wide, 239 cm. x 130 cm. **£900-1,100** B

A good 18th C. oak Dresser, 5'11'', 180.5 cm. wide. **£1,025-1,200** PWC

An 18th C. oak Dresser, 7'1½'', 217 cm., wide. **£1,000-1,100** KC

An early 18th C. oak Dresser, with Break-front base. 5'6¾'', 170 cm., wide. **£1,450-1,650** KC

An 18th C. oak and mahogany crossbanded Dresser. 5'10¾'', 180 cm. wide. **£1,800-2,000** KC

Unusual Anglesey Dresser in oak, banded with mahogany. **£1,600-1,800** RBB

An oak dresser on turned baluster legs and plinth base, 18th C., 69'', 175 cm. wide, **£1,000-1,100** CStJ

An early Georgian oak and elm dresser, 56½'', 144 cm. wide, **£2,800-3,000** CStJ

Late 17th C. oak Dresser with open shelves. £1,500-1,700 RBB

A yew dresser, 72 by 67 in; 184 by 170 cm; and a chest en suite, 34" by 38", 86 by 97 cm. probably American, early 20th C. £320-360 SBel

An Oak Dresser with concave cornice, protruding base, 60½", 159 cm. 18th C. £760-860 LC

CANTERBURY

- named after Archbishop of Canterbury, who reputably ordered the first in 1806
- basically a mobile music stand
- earliest have square tapered legs, with 2 or 3 divisions and a drawer

- round tapered legs made after 1810
- most Victorian canterburies were made to fit under the piano
- Victorian canterburies were more decorative than the austere styles pre-

viously, often used scroll carving

- Bamboo gained popularity in late 19th century
- many have been made from the bases of whatnots or pure reproduction

A large Walnut Canterbury in well-figured wood, 37", 94 cm., c.1860. £340-400 SBel

A walnut Canterbury, the three divisions above a frieze drawer. 2'0" wide, 61 cm. c.1860. £220-280 SBel

A Sheraton period mahogany music Canterbury. £500-600 PWC

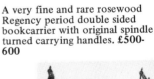

A very fine and rare rosewood Regency period double sided bookcarrier with original spindle turned carrying handles. £500-600

A Victorian mahogany Canterbury. £155-180 JWB

Late Regency book carrier in rosewood with pierced fretwork patterned sides. £350-400

A mahogany folio rack on trestle legs, 3'10", 107 cm. by 2'8", 82 cm. 1840's. £400-460 SBel

19th C. mahogany three-tier shoe rack. £42-52 PG

A Victorian walnut Folio Rack, 3'1" wide, 93.5 cm. **£520-570** OL

A Victorian burr walnut folio rack, 22½" wide, 57 cm. **£190-220** HKC

A good George IV rosewood bottle stand with turned spindle gallery and half bobbin mouldings. 11", 28 cm. dia. **£720-820** HKC

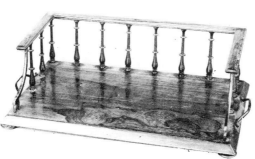

A William IV rosewood four-tier whatnot, fitted with a drawer, on castors, 1'8" wide, 50 cm. **£440-500** HKC

A George IV rosewood book tray with three-quarter gallery and turned spindles. 1'3½" wide, 39.5 cm. **£360-420** HKC

A Victorian rosewood three-tier whatnot with turned column 1'2" high, 35.5 cm., **£110-140** HKC

A late Georgian mahogany whatnot. Ebonised ringed support supports, 20" by 54", 51 cm by 137 cm. **£800-860** LC

A Victorian rosewood three tier whatnot with shaped shelves and turned supports 1'3" wide, 38 cm. **£200-250** HKC

A Papier Mache and Mother-of Pearl Whatnot, inlaid with flowers and leaves, 52½"; 133 cm., 1840's **£1,350-1,600** SBel

An English rosewood Etagere,
4'8", 142 cm. high. Mid 19th C.
£180-240 SBel

A Kingwood Etagere, gilt-metal
supports and handles carved with
shells and foliage, 33½" x 35";
85 cm., early 20th century.
£210-260 SBel

A Regency Mahogany Whatnot
with ringed and turned supports
joining the three cane tiers, 22"
x 63"; 56 cm x 160 cm high.
£320-380 LC

A Pair of Marquetry Etageres
shelves inlaid with flowers, the
strap-work on a rosewood ground
30¼" x 16⅛"; 77 cm. x 41 cm.,
c.1870. **£280-340** SBel

A French walnut etagere, the
top tier with drawer, three-
quarter gallery and inset with
painted porcelain plaque, on
ebonised supports, 18", 46 cm.,
late 19th C. **£270-300** LC

A two-tier mahogany Dumb
Waiter on a turned column claw
and ball feet, 1'9" wide, 34"
high, 52.5 cm by 90.5 cm. **£80-90**
VC

An early Victorian rosewood
teapoy 1'3" wide; 38 cm., **£130-
160** HKC

A Victorian walnut Workbox,
41", 103.5 cm. high. **£380-420**
OL

Sheraton period two tier dumb
waiter with circular folding
shelves, 23½", 61 cm. **£270-300**
WW

Antique Mahogany Teapoy on Pedestal with Brass Claw Feet. Interior fitted with three compartments. £160-190 W

William IV mahogany Teapoy with fitted interior 18"; 45 cm., £120-180 WW

A William IV rosewood teapoy, interior with four lidded caddies flanking two vacant mixing bowls. 1'7" wide; 47.5 cm., £180-220 HKC

A George III mahogany Wine Cellaret, 1'5½", 45 cm. £740-820 LC

A good 18th C. mahogany wine cooler, brass bound, 1'9", 52.5 cm. dia. 1'8", 50 cm. high. £880-980 PWC

A large solid rosewood Anglo-Indian wine cooler, 1'11", 58.5 cm. by 2'6", 76 cm. by 2'0½", 62 cm. c.1840. £180-220 SBel

A Georgian mahogany wine cooler. £330-380 JWB

A Georgian mahogany wine cooler. £450-500 JWB

A George III mahogany octagonal brass bound wine cooler with lead lined interior and brass ring handles, 1'6" wide 45 cm. £580-680 HKC

A Coaster. £140-160 JWB

A Georgian mahogany wine cooler. £330-380 JWB

A George III oval mahogany wine cellaret or jardiniere with brass bands and handles, 22"; 56 cm. £590-630 LC

207

Chippendale period oval mahogany wine cooler on original stand, c.1765. **£1,100-1,200** PG

Late 18th C. mahogany and inlaid Cellaret. **£400-500**

An 18th C. mahogany tripod stand with a 12″ galleried top, 1′8″, 50 cm. high. **£250-280** PWC

A marble-topped giltwood Pedestal. 2′8½″, 82 cm. by 1′5½″, 44 cm. Mid 19th C. **£500-600** SBS

A walnut Urn Stand, 1′10½″, 57 cm. Late 19th C. **£310-350** SBel

A pair of English early 18th C. elaborately carved wood and gilded plant stands, 3′9″, 113.5 cm. high. **£700-800** LJ

Edwardian mahogany plant stand, part banded in satinwood, 1′3″, 38 cm. **£30-40** WW

A pair of red and green tortoiseshell Boulle Centre Pedestals. c.1830. **£420-470** SBel

A rosewood Urn Stand, 2′8″, 81.5 cm. c.1880. **£320-380** SBel

Regency style Torchere, 12″, 30.5 cm. **£90-110** WW

A giltwood Torchere, 3′7″, 109 cm. high by 1′2″, 35 cm. diam., c.1700. possible German, reduced in height. **£950-1,100** SBS

A rosewood Urn Stand, 2′8¼″, 82 cm. c.1880. **£270-300** SBel

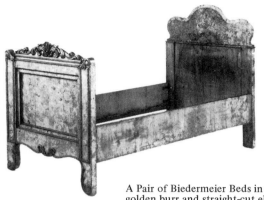

A Pair of Biedermeier Beds in golden burr and straight-cut elm with crossbanded serpentine topped headboards, 4'4" high by 6'5" long by 3'3½" wide, 132 cm. by 196 cm. by 1M; c.1840. **£750-850** SBS

A Dutch Marquetry Bedstead, of unusual form inlaid on a mahogany veneered ground, early 19th C. overall 6'2" by 3'2", 188 cm. by 96 cm. **£600-700** LC

An 18th C. carved oak Four-Poster Bed. 5'8", 173 cm. wide. **£940-1,200** KC

Antique oak cradle (probably Dutch). **£512-600** PG

A fine Hepplewhite mahogany four poster bed, the tester surrounded by an arched cornice. 107" high, 272 cm. 84" long, 213 cm., 73" wide, 185.5 cm. **£2,400-2,600** HKC

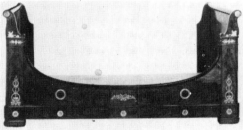

A Regency ormolu-mounted mahogany lit en bateau, 44", 112 cm wide, 88", 223.5 cm long. **£2,100-2,250** CStJ

A 19th C. mahogany four-poster Bed in the Hepplewhite manner, 3'6", 106 cm. wide. **£600-790** KC

A painted cradle. 40½", 103 cm wide. 18th C. Flemish or North German. **£550-600** CStJ

A French Empire style mahogany and parcel gilt Lit Bateau, 19th C. Overall 5'0", 152 cm. wide. x 7'8", 234 cm. long. **£300-400** LC

A Victorian brass Double Bedstead, 5'2", 157 cm. wide. **£550-650** OL

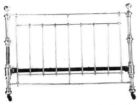

A brass half-tester Bed, the head and footboard with spindle supports. 7'10", 239 cm. x 6'4", 193 cm. c.1900. **£230-280** SBel

A giltwood bed, the headboard with a padded inset and swan's head finials. 5'2", 158 cm. wide, c.1900. **£360-400** SBel

An unusual chestnut bed screen, early 18th C., probably Spanish, 69½", 176.5 cm. wide, **£520-580** CStJ

A mahogany folding towel rail with turned supports and stretchers. **£30-40** WW

An oak aumbry with serpentine double plank top, 35", 89 cm. wide, **£1,400-1,600** CStJ

A pair of George III Cary's celestial and terrestrial table globes, 27", 69 cm high. **£2,600-2,700** CStJ

A serpentine fronted mahogany cheveret in the 18th C. style, herringbone stringing and rosewood crossbanding. 17" wide, 43 cm. **£340-380** HKC

A large Terrestrial Globe by Smith of London, the mahogany stand holding a compass in turned mahogany case, 39" high by 24" wide, 99 cm. by 61 cm. **£1,800-2,000** B

A 19th century early Georgian-Design Walnut Knee-hole Dressing Table, with chevron banding, 88 cm. wide, 2'10¾". **£530-600** KC

A Pair of George II Giltwood Wall Brackets in the rococo style, the D-shaped platforms supported by pierced swirling scrollwork, 1'9" high x 1'2½" wide 53 cm. x 37 cm., c.1760. **£3,700-4,200** SBS

A revolving mahogany bookcase, 15½" wide, 39.2 cm. **£85-100** HKC

An early 19th C. Napoleonic Prisoner-of-War coloured straw-work Ladies Table Dressing Chest, 17½" wide by 21½" high, 44.5 cm. by 54.5 cm., £145-185 OL

A Late Stuart Oak Chest in two sections, the lower portion with two cupboard doors enclosing three long drawers, 3'5"; 104 cm. £700-800 LC

A Fine Restoration Stuart Oak Chest, inlaid with bone and mother-of-pearl dated 1664, 43" wide; 108.5 cm. £850-950 KC

A 'Chippendale' painted wood Wall Shelf with Mirror back 4'1", 120 cm. 1920's. £220-250 SBel

A Charles II oak chest, inlaid in bone and mother-of-pearl, 42", 107 cm. wide, £1,600-1,800 CStJ

A Mid-17th C. Oak Spice Cabinet, 15" wide, 38 cm., wide, surmounted by grotesque masks. £320-380 KC

A French 17th C.-design small ornate carved oak Cupboard, with trellis and strapwork decoration. 2'1½" wide, 65 cm. £180-220 KC

19th C. satinwood veneered Toilet Cabinet banded in rosewood, fitted interior with mirror, trays, powder boxes, writing slide and pot cupboard. 2'4", 71 cm. £810-900 WW

A kingwood circular Cupboard, 2'11¼", 89.5 cm. c.1900. £120-150 SBel

Set of three Edwardian ebonised and gilt hanging wall cabinets, one 2'7", 78.5 cm. and two 20", 50 cm. angle cabinets. £155-175 RB

A Kingwood and Marquetry Poudreuse, mirror lined interior and mounted throughout with a gilt-metal scroll, 32 by 27"; 81 by 69 cm., possibly English, c.1880. £800-900 SBel

Pair of 16th C. Gothic trestle table supports. 29½", 75 cm. high. £600-700 B

Louis Phillipe Kingwood poudreuse, with brass and pewter inlay Rising top, interior with a mirror and lift-out tray. 2'; 61 cm. wide. £1,000-1,200 HKC

A George IV mahogany wash basin stand, 15" dia. 38 cm. £250-280 HKC

A 'Louis XV' Boulle Poudreuse, with scrolling cut brass on red tortoiseshell inlay, mirror-backed interior and lift-out compartment tray. 29 by 24"; 74 by 61 cm., c.1890. £350-400 SBel

Mid-18th century dummy board. £495-540 CAL

Sheraton style mahogany oval tea tray, having two brass handles. 2'0", 61 cm. £40-50 WW

A Pair of Louis XV Kingwood Chevron Veneered Bedside cupboards, 2'5¼" high by 12½" wide, 74 cm. by 32 cm., third quarter 18th C. restored. £450-520 SBS

A mid 18th C. Dutch burr walnut tea kettle stand with a copper liner and a stepped lid fitted with a deep drawer to the shaped apron, 1'11" high 11" wide, 58.5 cm. by 28 cm. £340-400 HKC

A late 18th C. Dutch Provincial Walnut Doughbin on stand with lined interior, 4'2", 127 cm. wide. £1,150-1,300 WW

A pair of late Georgian mahogany brass-bound Buckets, 1'2", 36 cm. diam. x 1'5", 43 cm. high. £1,150-1,250 LC

A Sheraton style mahogany half-round bijonterie table with glazed lid, lined interior. £34-45 WW

A French rosewood veneered bijonterie with gilt brass mounts, bevelled glass top and shaped glass sides, 19"; 47.5 cm., £260-300 WW

An oak dough-bin, early 18th C., 73½", 187 cm wide, £1,050-1,100 CStJ

POINTERS FOR CHAIRS

- in any chair made before 1845-50 the top rail must be contained within the back legs
- an overlapping top rail points to Victorian origin
- armchairs are always wider across the front than single chairs
- if chair is turned upside down, all seat rails should be same wood with equal patination
- cross-stretcher rails should not be too low, legs may have been cut
- original carving would not be flat
- round, turned legs tend to be Victorian or later

A XVII C. North Country Oak Wainscot chair with carved scroll shaped cresting rail with spandrel supports. £1,100-1,300 B

A Pair of XVII C. Oak Wainscot Chairs, central panel with lozenge decoration. £680-780 B

A XVII C. Oak Wainscot chair, shaped cresting rail with herring-bone decoration. £750-850 B

213

A Rare XVI C. Scottish Oak
Caquetoire Wainscot chair, gouge
decorated cresting rail with
initials "P.D." Trapezoid shaped
seat. £490-560 B

A 17th C. oak wainscot chair.
£490-550 HKC

Mid 17th C. carved Oak armchair.
£850-950 RBB

A XVII C. Oak Wainscot chair
with carved and shaped cresting
rail above a double panel carved
back. £710-800 B

A Charles I oak open armchair
on turned legs and square
stretchers. £1,050-1,200 CStJ

A William and Mary oak open
armchair with scrolled top rail
inscribed T. H. 1688, and
S-scrolled ears, the seat replaced.
£500-580 CStJ

A XVII C. Oak Wainscot chair,
incised carved straight cresting
rail. £540-620 B

A Charles II oak open armchair
on turned legs and square
stretchers. £900-1,000 CStJ

17th C. Oak Cockfighting Chair.
£900-1,100 RBB

A Charles II oak open armchair
the rectangular panelled back
with scrolled top rail, the seat re
placed. £650-720 CStJ

17th C. oak North country wainscot chair. £550-600   BA

An Oak elbow chair, second half 17th C. replaced seat and back stretcher. £760-860   LC

An oak open armchair on turned baluster legs and square stretchers, 17th C. £750-840   CStJ

A Late Stuart Oak elbow chair with characteristic West of England quatrefoil leaf design. £580-680   LC

An Unusual Stained Oak Debtor's Chair, carved with a figure of Christ, the wings containing shaped steel rods, early 20th C. £320-370   SBel

A XVII C. Oak Wainscot chair with arcaded carving to the pan-elled back. £980-1,100   B

A Charles II pale oak open arm-chair with scrolled top rail, on turned legs and square stretchers — squab cushion. £750-840   CStJ

A XVII C. Oak Wainscot chair with carved strapwork to the back surround, the centre of which has a carved devil in relief. £460-500   B

An oak open armchair, 17th C., squab cushion, carved with possible maker's initials I.L., £980-1,050   CStJ

An open arm oak childs chair 17th C. £800-900

A Pair of Florentine Walnut armchairs, stuffed seats upholstered in velvet and metal-thread embroidery, early 17th C. £800-1,200   SBS

A Walnut Armchair, 17th C., probably French. £350-400   SBS

An oak and elm armchair on turned legs and square stretchers, late 17th C., £820-900   CStJ

A Pair of Italian Walnut Armchairs, rectangular front stretcher with pierced geometric mouldings, late 16th C. probably Ligurian. £650-720   SBS

A fine Italian early 17th C. walnut elbow chair, bearing the arms of Cardinal Rampolla. £600-700 HKC

A Pair of Italian Walnut Armchairs, downcurved scrolled arms on plain supports, c.1620, possibly Lombard. £650-750 SBS

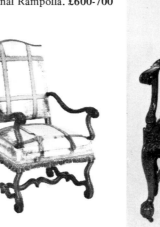

A William and Mary walnut open armchair. £420-500   CStJ

A Walnut Armchair, c.1680, possibly French. £1,150-1,300 SBS

An English Carved Mahogany Armchair, leather upholstered seat, mid-19th C. £120-180 SBel

A Set of Five Queen Anne caned walnut Chairs including an Armchair, c.1705, two with feet replaced. **£1,500-2,500** SBS

19th C. upholstered open armchair in walnut, c.1870. **£300-350**

A Pair of Venetian Walnut Armchairs, elaborately scrolled, c.1700. **£1,400-1,600** SBS

A 17th C. Oak and Upholstered Adjustable Wingback Armchair. **£480-540** KC

A Walnut Chair of George II design, the stuffed seat on cabriole legs with paw feet, **£110-150** HKC

A George III mahogany open armchair of Chinese Chippendale style, squab cushion. **£580-640** CStJ

A pair of Chinese hardwood open armchairs with waved top rails, curved solid splats, out-scrolled arms and inset wicker seats, turned legs. 18th C., Ch'ing. **£3,400-3,800** CStJ

A set of four Chinese rosewood open armchairs, 18th C., Ch'ing. **£8,500-9,500** CStJ

A yew wood Windsor elbow chair, 19th C. **£420-440** LC

Yew wood child's chair, c.1800. **£300-350** BA

A Pair of Chinese Bamboo Armchairs in the Brighton Pavilion taste. c.1800. **£1,500-2,000** SBS

Yorkshire ladder back beech armchair with rush seat, **£75-85** WW

A set of eight oak and elm Windsor armchairs with spindle backs and crinoline stretchers. **£1,700-1,900** CStJ

Fruit wood and elm windsor armchair. Hoop back with rails and pierced splat. **£105-125** WW

A Hepplewhite Shield back Mahogany open Armchair. Channelled carved frame and arms, front square tapering legs. **£650-750** WW

18th C. country made open armchair in mahogany, c.1785. **£150-200**

A set of 6 late George III mahogany open armchairs. **£2,400-2,500** CStJ

A pair of George IV cream painted
parcel gilt armchairs with a
moulded frame. Ball studded
horizontal rails and arms with
cornucopia style terminals.
£1,150-1,400 HKC

A Rare George III Giltwood Armchair. Beaded lyre-shape. c.1775.
£2,400-2,700 SBS

A Set of Four Cane-Seat and
Back Chairs,
£500-600 KC

A Good George II Mahogany
and Satinwood Inlaid Armchair
1890's. **£280-320** SBel

Early George III Mahogany
Armchair, a Lyre splat back with
brass strings and a leafy cresting,
upholstered in tan suede, c.1770.
£3,000-3,600 SBS

A Fine Chippendale period open arm chair, c.1740-45 (possibly American), with flat stretcher rails. £1,000-1,200

An early 19th Century rosewood horseshoe form armchair, the back and splat inlaid with boxwood, £1,050-1,200 HKC

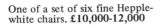

One of a set of six fine Hepplewhite chairs. £10,000-12,000

18th C. Queen Anne walnut elbow chair. £375-400 BA

An unusual fruitwood open armchair, late 18th C, possibly Maltese. £1,050-1,150 CStJ

An Empire mahogany Fauteuil, with overscrolled toprail, lions' legs headed by anthemion and ending in paw feet, c.1810, possibly German. £850-950 SBS

A pair of Regency elbow chairs with loose shaped cushions. £2,600-2,800 LC

A Pair of Regency Ornate Carved Oak Rail-back Armchairs, the seats covered in hide. £1,200-1,400 KC

A pair of Thomas Hope Regency style chairs. £2,500-3,000

An Early George III Mahogany Library Armchair with stop fluted arm supports and legs. £500-560 BON

A Rare Pair of George I Walnut Shepherd's Crook Armchairs with arched stuffed backs and bowed stuffed seats, c.1715. £3,800-4,300 SBS

An Italian giltwood open armchair. 18th C. £280-310   CStJ

A Pair of George III Carved Walnut Armchairs, c.1780. £1,000-1,500 SBS

A 19th C. mahogany framed Gainsborough chair in the Hepplewhite manner. £340-400 HKC

George II Mahogany Library Armchair. Serpentine-fronted seat, c.1755, upholstered in tan suede. £5,200-6,000 SBS

A Pair of George III Mahogany Frame Elbow Chairs, serpentine front seats with curved arm supports and square tapering legs and inlaid with stringing. £1,300-1,600 LC

A Mahogany Armchair, with tapering fluted legs, c.1870. £100-200 SBel

A Mahogany frame elbow chair, the sprung seats, back and arm rests in pink tapestry, £250-300 VC

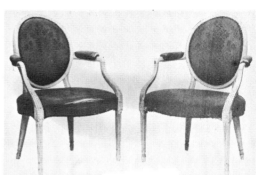

A Fine Pair of Adam Painted
wood oval back open Armchairs
Carved crests, reeded outswept
arms. Bow fronted seat in grey
damask, c.1770. £640-700 WW

A Pair of George III Mahogany
Armchairs French style, in the
manner of John Cobb, outlined
with gadrooning, c.1770. £5,800-
6,400 SBS

A pair of Adam style carved wood
and gilt armchairs. £350-400 LJ

A Pair of Giltwood Fauteils.
Backs carved with a leaf cresting
third quarter of 19th C. £400-
600 SBel

A Fine George III Mahogany
Cabriole-Leg Upholstered Gainsborough Armchair. Nailed hide
upholstery and padded arms.
£1,880-2,100 KC

A pair of George III cream-painted open armchairs. £2,600-2,800 CStJ

A Louis XIV design walnut fauteuil, the stuffed rectangular back and seat covered with chinoiserie gros and petit-point, £130-170 HKC

An Unusual Dieppe Ivory Fauteuil with cartouche-shaped padded back and bowed upholstered seat on cabriole legs, 19th C. £1,800-2,000 CStJ

A mid-Victorian walnut upholstered armchair. £300-400

A Suite of Louis XVI Gilt-wood Seat Furniture comprising a Canape and four Fauteuils, upholstered in Aubusson needle-work, c.1880. £3,300-4,000 SBel

Gainsborough chair with Soho tapestry. £1,525-1,625 VM

A pair of Regency carved wood and gilded fauteuils. The seat, back and arm pads upholstered floral Aubusson tapestry. £650-750 LJ

A Walnut Armchair, gilt-metal pierced acanthus mounts throughout, German, 1870's. £230-270 SBel

223

Barber's vintage chair. £23-30
ORM

A hardwood armchair, carved
with a shou emblem in a leaf-
shaped panel with some damage,
early/mid Ch'ing Dynasty, 39½",
100.5 cm. £1,000-1,200   CStJ

A Liberty & Co. Oak washstand,
Back inlaid with pewter flower-
heads, above a canvas flap and a
lead top shelf above cupboard
doors, 63 x 38½"; 159 x 98 cm.,
c.1900. £120-140   SBel

An Open Armchair of 'caquetteuse'
form decorated with sycamore
and satin birch marquetry,
possibly Scottish. £250-270   PL

A Mahogany Armchair. Tall
slender back, partly padded with
contemporary upholstery, and a
similar padded seat, probably
Scottish, c.1900. £230-250   SBel

A small Oak Rush-seated Armchair, designed by George Walton,
Back with pierced handhole and
trapezium rush seat, c.1900.
£820-1,000   SBel

A set of Four Oak Armchairs,
'U'-shaped back and stuffed
drop-in seat with central solid
splat and side splats forming
legs, c.1895. £90-120   SBel

A Walnut 'Grotto' Armchair,
carved as clam shell, the arms
carved as dolphins, third quarter
of 19th C. £210-250   SBel

An Unusual Pair of Stained Elm
revolving armchairs. Italian, late
19th C. £120-200   SBel

A matched set of eight Cromwellian oak Chairs, having nailed hide seats and backs, £1,675-1,875 KC

Eight 19th C. Continental Dining Chairs. £720-820 OL

Set of six Jacobean style carved walnut dining chairs. £300-350

A set of six 17th C. carved oak Derbyshire Chairs, with arcaded backs and panelled seats, including two carvers. £750-850 KC

A set of six 'Charles II' beechwood Dining Chairs, including a pair of armchairs. c.1930. £460-500 SBel

A set of five oak Chairs with hump shaped cresting rails, 18th C. with restorations. £1,200-1,300 LC

A Pair of William III Carved Walnut Chairs in the manner of Daniel Marot, c.1700, with restorations. £550-640 SBS

A carved Walnut Chair, the toprail with a leafy grotesque mask crossbar, mid 17th C. probably Dutch. £300-400 SBS

A Set of Six Oak Chairs, the panel seats with dished centres and the square and turned supports joined by stretchers, early 18th century. £2,300-2,600 LC

Old reproduction Carolean oak side chair with squab cushion. £40-50 WW

A set of eight Cromwellian oak Chairs, with nailed hide seats and backs. £800-900 KC

A near matching set of six Cromwellian oak Chairs, nailed tapestry seats and backs, £2,400-2,700 KC

A Set of Four Queen Anne Walnut Dining chairs with solid vase shape splats, tapestry lift-out seats. £2,850-3,100 LC

A Pair of Ebonised Side Chairs, inlaid and banded with ivory, c.1880. £180-220 SBel

A set of eight oak Dining Chairs, including one armchair, late 19th C. £280-340 SBel

A set of 8 red walnut dining chairs, including 2 arm chairs in early 18th C. style. £1,350-1,450 LC

Set of twelve oak carved Carolean design Dining Chairs. £1,220-1,495 W

Walnut chair with cane seat and back inserts, c.1710. £375-400 VM

Set of four 18th C. elm country made dining chairs in Queen Anne style. £140-180

A Set of Three Portuguese Dining Chairs, mid-eighteenth century. £280-320 SBS

Queen Anne Style single walnut chair. £240-300 MP

A Pair of George I Walnut Chairs with solid splats, cabriole legs ending in pad feet, c.1715. £800-900 SBS

A set of 8 beechwood and parcel-gilt dining chairs, early 18th C. Dutch or North German. £3,000-3,250 CStJ

A Set of Six George I Red Walnut Chairs, the bow-fronted drop-in seats with veneered seatrails centred by a shell, c.1720, possibly Irish. £2,200-2,600 SBS

A Set of Seven George I design Walnut dining chairs, the trap seats raised on shell carved cabriole supports with trefoil paw feet. £1,200-1,500 HKC

A Set of Six Early George III Mahogany Dining Chairs, the backs carved with shellwork and interlaced ribbon. c.1770. £2,300-2,800 SBS

A Set of Four Portuguese Japanned Dining Chairs, the frames carved and painted with rococo motifs, c.1760, distressed. £600-900 SBS

Set of six 19th C. mahogany Dining Chairs in 'Chippendale' ribbon back style, comprising 2 carver and 4 side chairs. £780-880 WW

1212

A pair of George I walnut Dining Chairs, having woolwork-covered drop-in seats. £340-400 K.C.

A set of 6 early George III mahogany dining-chairs, and a pair of George III armchairs. £4,800-5,000 CStJ

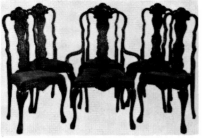

Six Dutch early 19th C. marquetry Dining Chairs; 5 single and 1 elbow chair. £1,400-1,600 KC

A Set of 12 Mahogany Dining Chairs including two armchairs c.1880. £1,900-2,200 SBel

A set of Chippendale design mahogany dining chairs, acanthus carved cabriole legs with claw feet, £1,050-1,250 MH

One of a set of eight Chippendale chairs (including two carvers) £4,750-5,000 MP

A set of eight mahogany 'Chippendale' dining Chairs, including a pair of armchairs, c.1920. £700-800 SBel

A set of 6 mahogany dining chairs in the Georgian style, 19th C. £420-440 LC

A set of six Chippendale-style carved mahogany Chairs. Rosette-decorated toprails; 4 standards and 2 carvers. £600-700 KC

A set of eight mahogany Dining Chairs including two Armchairs. early 20th C. £620-700 SBel

A set of six 19th C. mahogany Chippendale-style Chairs. Pierced and interlaced scroll vase-shape splats. £1,050-1,250 KC

A Set of Six Early George III Mahogany Chairs, the serpentine toprails outlined with scrolls splats pierced with gothic arches. c.1760. £2,200-2,600 SBS

Set of Eight George III Mahogany dining chairs. Square backs and reeded outer and plain inner vertical splats headed by stiff leaves. Dipped nailed stuffed seat. £5,000-6,000 HKC

A set of six mahogany Dining Chairs, including a pair of armchairs, central pierced splat, late 19th C. £300-500 SBel

A set of Eight Mahogany dining chairs in the Georgian style, including two arm chairs with camel backs, reeded vertical splats, upholstered seats. £750-850 LC

Set of Twelve George III Mahogany dining chairs. Hoop back and pierced vase splat. £2,300-2,800 HKC

Twelve Country Dining Chairs in ash and beech, lift out seats late 18th/early 19th century (all with repairs) £660-760 LC

A set of eight George III design mahogany dining chairs including two with arms. £650-750 HKC

A set of fourteen mahogany dining chairs in Hepplewhite style, 12 side chairs and 2 carving chairs. £1,900-2,100 LJ

One of a pair of 'Hepplewhite' mahogany chairs with pierced vase form splats, £140-170 DHBN

A fine set of eight George III mahogany Dining Chairs; 6 single and 2 elbow chairs. £1,800-2,000 KC

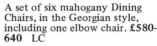

A set of six mahogany Dining Chairs, in the Georgian style, including one elbow chair. £580-640 LC

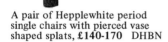

A pair of Hepplewhite period single chairs with pierced vase shaped splats, £140-170 DHBN

A Set of Eight Sheraton Mahogany dining chairs, the backs with reeded central clasps and moulded scroll uprights. £2,100-3,000 OL

A Set of Eight Walnut Chairs, including one armchair and one nursing chair, c.1890. £600-700 SBel

A Set of Eight George III Hepplewhite Wheatear Mahogany Dining chairs, two carvers and six single, with stuff-over velvet seats. £1,650-1,850 B

A fine set of six George III mahogany dining Chairs. £680-780 KC

A set of six George III mahogany Dining Chairs, the cresting rails decorated with satinwood crossbanding and stringing, £600-700 KC

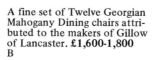

A fine set of Twelve Georgian Mahogany Dining chairs attributed to the makers of Gillow of Lancaster. £1,600-1,800 B

One of four mahogany Georgian chairs. **£300-350** JWB

A set of 6 George III cream-painted and parcel-gilt dining chairs. **£1,600-1,800** CStJ

A set of six George III painted chairs in the Hepplewhite style, including two elbow chairs. **£740-840** LC

A set of eight mahogany Dining Chairs, including two armchairs, in the Hepplewhite style. **£600-700** LC

Set of Sixteen Regency Mahogany dining chairs, including two with arms, each with a moulded top rail and horizontal splat, with an unusual reeded convex seat rail. **£5,400-6,000** HKC

A Set of Six Regency Mahogany Dining Chairs with leather lift-out seats and sabre legs. **£680-780** LC

A set of 6 Regency mahogany dining chairs. **£660-700** LC

A fine set of 18 Regency mahogany mahogany dining chairs with drop-in leather-upholstered seats. **£4,000-4,200** CStJ

A Set of Four Dutch Marquetry Chairs with padded backs and seats, inlaid with flowers on a mahogany ground, early 19th century. **£550-650** SBS

GUIDE TO STYLES		
Dates	Monarch	Period
1603-1625	James I	Jacobean
1625-1649	Charles I	Carolean
1649-1660	Commonwealth	Cromwellian
1660-1685	Charles II	Restoration
1685-1689	James II	Restoration
1689-1694	William & Mary	William & Mary
1694-1702	William III	William III or more often William & Mary
1702-1714	Anne	Queen Anne

A set of six Regency mahogany Dining Chairs, restored. **£575-660** LC

A set of six Regency Dining Chairs, the simulated rosewood frames. **£575-620** LC

A set of 6 Biedermeier oak marquetry dining chairs. **£1,450-1,590** CStJ

A set of Eight Regency-period simulated rosewood Dining Chairs. **£1,800-2,100** KC

A Set of Eight William IV Mahogany Dining chairs with high curved cresting rails, the plain supports headed by leafage, red velvet lift-out seats on turned front legs. **£850-950** LC

A set of four William IV rosewood Dining Chairs. Curved top rail and padded drop-in seats; early 1830's. **£290** SBel

An unusual set of six Regency Mahogany chairs in the classical taste. **£900-1,000** B

A Set of Eight Mahogany Dining Chairs, the drop-in seats on reeded 'jewelled' legs, late 1830's. **£800-900** SBel

A set of 6 Victorian mahogany dining chairs. **£300-330** LC

A Set of Six Victorian small mahogany chairs with waisted hoop backs, serpentine front seats and cabriole legs. £540-640 LC

A set of six Victorian mahogany frame Chairs. £420-510 LC

A set of six Victorian rosewood Chairs, £650-750 KC

A set of four Victorian rosewood small Chairs with shaped waisted backs, £340-400 LC

A Set of Five Mahogany Side Chairs, with balloon back and leaf carved horizontal splats c.1860. £290-350 SBel

A set of six Victorian carved walnut spoon-back Chairs, having pierced clasp-shaped mid-bars. £800-900 KC

Set of six William IV mahogany Dining Chairs. £660-760 PWC

A Set of five Victorian drawing room chairs with balloon backs. £290-360 LC

A Set of Four Victorian chairs, the frames simulating walnut with pierced leafage. £250-350 LC

A Set of Six Victorian Rosewood Drawing Room Chairs, with upholstered panels and seats. £600-700 LC

Set of four Victorian rosewood small chairs. £210-250 LC

233

A set of 6 Victorian mahogany dining chairs with lift-out seats. **£360-400**   LC

A set of six mahogany Dining Chairs, mid 19th C. **£310-350** SBel

A Set of Six Victorian Mahogany chairs with lift-out seats and octagonal baluster turned supports. **£350-450**   LC

A set of eight Victorian rosewood Dining Chairs with waisted balloon backs, **£620-680**   LC

One of a set of six early Victorian rosewood side chairs. Shaped backs with scroll carved rails. **£400-470**   WW

A set of 6 Victorian mahogany balloon back standard chairs. **£245-265**   ORM

A Pair of Oak Dining Chairs attributed to Alfred Waterhouse. Padded back with bobbin turned top-rail, and padded bowed seat, 1870's. **£130-180**   SBel

One of a set of six Victorian mahogany shaped back side chairs. **£340-400**   WW

A set of eighteen 'Empire' burr-walnut Dining Chairs, including two armchairs. Sprung seats with gilt-metal paw feet, bearing the label Krieger Paris; c.1910. **£2,800-3,100**   SBel

A Set of Six Mahogany Dining chairs after a design by E.A. Taylor, c.1895. **£150-250**   SBel

A Set of Ten Beech Spindle Back rush seated dining chairs including one with arms. £640-700 HKC

A set of eight 19th C. figured walnut dining chairs in the French style, £1,450-1,650 DHBN

A set of six early 19th C. spindle-back elm rush-seat Chairs, £600-700 KC

A set of six George III mahogany Dining Chairs; 4 single and 2 elbow chairs. £780-880 KC

A Pair of Ebonised Side Chairs, probably designed by E.W. Godwin. Geometric waisted backs and circular rush seats, 1870's. £60-80 SBel

Child's bentwood and cane chair. £36-46 MP

A set of 6 country chairs with elm seats and fruitwood backs, c.1800. £410-450 BA

Pair of late Victorian rosewood frame side chairs, ivory motif mask and line inlaid. £66-86 WW

A set of 6 late Victorian standard chairs. £185-200 ORM

Victorian ebonized bedroom chair, the shaped back inlaid mother-of-pearl and gilt flowers. £60-90 WW

A Set of Eight Ebonised Oak and Walnut Dining Chairs, including a pair of armchairs with a triple horizontal wavy splat, and sprung drop-in seats, 1930's. **£300-500** SBel

Unusual set of six second empire Thuyawood Dining Chairs, c.1850. **£180-220** SBel

A Set of Six Stained Oak Dining chairs, inlcuding a Pair of Arm- chairs with concave backs, carved side chairs, with 'U'-shaped stuffed seats, stamped Reg. No. 778034, one arm lacking, 1895- 1900. **£120-180** SBel

A set of six beech and oak West- morland dining chairs, including two with arms. **£800-900** HKC

A Mother-of-Pearl inlaid Papier Mache Chair with serpentine stuffed drop-in seat on cabriole legs, mid 19th C. **£260-300** SBel

A James I Oak Hall Chair, c.1615, restored. **£290-330** SBS

An Oak Turned Triangular Chair, **£350-450** SBS

A Victorian Child's Walnut fold- ing chair with rush seat and back. **£24-34** RB

An Italian painted and gilded sedan chair, the interior with velvet. 29", 74 cm wide, 18th C. **£950-1,150** CStJ

A Musical Beechwood Hall Chair, 3', 92 cm. high. German, late 19th C. **£250-300** SBel

A 17th C. oak box seat chair with door at rear, 19" by 42", 48 cm by 106 cm. **£300-330** LC

236

SOME LEGS AND FEET

Ball-foot
– a turned sphere found in late 17th and early 18th C. furniture.

Ball and claw foot
– a ball clutched by a claw – very popular on cabriole leg furniture from 1710.

Bracket foot
– introduced c.1690.

Bun foot
– a turned ball shaped foot – popular from 1650-1710 (in America called a ball foot).

Cabriole leg
– starts from just under the seat, curves outwards at knee and then curves backwards to the foot, popular into the early 18th C. until c.1760. Enjoyed a Victorian revival.

Cluster column leg
– usually found associated with revived Gothic style, has several slender columns joined together starting from a common base.

Hoof foot
– animal form of foot, very popular with early cabriole legs.

Pad foot
– a round foot.

Sabre leg
– a curved chair leg of the Regency period; examples from 1830's have sabre legs at back and turned legs at front.

Scroll foot
– used from mid 18th C., usually with cabriole leg.

Spade foot
– late 18th C. tapered foot with basic square section.

Set of four early George III mahogany hall chairs, after designs by Ince and Mayhew. Shaped and pierced carved back, dished saddle shaped seat. **£2,200-2,500 HKC**

A Folding Sedan Chair, inscribed 'J. Alderman Inventor, Patentee and Manufacturer, 16 Soho Square London'. 51 by 48 cm, 20" x 19", c.1840. **£80-150 SBel**

An unusual beechwood folding campaign chair, mid-19th C. **£420-480 CStJ**

A Bent Steel 'Digestive' Rocking Chair, patented by Dr. Calvert, 1870's. **£95-115 SBel**

A Pair of Late Georgian Mahogany hall chairs, the backs carved with honeysuckle motif and pendant husks. **£270-350 LC**

A Walnut Armchair with sprung serpentine seat on cabriole legs, c.1860. **£210-240** SBel

A George I Walnut Wing Armchair, the stuffed back and arms and petit-point needlework, c.1720, back legs restored. **£1,500-2,000** SBS

French carved gilt 'Fauteuil-de-femme' upholstered and seat. **£150-170** WW

A pair of Victorian walnut ladies and gentleman's spoonbacked chairs. **£500-590** HKC

Set of Two Walnut Drawing-room Chairs, armchair with an anthemion-carved serpentine moulded back, and a lady's chair, c.1860's. **£620-690** SBel

A Victorian rosewood frame drawing room chair with high over-scroll back, elbow rests and bowed seat. **£280-340** LC

French 18th C. gilt child's chair. **£350-400** BA

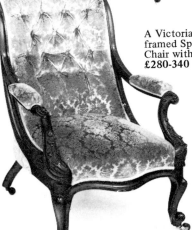

A Victorian Carved walnut-framed Spoon-back Occasional Chair with button upholstery. **£280-340** KC

A Walnut Button-back Armchair with an overscrolled top-rail and downswept padded arms, c.1860. **£260-300** SBel

A Walnut Button-back Armchair, c.1860. **£410-480** SBel

A Victorian Walnut Drawing Room chair and A Victorian Mahogany frame chair. **£150-170** each   LC

A Set of Four George I Walnut Side Chairs, early 20th C. **£200-350**   SBel

A Pair of Walnut Side Chairs, inlaid with scrolling foliage, Italian or South German, c.1850. **£360-400**   SBel

A Walnut Armchair with a moulded button-upholstered waisted back, c.1870. **£150-200** SBel

A set of 4 green-painted and gilded chairs, late 18th C. Italian. **£1,050-1,150**   CStJ

A Button-Upholstered Walnut Side Chair, c.1860. **£200-240** SBel

A good Oak and Elmwood
Settle, the coffered seat flanked
by downswept arm supports.
6'3"; 190 cm. wide, late 17th C.
£400-600 BON

A mid-Georgian oak hall settee of
Kentian style, 59", 150 cm. wide,
and another, en suite, smaller,
51", 129.5 cm. **£1,200-1,400**
CStJ

A 17th C. carved oak box-seat
Settle. 5'0¼", 150 cm. wide.
£600-700 KC

A 19th C. hall Settle, 4'8",
142 cm. **£320-400** LE

An 18th C. oak Settle with
carved panels, fitted lift top.
£520-600 LJ

A 19th C. ornate carved oak
Settle in the French Renaissance
style. 6'4¾", 195 cm. wide.
£1,000-1,300 KC

A 17th C. oak Settle, with strapwork frieze, 6'0", 183 cm. wide.
£500-600 KC

A walnut Settle. 3'8½", 113 cm.
by 4'3½", 131 cm. Italian, 1880's.
£440-500 SBel

A Victorian rosewood frame
settee, 68½", 174 cm. **£410-430**
LC

A Grained Rosewood Chaise
Longue, mid 19th C. **£170-200**
SBel

A George III Small Carved Mahogany Settee. Eagle-head arms and
shell-decorated cabriole legs,
3'8¼", 112 cm. wide. **£500-600**
KC

An unusual pair of mahogany
sofas, probably American, c.1840,
7', 213.4 cm. **£600-660** SBel

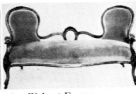

A Victorian Walnut Frame
Couch with double spoon shape
ends. 6'0", 183 cm. **£260-300**
LC

A Victorian Rosewood Frame Confidante with rosewood scroll handgrips and spiral twist supports, 53", 134.5 cm. **£550-630** LC

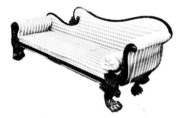

A pair of walnut settees covered in 17th C. tapestry, 83", 211 cm wide. **£4,000-4,300** CStJ

A pair of Victorian Rosewood Frame settees, the backs surrounded by C scrolls and flame ornament. each 55", 139.5 cm. **£680-780** LC

A Victorian walnut serpentine settee, the moulded frame with two spoon back corners, 74" wide, 188 cm. **£560-620** HKC

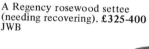

A Regency rosewood settee (needing recovering). **£325-400** JWB

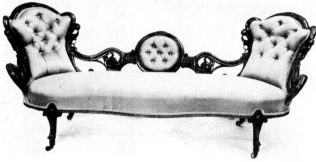

A Victorian Ornate Carved Walnut-Framed Serpentined Settee, 6'0", 183 cm. wide. **£480-580** KC

A Victorian walnut framed Settee, 6'0", 183 cm. wide. **£600-670** OL

A pair of George III giltwood settees. 86¼", 219 cm wide. **£2,400-2,600** CStJ

A Set of three Window seats with outscrolling stuffed arms and serpentine seats. 4'7"; 139 cm. wide. **£4,800-5,500** HKC

A William IV Mahogany Settee, the top-rail with a large scallop shell flanked by lotus and palms. 81"; 207.5 cm. wide, 1830's. **£100-200** SBel

An ebonised bench seat with chinoiserie style latticed work, 4'9''; 144.5 cm. wide. **£90-140** HKC

A George III Adam Gilt Wood Settee, gilded carved pine-wood frame. Covered in deep button upholstery 57''; 144 cm. wide. **£520-600** B

A George II Mahogany Settee, covered in contemporary gros and petit-point needlework, 6'2''; 188 cm. wide, mid-18th C. **£800-1,200** SBS

A Suite of Walnut Seat Furniture comprising six Dining Chairs, an Armchair and a Side Chair, 1880's. **£620-700** SBel

A Suite of Mahogany Seat Furniture, four Dining Chairs, Two Arm Chairs and a Settee, c.1900. **£210-240** SBel

A Suite of Empire Mahogany Seat Furniture comprising a Sofa and six Armchairs, sofa 5'6''; 168 cm. c.1810. **£2,000-2,300** SBS

A Suite of cream painted and parcel gilt salon chairs in the Louis XVI manner comprising a settee, two armchairs and four single chairs. **£1,000-1,300** HKC

A mahogany drawing-room suite with 2 seater settee, 47½'', 120.5 cm wide, 2 armchairs and 4 side chairs, late 1890's. **£160-190** SBel

A Louis XVI French carved wood and grey painted suite of canape and six fauteuils with aubusson Aesop fables and floral tapestry panels. £3,100-4,000 LJ

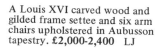

A Louis XVI carved wood and gilded frame settee and six arm chairs upholstered in Aubusson tapestry. £2,000-2,400 LJ

A fine quality Victorian nine piece walnut sitting room suite comprising a 5'10''; 178 cm, buttoned and upholstered settee, a ditto elbow and lady's chair and six side chairs, cabriole legs. £2,200-2,600 PWC

Louis Phillipe Five-piece Gilt-wood Salon Suite of Louis XV Design. Tapestry upholstered seats. £2,400-2,700 KC

A Suite of Eight Louis XV-Style Fauteuils, covered with 18th century Aubusson tapestry. Three matching footstools. £2,200-2,600 KC

A stained beechwood drawing-room suite with 4 side chairs, 2 armchairs and settee, piano stool and display cabinet, 58'', 147.5 cm., 1890's. £170-190 SBel

243

A Good William and Mary Ebonised Stool, with octagonal baluster shaped legs caned top, 23", 58 cm. wide. £320-360 B

Adjustable swivel piano stool. £25-30 ORM

A George III Gilt-Wood Stool, on moulded cabriole legs, 2'2" by 1'9", £200-300 BON

Pair of Carolean oak Coffin Stools. £540-600 RBB

An oak joint stool on fluted columnar legs and square stretchers, 18" wide, 46 cm., early 17th C. £1,050-1,200 CStJ

A James I Oak Joint Stool 1'7" high by 1'5½" wide, 48 cm. by 44 cm. c.1610. £290-350 SBS

An oak joint stool on turned legs and square stretchers, 18" wide, 46 cm. 17th C. £650-720 CStJ

An oak joint stool on turned legs and H-shaped stretcher, 17th C., 18", 46 cm. wide, £650-720 CStJ

A mid 17th C. oak joint stool. £340-380 HKC

A James I Oak Joint Stool, 1'9½" high by 1'6" wide, 55 cm. by 46 cm. c.1620. restored. £320-360 SBS

One of a pair of beaded rose-wood Footstools. £68-78 GA

An early Victorian walnut Foot-stool, the stuffed over top covered striped plush. 1'3", 38 cm. £20-30 WW

A bamboo Stool, with saddle seat on four legs, 1'6", 45 cm. high by 1'8", 50 cm. square. £250-300 SBS

Rare Hepplewhite period mahogany Stool still retaining the original wooden slats. £300-350

A fine George II carved red walnut Stool upholstered in 18th C. floral petit point needlework. £1,100-1,200 PL

A very rare 16th C. Gothic oak Box Stool, 2'0", 62 cm. wide x 1'9", 54 cm. high x 10", 25 cm. deep. £3,000-4,000 B

A pair of stained rosewood Stools, circular top inset with marble panel, 1'8", 51 cm. £510-610 SBel

A pair of Louix XV-Style Stools, 18th C. Aubusson tapestry, on painted and decorated scroll-shaped legs. £340-400 KC

A Rare Charles II Oak Footstool, baluster turned supports and stretchers, 17" by 15" by 14" high, 43 cm. by 38 cm. by 35 cm. £290-340 B

An unusual stained walnut Stool, 3'7", 110 cm. c.1890. £920-1,100 SBel

A pair of walnut Stools, with early 18th C. petit-point. 1'10½", 57 cm. wide, restored, £7,000-7,700 SBS

- folding screens were imported into Europe in large numbers from China and Japan from the early 16th century
- price is determined by size, number of folds, the quality of lacquer and inlay, whether the picture is complete and continues over the folds

- always check for hinge marks on edges of screens which show that originally the screen had more folds
- European screens were frequently japanned and were sometimes sent to China to be lacquered
- Pole screens were frequently converted into the

- more lucrative tripod tables
- the most sought after pole screens were made from 1750-1800
- as pole screens have now become more sought after there have been attempts to reconvert tripod tables and standard lamps

A Large Mother O'Pearl Inlaid Tsuitate Screen, on a carved hardwood stand, 59" high; 150 cm., Japanese, last quarter 19th century. £400-500 LC

Merton Abbey Tapestrywork, A Woven Panel, probably a student work. Green, Blue, madder and beige on a dark blue ground, in a mahogany firescreen, 36½", by 17¼", 93 cm. by 43.5 cm., 1900-1920. £100-200 SBel

A Famille-Rose and Blue and White Eight-Fold Screen, 32⅜", 82.2 cm., late 19th C. hardwood frame. £780-860 SBel

Antique 4 fold leather screen. £350-380 PG

A Hardstone Table Screen, the oval plaque set within a carved wood frame, matching wood stand, 46.5 cm. overall; 1'6½", second half of 19th century. £150-220 SBel

A Walnut Firescreen, containing a glazed woolwork panel, on trestle feet, 59" by 33", 150 cm. by 84 cm., 1860's. £280-360 SBel

Regency needlepoint polescreen. £62-80 CFA

Chinese porcelain table-screen, in coloured enamels depicting "A Village Scene", 21" x 16"; 52.5 cm. x 40.5 cm., in carved red-wood frame and stand. £500-600 RB

A Mahogany and Leather Five-Fold Screen, Large central fold with a leather embossed panel and four smaller panels and six panels with 'Gothic K' tracery, 61¾" by 85", 157 cm. by 216 cm. overall, c.1900. £310-350 SBel

Carved gilt firescreen with tapestry panel. £85-95 PG

An 18th century Dutch leather screen painted with chinoiserie figures on a silvery gilt ground, each fold 5'3" high x 5'4" wide; 159.5 cm. x 162 cm. £2,800-3,000 HKC

An English eighteenth century six-fold leather screen with chinoiserie painted decoration. £1,700-2,300 LJ

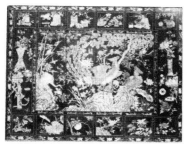

A Six-fold Coromandel Lacquered Wood Screen, decorated with an incised and tempera-coloured scene, each fold 42 cm. x 195 cm. 1'4½" x 6'4¾", period of K'ang Hsi. £2,500-3,200 KC

A Three-fold Painted Screen, one panel signed Jules Vernon-Fair, mahogany and gilt frame, the largest fold 78¾" x 22½"; 200 cm. x 56 cm., c.1910. £380-450 SBel

A Large Red Lacquer and Shibaya-Ama Two-fold Screen, each elaborate screen formed from inlaid carved and stained ivory, raised and carved lacquers and carved mother o' pearl, on a blue lacquered ground, red lacquered frame, each fold 75½" x 32½"; 192 cm. x 82.5 cm. Japanese, late 19th century. £1,200-1,300 LC

A Four-Fold Leather Screen, the centre painted with a view of 16th century London, each fold 75" by 22", 190.5 cm. by 56 cm. c.1880. £1,000-1,300 SBel

A Damascus Mishrabaya Hardwood three-fold Screen, with panels of bobbin-turned fretwork, inlaid with mother-of-pearl, each fold 78" x 23½"; 198 cm. x 60 cm., late 19th c. £250-320 SBel

A Six-fold Coromandel Lacquered Wood Screen, decorated with an incised and tempera-coloured scene, each fold 42 cm. x 195 cm. 1'4½" x 6'4¾", period of K'ang Hsi. £2,200-2,500 KC

A Six-fold Red and Black Lacquer Screen, each fold 50" x 12½"; 127 cm. x 32 cm. third quarter of 19th century. £150-250 SBel

An Ebonised Wood and Painted Leather four-fold Screen each fold 74¾" x 23"; 190 cm. x 58.5 cm., German, c.1860. £150-300 SBel

A Pair of Giltwood Mirrors, early 18th C. Italian. £750-830 CStJ

A Chippendale wall mirror, the four flower form candleholders converted to electricity, 66" high, 168 cm. £1,000-1,300 DHBN

A Chippendale wall mirror in finely carved wood and gilded frame, shoulders surmounted by squirrels. 4'7" x 2'7"; 139.5 cm. x 78.5 cm. £900-1,000   LJ

A George II Giltwood Mirror in the manner of John Vardy, 3'1" high by 2'9" wide, 94 cm. by 84 cm., c.1725. £600-700 SBS

A late 18th C. Neo-Classical gilt frame hanging mirror, 3'3½" by 4'8½", 100 cm. by 143.5 cm., overall. £250-350 GCH

A George II Carved and Gilt Wall Mirror, 5'10" by 3'2", 178 cm. by 96 cm., distressed. £2,200-2,500 BON

A George III giltwood mirror, 56" by 36", 142 by 91.5 cm. £2,300-2,450 CStJ

A Pair of George II Giltwood Wall Mirrors, the apron and cresting with elaborate cartouches, 3' 9" high by 2' wide, 114 cm. by 61 cm., c.1760. £1,900-2,200 SBS

A Pair of Thuringian Mirror Frames, encrusted with coloured flowers and putti, 99 cm., 3'3¼" overall, c.1880. £1,250-1,400 SBel

A Large Early 19th century Dresden Mirror Frame, of moulded scroll design, the moulding picked out in gilt, mounted on gilt frame 43" x 31½"; 108.5 cm. x 80 cm. £450-500   KC

A Pair of Giltwood 'Chippendale' Wall Mirrors the mirror plate intersected by bands of scrolls and foliage, 69" x 37"; 175 cm. x 94 cm. third quarter of 19th century. £1,550-1,700   SBel

A Painted and Gilded Mirror decorated in colours and mother-of-pearl, 41¼" by 34¼", 104.5 cm. by 87 cm., early 18th C. Dutch or North German. £1,000-1,100   CStJ

A William and Mary Large Rectangular Walnut Frame Mirror. 3'0" x 3'8"; 92 cm. x 112 cm. high. £900-1,100   LC

A Dresden Mirror Frame with brightly coloured floral trails and putti, bevelled mirror glass and wood backing, 1'11½"; 58.5 cm. overall, late 19th century. £450-520   SBel

18th century Mahogany 'Swansea' mirror, c.1765. 30" high; 76 cm. £150-250

A Copper and Enamel Mirror, the frame inset with enamel plaques, 21" by 40", 53.5 cm. by 101.5 cm; c.1900. £150-170 SBel

A Carved Wood and Gesso Mirror, 64½" by 47", 164 cm. by 119.5 cm., c.1880. £180-200   SBel

A pair of Giltwood Wall Mirrors, a rectangular plate within a scrolling foliate frame, 35½" x 40"; 90 cm. x 102 cm., mid 19th c. £190-230   SBel

A Mahogany and Parcel-Gilt Sheraton Period Wall Mirror, having carved acanthus and floral decoration, 1'9" wide x 3'2" high; 52.5 cm. x 96 cm., £1,200-1,300 KC

A Georgian mahogany and gilt hanging mirror with swan neck broken pediment and shaped apron. 54" high; 137 cm. £800-900 DHBN

An Early George III Mahogany and Parcel Gilt Wall Mirror, extensively restored, 41" x 23½"; 104 cm. 60 cm. wide. £650-720 LC

A Pair of Gilt-Plaster and Mahogany Wall Mirrors, applied with a pierced rope-twist mount in the arch, 45"; 114.3 cm., late 19th century. £500-550 SBel

A George I Walnut and Parcel Gilt Wall Mirror 2'2" x 4'5"; 66 cm. x 135 cm. £1,200-1,500 LC

A George I Parcel-Gilt Walnut Mirror, the broken pediment centred by a cartouche, 4'10" high by 2'2" wide, 147 cm. by 66 cm., c.1720. £1,550-1,700 SBS

An Ebonised and Mother-of-Pearl inlaid Pier Mirror and Table the breakfront lower part with a grey veined marble top. 103½" x 44"; 263 x 111.8 cm. 1870's £150-250 SBel

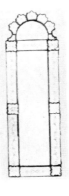

A Pair of Venetian Pier Mirrors, the lower part enclosing a bevel-glazed rectangular plate flanked by an etched floral frame, 84"; 213 cm., third quarter of 19th century. £1,200-1,400 SBel

A George II giltwood pier glass in the manner of John Vardy, 78¾" by 46", 200 by 112 cm. £1,200-1,350 CStJ

An early 20th century pair of Elephant Tusks supporting an oval oak framed Mirror, 37½" high; 95 cm. **£300-350** OL

A Walnut Dressing-Table Mirror, with pin-cushion with small drawer, 18", 46 cm., North Italian or Nicoise, c.1860. **£100-120** SBel

Satinwood veneered serpentine box mirror, 19", 47.5 cm. **£210-240** PG

Regency mahogany dressing mirror. **£35-45** HOA

Small Mahogany dressing mirror approx. 16" high; 40.5 cm. **£55-65** PG

A Giltwood Mirror, the top with a scrolling acanthus and shell cresting, 36"; 91.5 cm. circa 1880. **£100-150** SBel

A Queen Anne Black-Japanned Toilet Mirror, 1'5", 43 cm., wide, c.1710. **£850-950** SBS

Mahogany dressing mirror approx. 2'6" high; 76 cm. **£71-80** PG

Mahogany serpentine box mirror, 33½", 85 cm wide. **£95-105** PG

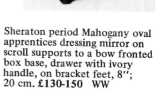

Sheraton period Mahogany oval apprentices dressing mirror on scroll supports to a bow fronted box base, drawer with ivory handle, on bracket feet, 8"; 20 cm. **£130-150** WW

Regency period faded rosewood tea caddy with gilt brass mounts, 11″, 28 cm. £46-56 WW

Chippendale period mahogany tea caddy, c.1760-70 £45-75

A George III satinwood octagonal Tea Caddy, crossbanded and strung borders, 14 cm. wide, 5½″, £150-180 PL

An early 19th C. veneered rosewood and boxwood line inlaid tea caddy, £100-120

A 19th C. painted satinwood Sheraton-design velvet lined box, £100-150 KC

A Regency tea caddy, 12½″, 32 cr £70-80 LC

Hepplewhite period octagonal shaped tea caddy in satinwood, £150-200

Burr yew tea caddy. c.1800. £85-95 LBA

A George III tortoiseshell polygonal Tea Caddy, strung and banded in ivory, 5″, 12.5 cm wide. £220-250 PL

Chippendale period mahogany and cross banded tea caddy. £70-100

A good Tunbridge ware Tea Caddy. 2 containers and mixing bowl, 14″, 35.5 cm. c.1845. £160-190 LC

A George III 'Pineapple' tea caddy in carved mahogany, 7½″ high, 19 cm., c.1800. £550-600 SBel

A Sheraton period mahogany tea caddy, 8″, 20 cm., £40-45 WW

A mid-19th C. tortoiseshell and silvered metal mounted small box, 18 cm. wide, 7⅛″, £105-155 KC

A George III mahogany octagonal Tea Caddy, strung with boxwood 5¾″, 14.5 cm. wide. £180-210 PL

A Victorian tortoiseshell and mother-of-pearl inlaid tea caddy, 32 cm. wide, 12½'', **£290-340** KC

A 19th century needle case. Mother-of-pearl and silvered metal. 5¼''; 13 cm. long. **£22-30** DHBN

Early 19th C. rectangular mahogany work box, (side handles missing), 10'', 25.5 cm. **£22-30** WW

An unusual 19th C. Antler sewing box, 14'' wide, 35.5 cm. **£260-290** KC

An English Mother-of-Pearl inlaid papier mache work box. 14'', 35 cm. wide, c.1840. **£180-280** SBel

Jewel Casket, with panels of glass, gilt-metal figures, swing handle, 19 cm. diam. 7½'', Continental, c.1880. **£450-520** SBel

A fine George III satinwood tea caddy, with two removable canisters, 8'' wide, 20.0 cm., **£320-400** HKC

A cast-iron Jewellery Casket, plaque stamped N. Strohmenger Kunstschlofserei Nurnberg, 12'' by 19'', 30 by 47 cm. lock mechanism, 17th C. style, casket mid-19th C. **£600-700** SBel

French rosewood inlaid pen box. **£28-34** TJC

Antique satinwood pen box. **£15-20** TJC

A late 18th C. German ivory and engraved gilt-metal bound casket, with ink bottle and pen tray, 7'' wide, 17.5 cm. **£800-900** KC

An apothecary's chest with bottles, English, early 19th C., 8'', 20 cm. **£260-280** SBel

A late Georgian mahogany medicine chest with accessories, 9'', 23 cm. **£200-220** LE

253

Georgian oak knife box. £20-25 PG

An early Victorian rosewood and mother-of-pearl inlaid writing box, 14¼", 36 cm. wide, £70-110　KC

A lacquered trinket box with musical movement, 14" wide, 35 cm. £10-15　RB

A George III mahogany square tantalus, with cut-glass decanters and 2 drinking glasses, 12" wide, 30.5 cm. £200-280　KC

A pair of George III mahogany and Kingwood banded knife boxes, 23 cm. wide, 9", £550-620　KC

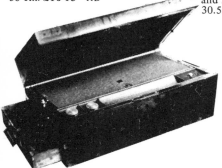

George IV mahogany brass bound writing desk with secret drawers. £100-120　HOA

18th C. apothecary's cabinet with scales, weights, etc. £300-340　HOA

A Victorian coromandel wood box by Baxter, 1856, maker's mark J.H., 8½" wide, 21.5 cm. £75-85　GC

A George III mahogany wedge shaped stationery box, 11" tapering to 8" wide, 28 cm. to 20 cm. £100-120　HKC

A lady's 19th C. walnut travelling dressing case, 12", 30.5 cm. £38-48　WW

A Victorian rosewood dressing case, complete with glass fittings and Sheffield plated lids, 12¾" wide, 32.5 cm. £135-160　HKC

A rosewoood vanity case, with silver-plated topped bottles and accessories, locks stamped Bramah Patent, 6¾", 16 cm. c.1860. £140-160　SBel

A lacquer box and cover, interior fitted with tray and set of tiered bowls, 10¼" x 6" x 4¾", 19th C. £380-440　KC

A cube form folding lacquered wood cabinet, with engraved bronze fittings, 19", 49 cm. Japanese, late 19th C. £850-950 LC

Small brass mounted, 3-sectioned oriental box. £28-32 MaH

19th C. inlaid box £32-40 TJC

A late George III Japanned box 7½" high by 12" wide, 19 cm. by 31 cm., c.1800. £600-700 SBS

18th C. candle box with pierced back plate. £65-75

A miniature lacquer and tortoise-shell cabinet, 18", 46 cm. wide. Japanese, mid 19th C. £400-440 LC

A Mitsumasa Shibayama and silver box of drawers, £1,050-1,150 SBel

18th Century Italian Ivory Box with painting inside the lid. £185-220 VM

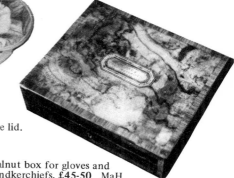

Walnut box for gloves and handkerchiefs. £45-50 MaH

A Komai box and hinged cover, the steel body damascened in gold, 3½", 9 cm., wide, inlaid seal mark, Japanese, early 20th C. £230-280 LC

17th C. oak bible box. £80-90 CAL

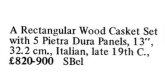

A Rectangular Wood Casket Set with 5 Pietra Dura Panels, 13", 32.2 cm., Italian, late 19th C., £820-900 SBel

19th century oval tortoiseshell mounted Jewel Box with silver hinged lid and lock. £115-140 AB

SILVER

Silver is one of the areas of collecting where a collector has slightly more certainty about authenticity of the pieces due to the highly efficient system of hallmarking. Hallmarks have been forged, frequently by grafting a genuine hallmark from a small, damaged piece onto a much larger and more valuable unmarked piece. The solder marks can often be detected by breathing on mark. There are now only 3 Assay Offices left in England: London, Birmingham and Sheffield.

Some dates of importance in study of silver:-

- 1660 restoration of Charles II — beginning of great era of domestic English silver
- c.1670 influence of acanthus leafage and fluted baroque
- 1685 The Revocation of the Edict of Nantes — brought Huguenot silversmiths to England
- 1697 introduction of Britannia standard. Lasted until 1720

- 1740's early signs of rococo
- 1750's revival of chinoiserie
- 1760's influence of neoclassicism.
- 1800-1820 tendency to add decoration to plainer style
- 1820's revival of rococo style
- By 1830's machines much in use
- 1880's Arts and Crafts movement — influence of Art Nouveau

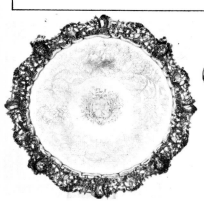

A George III salver, by Paul Storr, the base London 1804, the border and feet with additions marks, circa 1825. 21", 52.7 cm. diam. 118 oz. 18 dwt. **£2,600-2,900** SBS

A George III tray, by Crouch and Hannam, London 1792. 22", 56.0 cm. wide overall, 68 oz. 6 dwt. **£1,450-1,600** SBS

An early George III salver, 1763 by Richard Rugg. 11", 28.0 cm. 21 oz. **£380-440** LC

A George III circular salver, by Elizabeth Cooke, London 1772. 1½", 4.0 cm. diam. 35 oz. 2 dwt. **£620-700** SBS

A George IV salver, maker's mark M. & S., Glasgow 1825. 12", 30.5 cm. diam. 34 oz. 1 dwt. **£300-400** Sat HH

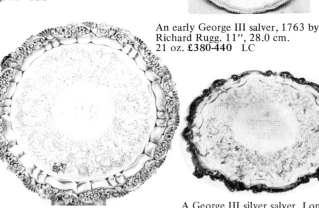

A George III silver salver, London 1819, 20½", 52.0 cm. diameter, 115 oz. **£1,000-1,200** KC

A Martin, Hall & Co. Ltd. shaped circular salver, makers' mark, London 1882, stamped: 1467, stamped: Wordley & Co./Liverpool'. 12½", 31.5 cm. diam. 25 oz. 18 dwt; 804 gm. **£260-290** SBel

A tea tray, 1912 by D. & J. Wellby. 30¼", 76.8 cm. 169 oz. **£500-560** LC

A tea tray, engraved with initials and dates, Sheffield 1908 by Martin, Hall & Co. 29", 74.0 cm. across handles, 160 oz. **£660-760** LC

A pair of George II salvers, by John Robinson, London 1747. 15¼", 38.7 cm. diameter, 94 oz. 11 dwt. **£900-1,000** SBS

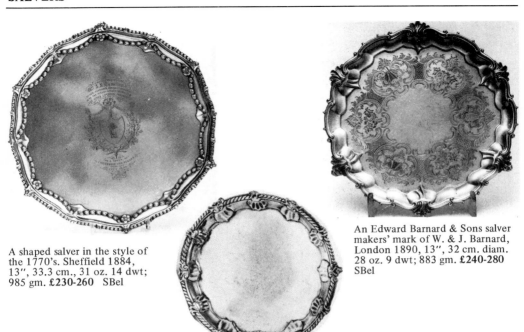

A shaped salver in the style of the 1770's. Sheffield 1884, 13″, 33.3 cm., 31 oz. 14 dwt; 985 gm. **£230-260** SBel

An Edward Barnard & Sons salver makers' mark of W. & J. Barnard, London 1890, 13″, 32 cm. diam. 28 oz. 9 dwt; 883 gm. **£240-280** SBel

An early George III circular silver salver, London 1760, probably by Ebenezer Coker. 7″, 17.5 cm. diam. 8½ oz. **£200-230** KC

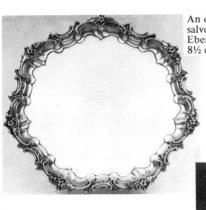

A shaped-circular salver, makers' mark ES/CS, London 1896, Stamped 'Mappin & Webb/London/ &/Sheffield'. 20″, 52.0 cm. diam. 95 oz. 8 dwt; 2,960 gm. **£550-650** SBel

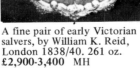

A fine pair of early Victorian salvers, by William K. Reid, London 1838/40. 261 oz. **£2,900-3,400** MH

A salver, makers' mark of E.B. & J. Barnard, London, 1852, stamped: 368. 15″, 38.0 cm. diameter, 40 oz. 8 dwt. 1,253 gm. **£280-330** SBel

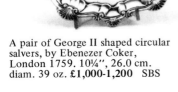

A pair of George II shaped circular salvers, by Ebenezer Coker, London 1759. 10¼″, 26.0 cm. diam. 39 oz. **£1,000-1,200** SBS

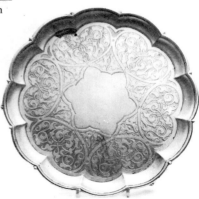

An Edward Barnard & Sons shaped circular salver, makers' mark of E. & J. Barnard, London 1864, 13″, 33.0 cm. diam. 30 oz. 17 dwt; 957 gm. **£200-240** SBel

A salver, London 1905. 7½", 19.0 cm. diameter, 10 oz. £90-110 AB

A Edwardian silver salver by Elkington & Co., Birmingham 1901, 100 oz., 20¼", 52 cm. diam., No. 17392. £640-700 OL

A James II Salver, 11½", 29 cm. diam., maker's mark R.L. London, 1685, 31 oz., 14 dwt. £3,200-3,500 SBS

An Atkin Brothers two-handled tea tray, makers' mark, Sheffield 1908. 28¾", 73.0 cm. over handles, 120 oz. 3,723 gm. £660-760 SBel

A George III Shaped Circular Salver, 12½", 32 cm., diam. by Elizabeth Cooke, London, 1763, 29 oz. £620-720 SBS

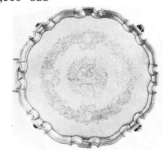

A George II salver with 'chippendale' border, London 1735. 15", 38.0 cm. diam. 56 oz. 5 dwt. £1,450-1,600 SBS

A D.& C. Houle oval tea tray, makers' mark, London 1872. 31", 79.0 cm. over handles, 170 oz. 5,276 gm. £1,250-1,500 SBel

A Pair of Early George II Waiters, 5¾", 14.5 cm., by Charles Hatfield, London, 1727, 16 oz. £1,150-1,250 SBS

A silver filigree and Shibayama tray with central gold lacquered ground panel, in inlaid hardstone, ivory and mother-of-pearl. late 19th C. 8¼", 21.0 cm. wide. £1,000-1,200 KC

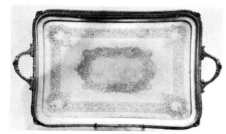

A Sibray, Hall & Co. tea tray, makers' mark, Sheffield 1896, engraved: 'Robt. Jones & Sons, Silversmiths, Liverpool'. 26½", 67.3 cm. 105 oz. 15 dwt; 3,282 gm. £580-680 SBel

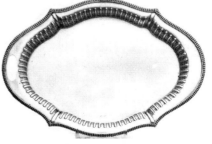

A Thomas Bradbury & Sons Ltd. makers' mark, Sheffield 1908, P.O.D.R. number: 442471. 25¾", 65.5 cm. across, 86 oz. 19 dwt; 2,698 gm. £420-500 SBel

A French serving dish, Paris c. 1860 maker's mark E.P. 13¼″, 33.5 cm. diam. 31 oz. **£140-170** LC

A pair of decorative dishes, maker's mark, London, 1883, stamped: 'Thomas/53 New Bond St'. 9½″, 24.0 cm. diam. 29 oz. 4 dwt; 905 gm. **£190-250** SBel

A pair of George II dishes, undersides with numbers and scratch weights, by Thomas Gilpin, London, 1758. 9½″, 24.0 cm. diam. 29 oz. 13 dwt. **£700-900** SBS

A fine early 18th C. alms dish by a Continental silversmith, Stamped with small Hallmark beneath the rim. 16¾″, 42.5 cm. diam. **£630-700** B

Two Victorian circular silver dishes, London 1890 and 1892, maker's mark JNM, also marked Mappin and Webb, Oxford Street. 10″, 25.5 cm. 28 oz. **£335-370** PWC

A pair of George II small dishes on three volute supports, by Paul Crespin, London, 1733. 6¼″, 16.0 cm. diam. 17 oz. 18 dwt. **£1,250-1,500** SBS

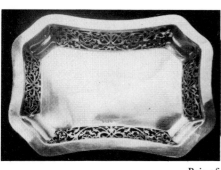

A pierced cake dish, Birmingham 1913. 13″, 33.1 cm. x 8″, 20.0 cm. 14 oz. **£50-60** AB

Pair of 18th C. scallop shell silver butter dishes, marked with Hibernia and crowned harp only. 9¾ oz. **£350-400** KC

A Martin, Hall & Co. Ltd. fruit Tazza, makers' mark, Sheffield, 1898, engraved: 'Cairns High St. Portsmouth'. 6″, 15.0 cm. high. **£200-250** SBel

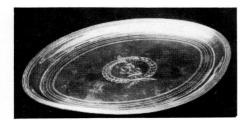

A Geroge III oval tea pot stand, London 1802, by P.A. & W. Bateman. 7″, 17.5 cm. x 5¼″, 13.0 cm. **£140-170** AB

An Atkin Brothers shaped circular cake stand, makers' mark, Sheffield, 1925. 11″, 28.0 cm. diam., 24 oz. 12 dwt., 763 gm. **£150-200** SBel

A Victorian Irish silver potato or dish ring, Dublin 1896, maker Wallace. 10″, 25.5 cm. 24 oz. **£350-450 PWC**

An Irish Dish Ring, Dublin, 1911, by Weir & Sons, 8″, 20.3 cm., blue glass liner, 12 oz. **£210-240 LC**

A pair of Dublin silver potato rings. Blue glass liners, fitted case, Dublin, 1910. 6¾ oz. **£200-240 KC**

A George III Circular Dish Ring, 8¼″, 21 cm., diam., by Joseph Jackson, Dublin, 1776, 13 oz. **£900-1.000 SIre**

A Pair of George III Silver-Gilt Tureens, Covers and Stands, stands 8½″, 21.5 cm. wide, by Wakelin and Garrard, London, 1800, 37 oz., 5 dwt. **£3,500-3,800 SBS**

A pair of entree dishes, covers and handles, makers' mark of S. Smith & W. Nicholson, London, 1857, some wear. 10¾″, 27.3 cm. wide, 81 oz. 9 dwt; 2,528 gm. **£600-700 SBel**

A pair of Hunt & Roskell entree dishes and covers, maker's mark of J.S. Hunt, London, 1862, 14″ 36.5 cm. 93 oz. 16 dwt., 2,911 gm **£1,050-1,200 SBel**

A pair of George III rectangular silver entree dishes, London 1805, probably by Thomas Robins, 8″, 22.0 cm. x 10½″, 26.5 cm. 103½ oz. **£1,500-1,800 KC**

A pair of Victorian oval entree dishes, 1884 by Martin, Hall & Co. and stamped 5762. 13″, 33.1 cm. across, 113 oz. **£1,050-1,200 LC**

A pair of George IV silver entree dishes, Dublin 1821, by James Le Bass. Total weight 126 oz., base size 8¼″, 21.0 cm. x 11″, 30.0 cm. **£1,350-1,500 KC**

A George III rectangular silver entree dish, London 1817 by Joshua Craddock and William Reid. size of base, 11″, 30.0 cm. x 9″, 23.0 cm. 64 oz. **£780-880 KC**

A Set of 4 George III Oval Entree Dishes and Covers, by Paul Storr, 12½″, 31.30 cm. wide, London, 1796, 141 oz., 18 dwt. **£2,500-2,700 SBS**

A Pair of George III Sauce Tureens and Covers, 9″, 23 cm. wide, by Wakelin and Taylor, London, 1782, 47 oz., 5 dwt. **£1,600-1,800 SBS**

A Pair of George III Boat-Shaped Sauce Tureens and Covers, 10¼″, 26 cm., by John Schofield, London, 1797, 37 oz., 16 dwt. **£1,900-2,100 SBS**

A George III oval soup tureen and cover, mark of Benjamin Laver struck over another on cover, London, 1799. 18″, 47.6 cm. wide, overall, 102 oz. 7 dwt. **£2,600-2,900 SBS**

A Pair of George III Boat-Shaped Sauce Tureens and Covers, 8″, 20 cm. wide, by F. Butty and N. Dumee, London, 1772, 49 oz., 14 dwt. **£1,200-1,400 SBS**

An early George III soup tureen and cover, marked on base and lid, by Frederick Kandler, London, 1761. 15″, 58 cm. wide overall, 100 oz. **£3,200-3,600** SBS

A Robert Hennell three-piece tea set. maker's mark, London, 1859. 54 oz. 19 dwt., 1,704 gm. (all in) **£700-780** SBel

A George IV three-piece silver tea service, the teapot London 1823, by William Bateman I, the basin and jug London 1820 by Crispin Fuller. total weight 48½ oz. **£175-215** KC

A Victorian three-piece tea set, maker's mark WRC; Edinburgh, 1845, 52 oz. 5 dwt (all in) **£450-550** Sat HH

A George III hemi-spherical three piece tea service. Maker WP, Edinburgh 1816, 42 oz. all in. **£550-620** HKC

A Victorian silver muffin dish, Edinburgh 1853, by J. McKay. 8½″, 21.5 cm. diam. 19 oz. **£135-155** KC

A three piece tea set, maker's mark WS, London, 1855. 34 oz. 18 dwt; 1,237 gm (all in) **£430-520** SBel

A George III tea set, by John Ziegler, Edinburgh. 4 pieces, 40 oz. 6 dwt (all in) **£480-580** Sat HH

A fine quality Victorian matching three-piece silver teaset, the teapot London 1839, makers Joseph and John Angell, the cream jug and sugar bowl London 1841, maker's mark WH. 45 oz. **£640-740** PWK

A three-piece tea set. Milk jug and sugar basin with gilt interiors, maker's mark of Robert Hennell, London, 1855, makers' mark of John Hunt & Robert Roskell, London, 1867, 45 oz., 12 dwt; 1,415 gm (all in). **£280-320** SBel

261

A matching four-piece tea and
coffee set, makers' mark of S.
Smith & W. Nicholson, London,
1861, London, 1918. 63 oz.
14 dwt. 1,977 gm. (all in) **£700-
800** SBel

A four piece tea and coffee set,
makers' mark WS/GS in a quatrefoil, London, 1871/72, 55 oz.
14 dwt; 1,728 gm. (all in) **£900-
1,200** SBel

A Joseph Rodgers & Sons Ltd.
four-piece tea and coffee set,
makers' mark, Sheffield, 1910/12,
stamped: 801. 74 oz. 12 dwt;
2,315 gm. (all in) **£600-700**
SBel

A Hayne & Cater four-piece tea
and coffee set, makers' mark,
London, 1843, 74 oz. 4 dwt;
2,302 gm. (all in) **£1,500-1,700**
SBel

A heavy quality four-piece silver
tea and coffee set, Sheffield
1918, maker's mark F. & F. 88 oz.
(all in) **£730-820** PWC

A Robert Hennell four-piece tea
and coffee set, maker's mark,
London, 1846. 81 oz., 16 dwt.
2,538 gm. (all in), erasures,
£1,050-1,200 SBel

A George III five-piece tea and
coffee set, by Solomon Hougham,
London, 1802/3, 57 oz., 2 dwt.
£1,200-1,400 SBS

A Victorian four piece tea and
coffee service. 1889 by Martin,
Hall & Co. and stamped 9558,
the coffee pot plated, with maker's
mark, 36 oz. of weighable silver.
£480-560 LC

William IV silver tea and coffee
service, engraved, London 1835,
by J. and J. Aldous, 69 oz.
£1,200-1,400 KC

A fine Georgian-style four piece
silver tea service, Sheffield 1931,
by John Deakin and Sons, gross
weight 64 oz. **£500-600** KC

An ornate four piece silver tea
service, Sheffield 1871, by
Walker and Hall, total gross weight
75 oz. **£700-800** KC

A silver three-piece tea set, 4½",
11.5 cm., stamped marks and
HM, c.1900. 37 oz. 941.91 gm.
£270-310 SBel

A Hayne & Cater three-piece tea
set, makers' mark, London,
1846, stamped respectively:
2646, 2923, and 2647, 46 oz.
1 dwt. 1,429 gm. (all in) £600-
700 SBel

A George III tea service, the tea
pot 1817 maker's mark rubbed,
the other two pieces 1817 by
Samuel Whitford II (G. 2663).
51 oz. £500-580 LC

A William IV three-piece tea set,
by Paul Storr, the teapot 7½",
19.0 cm. high, stamped Storr &
Mortimer, 372, London, 1836.
47 oz. 6 dwt. (all in) £1,300-1,600
SBS

A George III Oblong Teapot, Milk
Jug and Sugar Basin. 6", 15 cm.,
teapot marked by James Scott,
1818, Milk Jug and Sugar Basin
by Richard Sawyer, 1810, all
Dublin, 42 oz. £580-640 SIre

A Martin, Hall & Co. three-
piece tea set. makers' mark,
Sheffield, 1859, 49 oz. 16 dwt.
1,545 gm. (all in) £550-650 SBel

A Victorian silver teaset, London
1854, maker's mark IF. 51½ oz.
£640-720 PWC

A George III 3-piece Tea Set.
by James Le Bas, Dublin, 1816-
17, 35 oz. £750-850 SIre

A George III Irish Tea Service,
tea pot and milk jug, 1815,
maker's mark W.D. sugar basin
1810 by Richard Sawyer. 36 oz.
£380-440 LC

Three pieces from a Victorian tea
service. 1840-44 by Charles
Reily and George Storer. 62 oz.
£660-760 LC

A William IV four-piece tea and
coffee set, by John Wakefield,
London, 1834/35, 87 oz. 17 dwt.
(all in) £1,450-1,650 SBS

263

A George III Oval Teapot, by Hester Bateman, 5½", 14 cm., London, 1785, 13 oz., 1 dwt. **£600-670** SBS

A George III Argyle, by Hester Bateman, 4½", 11.5 cm., London, 1781, 9 oz., 5 dwt. **£1,200-1,300** SBS

A small Henry Wilkinson & Co. tea pot, Sheffield 1853, 6¼", 16 cm., 13 oz., 15 dwt., 427 gm. **£140-170** SBel

A William IV tea pot, by Paul Storr, London 1836, 4", 10 cm., 14 oz. **£500-600** SBS

A George II tea pot, by Thomas Whipham, London 1748. 5¾", 14.5 cm., 16 oz., 7 dwt. **£400-500** SBS

A George III tea pot, 1799 by William Allen III. 6¼", 16.0 cm., 18 oz. **£240-280** LC

A.J. & J. Angell tea pot. London 1841, 21 oz. 13 dwt., 671 gm. **£160-200** SBel

A Victorian silver teapot, engraved rococo scrolls and foliage, London 1847, maker Joseph Angell. 20½ oz, **£250-290** PWC

A William IV bachelor's tea pot, 1833 by Edward Barton. 5½", 14.3 cm. 13.2 oz. **£150-170** LC

A.J.J. Keith tea pot, London 1842, 6½", 16.5 cm., 24 oz., 15 dwt., 768 gm. **£230-260** SBel

An 18th C. tea pot, by Jan de Vries, Amsterdam, c.1735, 6", 15.4 cm. 9 oz. 5 dwt. **£520-590** SBS

A George II bachelor's tea pot, 1729 by John Chartier. 4¼", 10.6 cm. 12.5 oz. **£800-890** LC

A George IV circular tea pot by Philip Rundell, London, 1821. 7¼", 18.5 cm. 30 oz. **£400-500** SBS

A George I silver tea pot, marked London 1724, by Fras. Nelme. 11½ oz. **£1,750-2,000** KC

A Tea Pot and Coffee Pot, Birmingham 1842, 54 oz. **£640-700** LC

A Queen Anne silver tea pot by Gabriel Sleath, London 1713. 6¼", 16.0 cm. 16 oz. **£2,900-3,500** OL

A William IV silver teapot. London 1835, by Charles Fox II. 26 oz. **£560-660** KC

An Early Victorian Bachelor's Tea Pot, 1839, by John Tapley, 5", 13 cm., 16.7 oz. **£270-300** LC

A George III oval teapot, by John Younge & Co., Sheffield 1781. 5¼", 13 cm., 16 oz., 2 dwt. **£480-540** SBS

A George II coffee pot, by John Swift, London 1751. 13", 33 cm., 55 oz., 19 dwt., **£2,900-3,100** SBS

A.J. Smyth coffee pot, Dublin 1852. 27 oz., 7 dwt. **£320-350** SBel

A George II coffee pot, by Charles Sprage, London 1736. 9½", 24 cm., 26 oz., 19 dwt., (all in) **£950** SBS

A George II silver coffee pot, London 1731, by Richard Beale. 8", 20.5 cm. 15½ oz. **£700-800** KC

A plain coffee pot, Sheffield 1921. 20 oz. **£150-170** AB

A fine rare Channel Island coffee pot, 1740. 15", 38.1 cm. 34 oz. **£6,000-7,000** LJ

A plain urn design coffee pot, Chester 1921. 7", 17.5 cm., 10 oz. **£95-105** AB

A George II coffee pot, London 1736, by John Pero. 7¼", 18.5 cm. 15 oz. **£540-620** KC

An A.B. Savory & Sons coffee pot, London 1837. 9⅜", 23.7 cm., 27 oz., 838 gm. **£380-430** SBel

A George IV baluster coffee pot, by Michael Starkey, London 1823. 9½", 24 cm., 30 oz., 10 dwt. **£580-640** SBS

A George III coffee pot, London 1764, maker B.M. 26.5 oz. **£680-740** PK

A George III coffee jug, by Richard Gardner, London 1775, 11¼", 28.6 cm., 26 oz., 11 dwt. **£800-900** SBS

A George III Baluster Coffee Pot, 11½", 29 cm., by John Robins, London, 1788, 23 oz., 9 dwt. £750-850 SBS

An Italian Coffee Pot, 8¼", 20.8 cm., maker's mark I.P., Rome, c.1825, 13 oz., 5 dwt. £700-800 SBS

A George II chocolate pot, marked by Pentecost Symonds, Exeter, 1740. 8½", 21.5 cm., 20 oz., 8 dwt. £2,200-2,400 SBS

A George III Balsuter Coffee Pot, 11", 28 cm., maker's mark I.D. W.B. London, 1765, 33 oz., 2 dwt. £1,650-1,850 SBS

A George III Baluster Coffee Pot, 12½", 32 cm., by John Laughlin, of Dublin, c.1775, 31 oz., 10 dwt. £1,050-1,150 SIre

A Rare George III Baluster Chocolate Pot, 10", 25.5 cm., by Richard Williams, Dublin, c.1770, 36 oz. £2,600-2,800 SIre

A George III Baluster Coffee Pot, 11", 28 cm., maker's mark J.W. Dublin, c.1770, 28 oz., 10 dwt. £1,000-1,100 SIre

An early George III coffee pot, by William Grundy, London, 1762, 12", 30.5 cm., 31 oz., 6 dwt. £950-1,050 SBS

An Italian Coffee Pot, 9¾", 24.8 cm., Naples, c.1810, 17 oz., 14 dwt. £650-750 SBS

A miniature Maltese coffee pot, with domed lid and scrolled handle, by Mario Schembi, c.1800 2", 5 cm. £200-230 LJ

A Charles Fox II coffee pot, London 1839, 9½", 23.7 cm., 27 oz., 8 dwt., 850 gm. **£270-300** SBel

A George II baluster coffee pot, by Fuller White, London, 1758. 10½", 26.6 cm., 27 oz. 8 dwt. **£1,000-1,100** SBS

A George III coffee jug, by Paul Storr, London 1792. 10", 25.5 cm., 16 oz., 16 dwt. **£1,250-1,350** SBS

A William Smily coffee pot and sugar basin. 1857/59, 41 oz., 2 dwt., 1,275 gm. **£450-550** SBel

A George III coffee pot on lampstand, 1808 by Benjamin Smith II. 11¼", 28.7 cm. 45 oz. **£600-660** LC

A 'George III' style coffee pot on lampstand, 1925 by J. Parkes & Co. 11¼", 28.7 cm. 49 oz. **£450-520** LC

A George II silver coffee pot, London 1742, by Jonathon Fossy. 24 oz. **£900-1,000** KC

A George II silver coffee pot, London 1746, possibly by Shaw and Priest, 9", 23 cm. 21½ oz. **£820-1,000** KC

A George II coffee pot, by Thomas Whipham & Charles Wright, 1757. 30 oz. **£480-560** PK

A George III coffee jug on lampstand, with bruner, by Robert Garrard, London 1818/19. 11½", 29 cm., 38 oz., 11 dwt. **£750-850** SBS

A Persian silver coffee pot, late 19th C., 12½", 31.4 cm, and 23 oz., 8 dwt. **£150-190** SBel

A pair of coffee pots, mark of E. & J. Barnard, London 1864, 10½", 26.5 cm., 51 oz., 10 dwt., 1,598 gm. **£1,000-1,200** SBel

267

A George Edward & Son oval tea kettle on lampstand, with burner, engraved with a monogram and coronet, makers' mark Glasgow, 1902. 10¾", 27.3 cm., high, 44 oz. 5 dwt. 1,372 gm (all in) **£330-380** SBel

A George III spherical tea urn with detachable heater iron sleeve and domed lid, 17½", 44.25 gm. high, by George Ashworth & Co., Sheffield, 1802, 88 oz. 19 dwt. (all in) **£900-1,100** SBS

A tea urn, detachable burner, makers' mark of J. Aldwincle & T. Slater, London 1888, the burner engraved: 'Cairns. High Street, Portsmouth' 14", 35.5 cm., high 39 oz. 17 dwt; 1,236 gm (all in) **£700-800** SBel

A Victorian silver spirit kettle. Lower half of segmented design, the upper half ornately embossed. Hinged dome cover with national emblems finial and tongue and dart lip, base with embossed pierced frieze, Edinburgh 1837, by Robb and Whittet. Total weight 74 oz. **£890-990** KC

A fine George II Irish tea kettle on stand. Although marked on each piece a date letter is lacking. Dublin, c. 1740 maker's mark TI, a crown over, an original scratch weight on burner. 13¼", 33.5 cm., 68 oz, **£950-1,200** LC

A George II tea urn engraved with armorials, fully marked, by Smith & Sharp, London, 1763. 17½", 44.4 cm., high 86 oz. (all in) **£800-1,200** SBel

A George III tea urn, marked on body and lid by Benjamin Smith, London 1818. 16", 40.6 cm., high 135 oz. 10 dwt (all in) **£1,100-1,400** SBel

A George III tea urn with leaf chased tap, London 1771 by Charles Wright 80 oz. **£640-700** PK

A pair of fine George II Tea Caddies, 5", 12.5 cm., by Jerimiah King, London, 1752, 25 oz., **£1,700-1,900** HKC

A George III oval tea caddy, by Hester Bateman, London 1784, 5¾", 14.5 cm., 10 oz., 18 dwt. **£1,400-1,600** SBS

A George III vase-shaped tea urn 20½", 51.25 cm. high, marked, by Butty & Dumee, London, 1768. 99 oz. 16 dwt. (all in) **£1,250-1,500** SBS

A George III Tea Caddy, 5¼", 13 cm., by William and Aaron Lestourgeon, London, 1769, 14 oz., 15 dwt. **£1,400-1,600** SBS

A 19th C. Continental Silver Tea Caddy, London import mark 1895, 5½ oz., 3½", 9 cm., **£150-200** KC

An early 19th C. Dutch tea caddy, by Geradrus Hendrikus Nieuwenhuyzen, Leiden, 1804. 4½", 11.7 cm. high, 10 oz. 12 dwt. (all in) **£580-700** SBS

Three matching casters, by R. Peaston, 1762. 8", 19.5 cm. high, the pair by Samuel Wood, 1754, 6½", 16.5 cm. high, all London, marked 20 oz., 17 dwt. **£850-950** SBS

An early 18th C. caster, marked by Charles Adam, London, c.1720. 8¼", 21.0 cm. high, 12 oz. 4 dwt. **£500-580** SBS

A George II silver sugar caster. London, 1751, probably by Sam Wood. 4½", 11.5 cm. high, 2¼ oz. **£200-230** KC

A George I Caster and Dry Mustard Pot, 4½", 11.5 cm., by Starling Wilford, London 1722, 5 oz., 13 dwt. **£1,000-1,100** SBS

A George II octagonal caster, by James Ker, Assay Master Archibald Ure, Edinburgh, 1731. 9″, 22.0 cm. high, 15 oz. 13 dwt. **£900-1,100**   Sat HH

A pair of Queen Anne casters, by Charles Adam, London, 1713. 6¼″, 16.0 cm. high, 12 oz. 4 dwt. **£800-900**   SBS

A George II silver sugar caster. London 1735, maker: C.A. 6½″, 16.5 cm. 6½ oz. **£280-340**   KC

A set of three Queen Anne casters, marked by Charles Adam, London 1713. 7¼″, 18.5 cm. and 6″, 15.0 cm high, 16 oz. 10 dwt. **£1,900-2,100**   SBS

A set of three George III casters, marked by John Delmester, London, 1762. 6″, 15.0 cm. and 7½″, 19.0 cm. high, 18 oz. 8 dwt. **£750-820**   SBS

A George III Baluster Caster, 5¾″, 14.5 cm., by James Warner, Cork, c.1790, 3 oz. **£540-640**   SIre

Two William III 'Lighthouse' casters, maker's mark of David King struck over another, Dublin, 1693/5. 6¼″, 16.0 cm. and 5″, 12.5 cm. high, 11 oz. **£1,100-1,300**   SIre

A George I Vase Shaped Caster, 7¼″, 18.5 cm., Dublin, 1717, 9 oz. **£580-680**   SIre

A Charles Stuart Harris sugar caster in late 17th C. taste, Britannia standard, maker's mark, London 1889. 10½″, 26.3 cm. high 19 oz. 7 dwt; 600 gm. **£190-230** SBel

A George III plain pepper pot, London 1776 by T. Daniel. 5½", 14.0 cm. £95-115 AB

A George II plain pepper pot, London 1749, by Walter Brind. 4½", 11.5 cm. £120-140 AB

An E.H. Stockwell pug-dog pepperette, detachable head, maker's mark London 1877, 6¾", 7.0 cm. high, 3 oz. 6 dwt; 102 gm. £260-320 SBel

A J.B. Hennell cast pig pepperette with detachable head, maker's mark, London 1879. 3", 7.8 cm. long, 2 oz. 5 dwt; 70 gm. £200-240 SBel

A cast pig mustard pot, maker's mark JB, London 1881, with Mustard Spoon, makers' mark of E. Barnard & Sons Ltd., London 1970. 3", 7.8 cm. long, 3 oz. 7 dwt; 104 gm. £150-180 SBel

A C.T. & G. Fox pepperette, maker's mark of George Fox, London 1895. 4", 10.0 cm. long, 3 oz. 5 dwt; 101 gm. £220-250 SBel

A pair of Thomas Johnson pepperettes, maker's mark, London 1882. 3¾", 9.5 cm. long, 4 oz. 9 dwt; 138 gm. £260-300 SBel

A George I kitchen pepper, by John Hamilton, Dublin, 1715. 2½", 6.5 cm. high, 2 oz. 9 dwt; £330-370 SIre

A Victorian silver mustard pot, London 1844, by John Figg. 6 oz. £320-360 KC

A Mustard Pot, 3¾", 9.4 cm., maker's mark WE, London, 1865, and mustard ladle, London, 1846, 6 oz., 11 dwt., 203 gm. £90-110 SBel

A Maltese silver spice box in the form of a jug, de Rohan period. Probably by Francisco Cauchi marks crowned 'M' and crowned Mascle, 2", 5 cm. £250-270 LJ

A Maltese silver spice box in the form of vase and cover, with shell and foliate scroll engraving, mark M.A. under Maltese cross and crown, c.1800. 2", 5 cm. high. £250-270 LJ

271

A George III Cruet Frame by Paul Storr, 11½", 29 cm., fully marked, London, 1814, 31 oz., 1 dwt., **£950-1,100** SBS

A George III silver cruet stand. Sheffield 1806 by Alexander Goodman and Co. Base 5¼", 13.0 cm. 8¼", 21.0 cm. overall height 10", 25.5 cm. 17 oz. **£180-240** KC

A George III silver cruet set, dated London 1794, **£400-440** KC

A George IV silver cruet set with four bottles, London 1828, by John Wrangham and William Moutson; **£240-280** KC

A George III boat-shaped silver cruet stand, eight cut-glass bottles London 1788. overall length 15", 38.5 cm. height, 9½", 24.5 cm., 25 oz. **£460-510** KC

A George III silver cruet stand, four bottles, London 1809, two later mustard spoons. **£300-340** PWC

A George IV seven-bottle silver cruet stand, all silver parts fully marked London 1824, maker E. F. **£380-440** KC

A Georgian silver cruet set by London Silversmith Thomas Daniel. 7½", 19.0 cm. high, **£160-180** B

A George III silver egg cruet, frame and salt cellar hallmarked London 1798, maker's mark IT, the cups hallmarked London 1787, maker Robert Hennell. 12-oz. **£240-** PWC

A five-bottle Georgian silver cruet. marked with lion and made by Edmond Lowe, c.1770. **£400-460** KC

A George III wire sauce cruet frame, London 1761 by Francis Crumb, with six bottles. 5½", 14.0 cm. diam. **£155-175** AB

A pair of George III circular silver salts, London 1764. 4¾ oz. **£75-95** KC

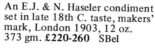

An E.J. & N. Haseler condiment set in late 18th C. taste, makers' mark, London 1903, 12 oz. 373 gm. **£220-260** SBel

A pair of George III salt cellars, by Benjamin Laver, London 1781. 3", 7.5 cm. diameter, 22 oz. 4 dwt. **£420-480** SBS

A Pair of George II Salt Cellars, 3¼", 8 cm. diam., by David Hennell, London, 1752, 13 oz., 6 dwt. **£650-730** SBS

A set of six silver trencher salts. made by Edward Wood, four London 1730 and two London 1727, size of each base, 3", 7.0 cm. x 2½", 6.0 cm. total weight 19 oz. **£800-900** KC

A George III silver salt cellar, London 1790, maker William Abdy. 2½ oz. **£86-96** PWC

A fine set of four George IV salt cellars by Joseph Wilson, 1822. 35 oz. 15 dwt. **£750-850** NN

Six matching George IV silver salts, all London hallmarked, four 1827, and two 1828, by William Eaton. 3¾", 9.5 cm. diam., total weight 37 oz. **£520-620** KC

A pair of George III salt cellars, by Paul Storr, London 1812. 4½", 11.5.cm. wide, 12 oz. 6 dwt. **£680-780** SBS

Four matching George III silver spool-shaped slats, London hallmarked by Thomas Robins, two dated 1805, the other two 1817. **£180-220** KC

A pair of late silver salts in Adam style with blue glass liners, made in London by Dobson and Sons, 1917. 21 oz. **£400-500** KC

A heavy Hunt & Roskell double salt cellar, maker's mark of John S. Hunt, London 1844, 6", 15 cm. long, 23 oz. 4 dwt; 720 gm **£380-460** SBel

A George I silver kitchen salt. Marked with lion passant, and grouped hallmarks London 1726 by William Darkeratt. 4", 10.0 cm. 3¼ oz. **£770-870** KC

A Chinese silver ewer, 1871.
12½", 32 cm. 30 oz. 16 dwt.
955 gm. **£600-700** SBel

A Scottish vase-shaped ewer, by
Robert Gray & Son, Glasgow 1841.
11", 28 cm. 36 oz. 2 dwt. **£440-500**
Sat HH

An Edward Barnard & Sons hot-
water ewer, London 1851, 12¼",
31.3 cm. 24 oz. 12 dwt. 763 gm.
£400-500 SBel

A William IV frosted glass ewer
with silver-gilt mounts, by Paul
Storr, London 1836. 8¾", 22.0
cm. **£3,200-3,600** SBS

A Victorian claret jug, Sheffield
1853 by Roberts and Slater.
13½", 34.6 cm., 29 oz. **£400-480**
LC

An Atkin Brothers silver-mounted
cut-glass claret jug, Sheffield
1892. 12", 30.4 cm. **£260-300**
SBel

A Tiffany baluster jug, 7",
17.5 cm. 25 oz. **£360-420** HKC

A George II silver jug, Newcastle
1732, by William Dalton, 4½",
11.5 cm., 12½ oz. **£430-500** KC

A Victorian Claret Jug, 1893 by
Edward Hutton, 12", 30.5 cm.,
£160-190 LC

A George III hot water jug, by
John Schofield, London 1785.
11'4", 30 cm. 24 oz. **£480-580**
SBS

A William Smily vase-shaped hot-water ewer, London 1857. 12″, 30.5 cm. 28 oz. 18 dwt. 896 gm. **£580-670** SBel

A William IV Baluster Jug, 10½″, 26.5 cm., by John Nicklin, Dublin, 1833, 40 oz., 14 dwt. **£820-900** SIre

A George III silver cream jug. Bead rim and double scroll handle London 1786, by Charles Haugham. 2¼ oz. **£80-110** KC

A Pair of Large Oval Sauce-Boats, 10″, 25.4 cm., maker's mark H.S., London, 1900, 40 oz., 3 dwt. **£340-400** SBel

A William IV Sauce Boat, 9¼″, 23.5 cm., by Charles Fox, London, 1830, 20 oz., 16 dwt. **£460-560** SBS

A Pair of George III Oval Sauce Boats, 6¾″, 17 cm., by William Skeen, London, 1769, 20 oz., 12 dwt. **£800-900** SBS

A pair of George III silver sauce-boats. London, c.1800. maker's mark unclear. 9¼ oz. **£500-580** KC

A Pair of George III Shell-Shaped Sauce Boats, 8″, 20 cm., by John Craig, Dublin, 1771, 37 oz., 10 dwt. **£2,500-2,700** SIre

A Goldsmiths & Silversmiths Co. Ltd. rose bowl, makers' mark, London, 1909. 10 1/8″, 46.0 cm. 105 oz. 18 dwt. 3,282 gm. **£850-950** SBel

A Latino Movio rose bowl, makers' mark of W. Walker & B. Tolhurst of Johnson, Walker & Tolhurst, 1904, 10″, 25.5 cm. high, 75 oz. 19 dwt; 2,357 gm. **£850-950** SBel

A Fenton Brothers rose bowl, makers' mark Sheffield, 1890, erasure. 15″, 38.0 cm. 36 oz. 18 dwt; 1,145 gm. **£340-380** SBel

A rose bowl, makers' mark apparently that of Slater, Holland & Slater of Holland, Aldwincle & Slater, London, 1899. 13 5/8″, 34.5 cm. 35 oz. 9 dwt; 1,100 gm. **£380-460** SBel

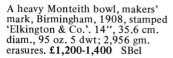

A heavy Monteith bowl, makers' mark, Birmingham, 1908, stamped 'Elkington & Co.'. 14″, 35.6 cm. diam., 95 oz. 5 dwt; 2,956 gm. erasures. **£1,200-1,400** SBel

An unmarked silver bowl, plain interior, late 19th C. 14 1/8″, 36 cm. diam. **£550-600** KC

A George III Circular Bowl, 7″, 17.5 cm., by John Laughlin, Dublin, c.1750, 18 oz., **£950-1,050** SIre

A Maltese sugar bowl and cover, c.1785 maker's mark of Guiseppe Cousin (Warrent 1770). 5½″, 14.0 cm. high, 7.6 oz. **£295-350** LC

A Victorian embossed sugar bowl and tongs in case, London 1833/1835. **£46-60** AB

A pair of ornate Victorian silver bowls, London, 1899. 7″, 17.5 cm. diam., 4¾″, 12.0 cm. high, the pair 23 oz. **£200-240** KC

A William Comyns rose bowl and two fruit dishes, maker's mark, London, 1903/04, the bowl P.O.D.R. number 430118. 13½″, 34.5 cm. and 8″, 20.5 cm. diam. respectively, 86 oz. 1 dwt; 2,670 gm. **£380-450** SBel

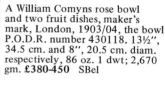

A William IV Sweetmeat Bowl, 4½″, 11.5 cm., by E.E. J. & W. Barnard, London, 1831, 16 oz., 13 dwt. **£400-460** SBS

A fine bowl and cover inscribed, 'St. David Exon, 1717', Exeter 1718, by Ed. Richards. 5¼″, 13.0 cm. diam. 13 oz. 10 dwt. **£1,850-2,000** LJ

A replica of the Warwick vase, makers' mark, Sheffield, 1881, stamped: 'Thomas Bradbury & Sons/Arundel St./Sheffield'. 10¾″, 27.5 cm. high, 138 oz. 10 dwt. 4,098 gm. **£820-920** SBel

A posy vase, maker's mark JB, London 1884. 4¼″, 10.8 cm. long, 12 oz. 10 dwt; 388 gm. **£65-75** SBel

An enamelled silver and gold-inlaid vase. c.1900. 15″, 38.0 cm. **£430-510** KC

A Dutch Brandy Bowl, cast 9¾″, 24.5 cm., wide, possibly by Wieger Cornelis Schreuder, Sneek, 1732, 7 oz., 15 dwt., **£1,000-1,100** SBS

A pair of George III silver-gilt sugar vases and covers, by Paul Storr, London, 1816. 8¼", 21.0 cm. high, 61 oz. 7 dwt. **£4,000-4,500 SBS**

A George III Ice Bucket, 4½", 11.5 cm., by Robert Sharp, London, 1794, 21 oz., 12 dwt. **£950-1,100 SBS**

A pair of George IV wine coolers, fully marked, by Matthew Boulton, Birmingham, 1829. 10½", 26.5 cm. high, 184 oz. 8 dwt. **£2,800-3,100 SBS**

Oval cake basket, London 1756, makers' Edward Aldridge & John Stamper. 12½", 31.7 cm. wide, 27 oz. **£600-700 LJ**

A George III sugar basket, by Robert Breading, Dublin 1784. 5¾", 14.5 cm. high, 8 oz. 10 dwt. **£280-320 SIre**

A cast cake basket with handle, London 1755, by Edward Aldridge and John Stamper. 15", 38.1 cm. long 62 oz. **£2,200-2,500 LJ**

A Manoah Rhodes & Sons Ltd. fruit bowl, maker's mark, London 1926, P.O.D.R. number: 700773. 10¾", 27.0 cm. diam., 36 oz. 2 dwt; 1,120 gm. **£260-300 SBel**

A George III sugar basin, by Joseph Jackson, Dublin 1782. 4¾", 12.0 cm. diam., 5 oz. **£200-250 SIre**

A George II sugar basket, 1786 by Robert Hennell. 6 oz. **£310-400 PK**

A Goldsmiths & Silversmiths Co. Ltd. fruit basket, makers' mark, London, 1899. 12¾", 32.5 cm. across, 21 oz. 18 dwt; 679 gm. **£200-240 SBel**

A Victorian rectangular silver dessert basket, London 1894. 14", 35.6 cm. diam. 26½ oz. **£270-330 PWC**

A Robert Harper cake basket, maker's mark, London 1873, stamped: 7877. 9⅝", 24.5 cm. diam. 39 oz., 1,210 gm. **£340-400** SBel

A George IV cake basket, by Kirkby Waterhouse & Co., Sheffield 1821. 13½", 34.3 cm. wide, 38 oz. 12 dwt. **£520-600** SBS

A George III cake basket, by Richard Morton & Co., Sheffield, 1777. 12½", 31.7 cm. wide, 23 oz 8 dwt. **£600-700** SBS

A cake basket, with swing handle, makers' mark of E. & J. Barnard, London 1860. 13⅛", 33.3 cm. diam., 38 oz. 10 dwt; 1,195 gm **£400-480** SBel

A fine set of two silver tazzas, and cake basket, with swing handle. London 1926, maker S.G. for Garrard and Co. Ltd. Total weight 61½ oz. dia. of tazzas 8⅞", 22.5 cm., dia of basket 26 cm. **£520-600** KC

A cake basket makers' mark of E., E., J. & W. Barnard, London, 1841, minor repairs to piercing 13⅜", 34 cm. diam., 38 oz. 6 dwt; 1,189 gm. **£320-400** SBel

A Henry Wilkinson & Co. makers' mark, Sheffield, 1845. 10¾", 27.5 cm. diam. 23 oz. 714 gm. **£320-400** SBel

An oval cake basket pierced, makers' mark HEB/FEB Chester, 1911. 13¼", 33.8 cm. long. 22 oz. 10 dwt; 698 gm **£160-200** SBel

An early George III cake basket, by William Plummer, London, c.1768. 14¾", 37.5 cm. wide, 36 oz., 18 dwt. **£1,300-1,450** SBS

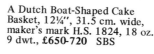

A Dutch Boat-Shaped Cake Basket, 12¼″, 31.5 cm. wide, maker's mark H.S. 1824, 18 oz. 9 dwt., £650-720 SBS

A Pair of Danish Baskets, 12½″, 31.8 cm. wide, by Frederik Moritz Klos, Copenhagen, 1812, 38 oz., 5 dwt. £850-950 SBS

A George II sweetmeat basket, by Hester Bateman, London 1784. 5½″, 14.0 cm., diam. 5 oz. £260-300 SBel

A George III Oblong Sweetmeat Basket, 6″, 15 cm., by William Abdy, London, 1798, 8 oz., 19 dwt. £480-560 SBS

A George III Boat-Shaped Sweetmeat Basket, 7″, 17.5 cm. wide, maker's mark G. & P.W., Dublin, 1800, 8 oz., 4 dwt. £240-280 SIre

An Early Victorian Circular Cake Basket, 1840 by Messrs. Barnard, 13″, 33 cm., across, 34 oz. £475-575 LC

A George IV Shaped Oval Cake Basket, 13¾″, 35 cm., probably by James Fray, Dublin, 1824, 50 oz. £580-640 SIre

A Goldsmiths and Silversmiths Co. Ltd. sugar basket, makers' mark, London, 1902. 5½″, 13.9 cm. 10 oz. 8 dwt. 322 gm. £140-170 SBel

An Elizabeth I provincial chalice, probably by Erasmus Coke of Bury St. Edmonds, c.1580. 6″, 15.0 cm. 6 oz. 14 dwt. £900-1,100 SBS

A Charles I wine cup, maker's mark R.S. London 1628. 7″, 17.5 cm. high, 10 oz. 13 dwt. £1,350-1,550 SBS

A Victorian coco-nut cup, 1848 by Charles T. and George Fox. 6″, 15.2 cm. high, £190-250 LC

A bell-shaped cup, maker's mark of John S. Hunt, London 1861, 4¾″, 12.0 cm. high, 5 oz. 155 gm. £190-250 SBel

A plain trophy cup, Birmingham
1922. 7″, 17.5 cm. high, £44-55
AB

A rare William and Mary cup and
cover, by James Penman, Assay
Master John Borthwick, Edinburgh
1693. 7¾″, 19.5 cm. high, 28 oz.
14 dwt. £2,500-3,500   Sat HH

A George I Cup and Cover, 8¾″,
22 cm., by George Boothby,
London, 1722, 29 oz., 6 dwt.
£600-660   SBS

A Suite of 3 George III Covered
Cups, 15½″ & 9½″, 38 cm. &
24 cm. high, by Joseph Jackson,
Dublin, 1787, 89 oz. £1,050-
1,150   SIre

A Pair of George III 2 Handled
Cups, engraved, 5½″, 14 cm.,
by Matthew West, Dublin, 1782,
27 oz., 10 dwt. £360-400   SIre

A Queen Anne silver-gilt cup and
cover, marked by Benjamin
Pyne, London 1702. 13″, 33.0 cm.
high 86 oz. £4,000-5,000   SBS

An Early Charles II Caudle Cup
and Cover, 4¾″, 12 cm., maker's
mark P.D., London, 1663, 11 oz.,
12 dwt. £2,700-2,900   SBS

A George Angell cup and cover,
maker's mark, London 1867.
15¾″, 40.0 cm. 67 oz. 7 dwt.
2,090 gm. £620-720   SBel

A Guild of Handicrafts Ltd.
silver and enamel cup. makers'
mark, London 1901. 7″, 17.5 cm.
£500-800   SBel

A George III Goblet, 1813 by
Samuel Hennell, 6¾″, 17 cm.,
10.9 oz. £200-240   LC

A Medieval pattern squat goblet,
Chester 1902. 4″, 10.0 cm.
£56-80   AB

An Elizabeth I Chalice and Paten, 1574, 8½", 21.5 cm., mark I.F. (Jasper Fysher?), London, 1570, 12 oz., 16 dwt. **£2,400-2,600** SBS

A pair of silver stemmed cups, makers' mark, Chester 1905. 7", 17.5 cm. **£220-250** SBel

A George II cup, by Robert Calderwood, Dublin, c.1752. 4¾", 12.0 cm. high, 14 oz. **£270-350** SIre

An octagonal punch set complete, each with glass liners. 39 oz. **£400-450** HKC

A pair of George III wine cups, by Solomon Hougham, London 1800. 8½", 21.5 cm. high, 25 oz 15 dwt. **£480-570** SBS

A large Martin, Hall & Co. Ltd. presentation bowl, makers' mark, Sheffield, 1910. 22", 56 cm., 121 oz. 3,754 gm. **£580-680** SBel

A George II 2-handled silver cup. Dublin, c.1736 by John Wilme. 7¾", 19.5 cm. high, 5¾", 14.5 cm. diam. 38 oz. **£420-500** KC

A Silver Standing Cup and Cover, signed Omar Ramsden & Alwyn C.E. Carr, 10", 25.5 cm., London, 1905. **£500-560** SBel

A presentation cup, Birmingham 1922. 7", 17.5 cm. 15 oz. **£40-50** AB

An R. & S. Garrard & Co, presentation cup, London 1865, 11½", 29.3 cm. 24 oz. 8 dwt. 446 gm. **£400-500** SBel

An Edward Barnard & Sons presentation cup, London 1873, scratched. 10½", 26.4 cm. 30 oz. 13 dwt. 1,216 gm. **£550-600** SBel

An R. & S. Garrard & Co. presentation cup, London 1864, 9¾", 24.8 cm. 20 oz. 17 dwt. 647 gm. **£350-400** SBel

A Charles II Mug, 4″, 10 cm., by Jonah Kirk, London, 1683, 9 oz., 8 dwt. **£600-660** SBS

A William and Mary Baluster Mug, 3¼″, 8 cm., maker's mark I.C., London, 1691, 4 oz., 18 dwt. **£650-730** SBS

A William IV fluted mug, London 1830. **£80-100** AB

A rare pair of Queen Anne thistle-shaped mugs, by George Scott, Jr., Assay Master James Penman, Edinburgh 1703. 3¼″, 8.0 cm. high, 10 oz. 1 dwt. **£3,500-4,500** Sat HH

A Queen Anne thistle-shaped mug, maker's mark 'R', Assay Master James Penman, Edinburgh 1703. 2¾″, 7.0 cm. high, 4 oz. 2 dwt. **£450-550** Sat HH

A North American christening mug, by Gale and Willis, New York, c.1840. 3½″, 9.0 cm. 5.9 oz. **£100-160** LC

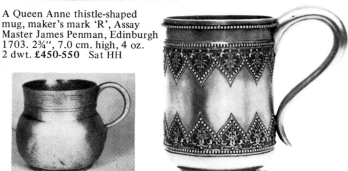

An early George III silver mug, London 1762, By William Cafe. 13 oz. **£380-440** KC

A late 17th C. provincial mug, dated 1685. Maker's mark of Lionel Girling. 3½″, 8.9 cm. high, 6.9 oz. **£820-930** LC

A Henry Holland & Son mug, London 1871. 5¾″, 14.7 cm. high 12 oz. 13 dwt. 393 gm. **£200-240** SBel

A Victorian silver christening mug, London 1848. **£165-200** 7½ oz. KC

A George I silver mug. London 1721, by Hugh Arnett and Edward Pocock, 4″, 10.0 cm. 5½ oz. **£195-265** KC

A George III silver mug. Newcastle 1769, by John Langlands. **£290.** 4½″, 11.5 cm. high, 9 oz. **£310-350** KC

A George II silver mug, London 1752, by Robert Albin Cox. £160. 3¾", 9.75 cm. 7½ oz. **£160-190** KC

A George III silver tankard, London 1762, probably by W. and R. Peaston. 5", 12.5 cm. high, 11½ oz. **£280-360** KC

A George III silver tankard, London 1766, probably by Joshua Bell. 5¼", 13.0 cm. 12½ oz. **£220-290** KC

A Norwegian Tankard, engraved date 1752, 9½", 24.2 cm., maker's mark C.H., 38 oz., 3 dwt. **£2,900-3,100** SBS

A Charles II Tankard, 6½", 16.5 cm., by Marmaduke Best, York, 1664, 24 oz., 19 dwt. **£4,200-4,600** SBS

A Large Charles II Tankard, 8¾", 22 cm., by Thomas Jenkins, London, 1671, 45 oz. **£7,000-9,000** SBS

A George III cylindrical tankard, by Hester Bateman, London 1790. 8¼", 21.0 cm. high 25 oz. 18 dwt **£1,300-1,500** SBS

A Victorian 10¼", 26 cm., silver inkstand, silver taper holder and two silver topped cut glass receivers, Sheffield 1893 and Birmingham 1893, 14¾ oz. of weighable silver. **£200-230** PWC

A rare 19th C. oval silver inkstand, bearing the crown of the Sheffield assay office, inscribed 'PDP to HP Nov. 1867'. 8", 20.0 cm. wide, 26½ oz. **£600-700** PWC

A George IV silver inkstand, hallmarked London 1822, maker S.R. 5¼", 13.0 cm. overall length, 5 oz. **£300-350** KC

A Victorian silver inkstand, Birmingham 1837, by Robinson, Edkins and Aston, 13", 33.0 cm. x 9", 23.0 cm. 28 oz. **£300-350** KC

A George III oval inkstand, by Burrage Davenport, 1772, 3 oz. **£270-330** PK

A Georgian-style silver inkstand. London 1909, maker: C.S. and H.S. 14", 35.6 cm. x 9¾", 24.5 cm. 60 oz. **£520-600** KC

An Edward Barnard & Sons two-bottle inkstand, and a central detachable taperstick, makers' mark, London, 1847, 14", 34.5 cm. long, 27 oz. 16 dwt; 862 gm. £280-360 SBel

A George II inkstand, marked on base and holders, by Samuel Herbert & Co., London, 1758. 9¾", 24.5 cm. wide, 20 oz. 8 dwt. £520-620 SBS

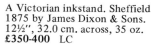

A Victorian inkstand. Sheffield 1875 by James Dixon & Sons. 12½", 32.0 cm. across, 35 oz. £350-400 LC

A George III Globe Inkstand, 2 glass silver-mounted wells, a pen and tablet, 6½", 16.5 cm., by John Robins, London, 1792, 7 oz., 10 dwt. £1,100-1,200 SBS

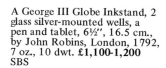

Inkstand with pair of bottles, Sheffield, 1910. 10", 25.5 cm. x 4", 10.0 cm. £70-80 AB

A Victorian inkwell, gilt interior, maker's mark J.A., Edinburgh, 1897, 3½", 9.0 cm. high, 9 oz. 18 dwt; (all in) £320-400 Sat HH

A George II silver-gilt inkstand, fully marked, by Eliza Godfrey, London, 1741. 13½", 34.3 cm. wide, 46 oz. 10 dwt. £5,500-6,200 SBS

A George IV inkstand by Paul Storr, inkwell dated 18 Sept. 1832, London 1829. 9", 23.0 cm. wide, 16 oz. 10 dwt. £1,250-1,500 SBS

A Victorian oval inkstand, one glass bottle missing, 1845 by Edward Barnard & Sons. 10½", 26.7 cm. 15.8 oz. £240-280 LC

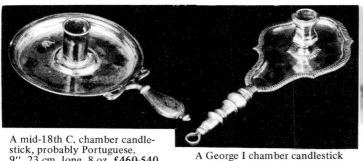

A mid-18th C. chamber candle-stick, probably Portuguese. 9'', 23 cm. long. 8 oz. **£460-540** HKC

A George I chamber candlestick by John Cafe, London 1746. 5¾'', 14.5 cm. 6 oz. **£580-680** HKC

A William IV silver chamber candlestick with extinguisher, London 1832, maker Joseph Angell. 5¼ oz. **£260-300**   PWC

A Pair of plain chamber sticks and snuffers with vase shaped candle holders, London, 1803, W. Bayley, 23 ozs. **£700-800**   LJ

A Henry Wilkinson & Co. taper-stick, Sheffield 1838, loaded. 5½'', 14 cm. **£180-240**   SBel

A pair of George III chamber candlesticks, maker's mark W.S., 1814, 2 pairs of Snuffers, by Wilkes and John Booth, 1810, all London. 6½'', 16.5 cm. wide. 40 oz. 14 dwt. **£1,600-1,900** SBS

A George III silver chamber-stick, London 1787, by Hester Bateman. 6'', 15 cm. diam. **£260-330**   KC

A set of 4 chamber candlesticks with snuffers, maker's mark of J.S. Hunt, London 1853-56, 6½'', 16.7 cm. 58 oz. 12 dwt. q,818 gm. **£1,400-1,818**   SBel

2 George II Tapersticks, 4¼'', 10.5 cm., by William Gould, London, 1733-4, 9 oz., 15 dwt. **£1,350-1,550** SBS

An Unusual George Ivory and silver Taperstick, 3¼'', 7.9 cm., maker's mark, London, 1850, 3 oz., 13 dwt., 113 gm. **£280-340**   SBel

A pair of George III chamber candlesticks with extinguishers. By Thomas Hannam and John Crouch, London 1774. 5½'', 14 cm. diam. 16 oz. **£700-800** HKC

285

A pair of Georgian-style silver candlesticks, Sheffield 1901. 11½″, 29.0 cm. **£260-300** KC

A set of four George III candlesticks, Sheffield 1774 by John Winter & Co., loaded. 11¾″, 30.0 cm. **£680-780** LC

A pair of cast silver candlesticks, c.1750 by Guillaume Henry of Guernsey. 8¾″, 22.0 cm. **£2,600-3,400** LJ

A large pair of table candlesticks in George II style, 1 nozzle damaged by William Hutton & Sons Ltd., Sheffield 1904 (loaded) 12″, 30.5 cm. **£250-350** Sat HH

A set of 4 C.S. Harris table candlesticks, London 1884-85, loaded. 5″, 12.5 cm. **£390-470** SBel

An unusual set of 4 silver table candlesticks in late 17th C. style, London 1913, maker's mark HL. 12″, 30.5 cm. 69 oz. **£860-960** PWC

A set of 4 Adam-style silver candlesticks, Sheffield, two 1901 and two 1902. 9¼″, 23.5 cm. **£600-700** KC

A pair of William and Mary table candlesticks, by Pierre Harache, London 1692. 2 later nozzles 8″, 20.0 cm. high, 41 oz. 11 dwt. **£3,400-4,000** SBS

A pair of George II Table Candlesticks, 9½″, by Ralph Beilby, Newcastle 1757, 46 oz., 8 dwt. **£2,000-2,500** SBS

A pair of William IV silver candlesticks, Sheffield 1836, by Henry Wilkinson and Co. 9″, 23.0 cm. **£400-450** KC

A set of 4 Hawksworth, Eyre & Co. Ltd. table candlesticks, makers' mark, Sheffield 1898-99, loaded. 10¼″, 26.0 cm. **£680-780** SBS

A William IV silver chamber candlestick Sheffield 1837, maker's mark HW & Co. 4½ oz. **£85-100** PWC

A fine set of 4 Victorian silver candlesticks. Sheffield 1898 by Martin Hall and Co. Ltd. 12¼″, 31.0 cm. **£1,700-2,000** KC

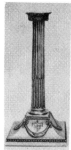

A Pair of George III Table Candlesticks, Sheffield 1775, John Young & Sons, 11½", 29 cm. £1,400-1,600 LC

A Pair of George II Table Candlesticks, 8", 20 cm., by John Cafe, London, 1754, 31 oz., 6 dwt. £1,200-1,400 SBS

A Pair of George II Cast Table Candlesticks, 1759 by Arthur Annesley, 10¼", 25.9 cm., 42 oz. £1,000-1,100 LC

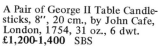

A Set of 4 Late Georgian Candlesticks, Sheffield 1819 and 1822, by John and Thomas Settle, 6¾", 17.2 cm. £780-880 LC

A Pair of George II Figure Candlesticks. 14", 35.5 cm., by James Scott, Dublin, 1803, 1814, 56 oz. £2,600-2,800 SIre

A pair of Victorian silver table candlesticks, London 1892-3, maker's mark HW & Co., loaded bases. 11½", 29.0 cm. £400-500 PWC

A Good Set of 4 George II Irish Table Candlesticks, 9¾", 24.5 cm. by William Townsend, Dublin, c.1759, 83 oz. £3,000-3,300 SIre

A pair of 18th C. Austrian table candlesticks, Vienna, apparently 1792. 6¾", 17.5 cm. 19 oz. £750-850 SBS

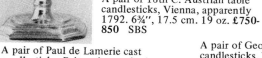

A pair of Paul de Lamerie cast candlesticks, Britannia standard, London 1719. 6¼", 16.0 cm. 25 oz. £6,600-7,600 LJ

A pair of George II cast table candlesticks, by John Cafe, 1756, 10", 25.5 cm. 41 oz. £800-900 NN

A pair of Edwardian candlesticks, Sheffield 1901 by T.A.S. 10", 25.5 cm. £300-380 AB

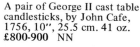

A pair of Henry Wilkinson & Co. table candlesticks in George II style, Sheffield 1843, loaded. 9", 23.0 cm. £370-450 SBel

A pair of George II table candlesticks, by Thomas Heming, London 1748. 8¾", 22.0 cm. 39 oz. 10 dwt. £1,750-2,000 SBS

A pair of George II cast table candlesticks by John Cafe, 1758. 10", 25.5 cm. 40 oz. £680-780 NN

287

A set of William IV silver table candlesticks. **£1,250-1,450** RBB

A George II silver taperstick, London 1750, makers William Shaw and William Priest. 4½", 11.5 cm. 3¾ oz. **£320-370** PWC

A pair of Walter Latham & Son 2-light candelabra, makers' mark, Sheffield 1907, loaded, 16½", 42.0 cm. **£440-520** SBel

A pair of Victorian 3-light candelabra, by S. Roberts & Co., Sheffield 1837 (loaded). 24", 61.0 cm. high. **£2,400-2,700** SBS

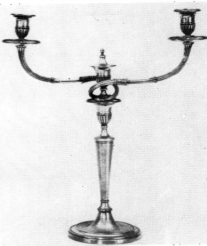

A pair of George III 2-light candelabra, marked W. Fountain and D. Pontifex, London, 1788-91. 17½", 44.4 cm. 87 oz. 4 dwt. **£3,200-3,500** SBS

A pair of Hawksworth, Eyre & Co. Ltd. 3-light candelabra, makers' mark, Sheffield 1865-1876, loaded. 17½", 44.5 cm. **£900-1,100** SBel

A William IV candelabrum, for 6 or 7 lights, marked by E., E., J. & W. Barnard, London 1834, 7th nozzle by Paul Storr, 1835. 26¾", 68.0 cm. 174 oz. 7 dwt. **£2,200-2,500** SBS

A pair of William Moulson 3-light candelabra, maker's mark, London 1852. 20¼", 51.0 cm. 65 oz. 18 dwt. 2,054 gm (of weighable silver) **£1,500-1,700** SBel

Georgian silver wine label 'Sherry' London 1802. **£30-40** PG

Silver Georgian wine label 'Gin' Birmingham 1837. **£30-40** PG

Silver gilt Georgian wine label 'Brandy'. **£40-50** PG

Georgian silver wine funnel 2½ ozs. c.1808. **£196-230** PG

3 George III Wine Coasters, 1793 by Michael Plummer, 5", 13.2 cm. diam, loaded. **£775-875** LC

A William IV Wine Funnel and Filter, London 1833, by W. Bellchambers, 7¼ oz., 6″, 15 cm. high **£220-250** KC

A George IV Silver Wine Funnel, four narrow flutes to funnel, filter with gadroon trim and shell hook, London 1824, by Rebecca Emes and Edward Barnard I, 6 oz., height 6″, 15 cm. **£180-240** KC

Wine Funnel (marks rubbed) on 3¾″, 9.5 cm. stand, London 1793 by Henry Chawner **£46-60** AB

Pair of silver wine labels (Madeira) London 1826. **£60-80** PG

A pair of George IV wine coasters, by S.C. Younge, & Co., Sheffield, 1828/9. 7″, 17.5 cm. diam. **£650-750** SBS

A set of four George III silver-gilt wine coasters, by Digby Scott and Benjamin Smith, London, 1804/5/6, with the Latin signature of Rundell, Bridge and Rundell. 5½″, 14.0 cm. diam. **£5,000-6,000** SBS

A Pair of William IV Coasters, 5½″, 14 cm. diam. by Edward Farrell, London, 1835. **£600-660** SBS

A William IV Silver-Gilt Snuff Box, 4¾″, 12 cm. wide, by A.J. Strachan, London, 1830. **£700-800** SBS

A pair of George III wine coasters, by Robert Hennell, London, 1793. 4½″, 11.5 cm. diameter. **£720-800** SBS

A Russian Niellow snuffbox. Good marks, Moscow 1846 maker's mark AS and Assay masters mark A.K. 3¼″, 8.4 cm. **£170-190** LC

A William IV snuffbox, in original morocco case. 1833 by Edward Edwards II. 3⅜″, 8.6 cm. **£210-240** LC

A George III silver sunffbox. Maker C.R. London 1819. 3¼″, 8.0 cm., 3 oz. **£130-170** DHBN

A William Summers snuffbox, hinged cover, gilt interior, 3¼″, 7.8 cm. long, maker's mark, London, 1890. 4 oz. 2 dwt., 127 gm. **£160-190** SBel

A Continental Silver Snuff Box of Bombe Shape, London import mark 1901, 4½ oz., base 3½″, by 2¾″, 9 cm. by 7 cm., **£190-250** KC

A George III octagonal snuff box
by Richard Sawyer, Dublin 1806.
3½″, 9.0 cm. wide. **£440-500**
SIre

A 19th C. snuff mull, unmarked,
c.1860. 10½″, 26.5 cm. wide.
£300-350   Sat HH

A Gold-mounted carved-nut scent
flask, struck with the Valenciennes
import mark, 1819-1838. 1½,
4 cm. high. **£80-120**   SBel

A Gold-mounted tiger's claw
vinaigrette, Anglo-Indian, c.1850,
the grille missing, 1¾″, 4.5 cm.
long. **£100-120**   SBel

A Gold-mounted tiger's claw
vinaigrette, Anglo-Indian, c.1850.
1⅝″, 4.1 cm. long. **£150-170**
SBel

A parcel gilt vinaigrette, by
H. and Thompson, Birmingham
1881, **£250-270**   KC

An octagonal nutmeg grater, by
T. Phipps and E. Rollinson,
London 1790. **£170-210**   KC

A silver card case, by N. Mills,
Birmingham 1844. **£220-240**
KC

A Scottish silver-mounted mull
vinaigrette, unmarked, c.1840.
6½″, 6 cm. long. **£150-170**   SBel

A rectangular vinaigrette,
Edinburgh, c.1810. maker 'J.M.'.
£95-115   KC

A silver visiting card case, by N.
Mills, Birmingham 1851, **£120-
150**   KC

A French table seal with tapering
handle, marked 800, c.1850. **£75-
95**   KC

A William IV 18 Carat Gold
Presentation Snuff Box by
Joseph Willmore, Birmingham,
1834, 3¼", 8 cm. wide. 1834,
4 oz. (fitted case). **£1,150-1,300**
SBIre

A George III 18 Carat Gold
Freedom Box, by Edward Murray,
Dublin, 1817. 3", 7.5 cm. diameter.
3 oz. 10 dwt. **£2,700-3,000**
SBIre

A George III silver vinaigrette.
Maker TB, Birmingham 1797.
1½", 4.0 cm. **£110-130** DHBN

A silver vinaigrette, London 1800.
£320-350 KC

An octagonal silver vinaigrette,
I. Angel, London 1801. **£300-
330** KC

A silver vinaigrette, J. Timms,
c.1840. **£300-340** KC

A silver vinaigrette by Shaw, 1803,
£230-260 KC

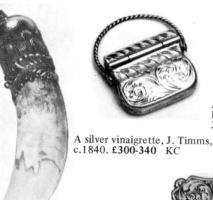

A Good Tiffany & Co. Gold-
Mounted Tooth Scent Flask, 5",
12.2 cm., c.1895, **£320-350** SBel

A silver-gilt vinaigrette by N. Mills,
1848, **£250-280** KC

An oval scalloped silver vinagrette
by N. Mills, Birmingham 1846.
£280-310 KC

A rectangular silver vinaigrette, by
J. Barber, 1823. **£220-240** KC

A rectangular vinaigrette, Matthew
Linwood, Birmingham 1814.
£170-190 KC

A silver rectangular vinaigrette,
J. Willmore, Birmingham 1821.
£160-190 KC

A rectangular parcel gilt silver
vinaigrette, Matthew Linwood,
Birmingham 1809. **£210-240** KC

A rectangular silver vinaigrette,
£230-260 KC

A scalloped rectangular vinaigrette
by N. Mills, 1846. **£300-340** KC

An Unusual Agate-Set Casket. Top panel applied with a monogram and coronet, 6½", 16.3 cm., long, maker's mark JB/LW, London, 1895. Interior fitted with a part Manicure Set, maker's mark of George Unite, Birmingham, 1894. **£250-300** SBel

An Oval Biscuit Box, 1867, by Stephen Smith, 9", 22.8 cm., 30 oz. **£380-420** LC

A George II Silver Brandy Warmer. Reeded circular foot, turned wood handle and wood finial to cover, London 1727, by William Fordham. **£300-380** KC

A Thomas Johnson Vesta Box, with hinged tortoiseshell back, 3½", 9 cm. long, maker's mark London, 1881, engraved 'W. T Thornhill & Co., 144 New Bond St. W.' **£160-190** SBel

A brandy warmer supported by a stand burner, London 1814 Emes & Barnard, 14 ozs. in all. **£440-500** LJ

A George IV Large Brandy Saucepan and Cover, 5½", 14 cm., by James Scott, Dublin, 1824, 21 oz., 10 dwt. **£580-640** SIre

A George V silver tortoise Table Bell, London 1910, 18 oz. (all in) 7", 17.5 cm. long. **£90-110** OL

A table bell. Late 19th C. French marks signifying importation from a country without assay regulations and another mark, possibly that of Valentin Adrian, Estonia, c.1720, 5 ozs. 5¼" high, 13 cm. **£300-400** LJ

A child's rattle, with revolving punch bead centre hung with six bells. Marks poor, probably French, second half 19th C. **£80-90** LC

A German Silver Figure, 4¾", 12 cm., importer's mark BP, London, 1901. **£260-290** SBel

A Large Unmarked Silver Model of an Eagle, 15¾", 40 cm., long, 34¾", 88.5 cm. overall, Japanese, late 19th C. **£1,650-1,850** LC

A Silver Dragon, 4", 9.8 cm., incised mark, stamped jun gin, late 19th C. 14 oz. 18 dwt. 462.42 gm. **£300-350** SBel

A pair of cockfighting spurs, 1¾", 4.5 cm. maker's mark T.S. in script, probably late 18th C. **£160-190** SBS

Silver picture frame approx. 8", by 4", 20 cm. by 10 cm. Birm. 1929. **£22-30** GA

An Unusual Table Lighter with three spirit containers on tapering supports, the cover of each equipped with a dipstick, 5½", 14 cm. high, maker's mark W.R. Longon, 1861, 12 oz. 3 dwt. 377 gm. **£120-160** SBel

An Unusual Pair of George III Wall Sconces, in the form of hanging lamps, 10¼" wide, 26 cm. height to ring holder 17", 42.5 cm., fully marked by W. Pitts and J. Preedy, London, 1796, with two Wall Brackets, in similar taste by Garrard and Co. Ltd., London, 1959, 76 oz. 5 dwt. **£1,800-2,100** SBS

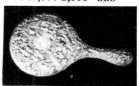

Silver dressing mirror, Birmingham 1909. **£38-48** GGA

A George III honey pot and stand by Paul Storr, with gilt interior, London, 1797. 4¾", 12.0 cm. high 14 oz. 8 dwt. **£3,800-4,200** SBS

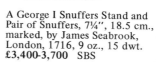

A George I Snuffers Stand and Pair of Snuffers, 7¼", 18.5 cm., marked, by James Seabrook, London, 1716, 9 oz., 15 dwt. **£3,400-3,700** SBS

Pair of Victorian engraved napkin rings in case, London 1874. **£28-38** AB

488 A Victorian boatswain's whistle 4½", 11.5 cm. long by H. & T. Birmingham 1899. **£90-110** HKC

A Victorian ceremonial horn with silver mounts. Inset with foiled crystal, maker's mark J.C., c.1870. 13¾", 35 cm., overall. **£250-350** Sat HH

A Pair of George IV Grape Tongs, the grips in the form of escallop shells, fully marked, by Mary and Charles Reily, London, 1828, 3 oz. 7 dwt. (all in). **£140-180** SBS

A Pair of H. & H. Lias Parcel-Gilt Harlequin Sugar Nips, cast and textured, 12.2 cm. 4¾" long, maker's mark, London, 1865, 2 oz. 53 gm. **£85-105** SBel

A Pair of C.S. Harris Grape Scissors, the interior fitted with a child and a small stork, 5¾", 14.5 cm. high, maker's mark, London, 1887, 2 oz. 16 dwt; 87 gm. **£150-190** SBel

A Carrington & Co. epergne in mid 18th C. style, makers' mark, London, 1900. 22", 56.0 cm. overall length, 123 oz. 3dwt; 3,822 gm. **£1,900-2,100** SBel

A Nathaniel Mills card case, maker's mark, Birmingham, 1839, 3¾", 9.5 cm. long. **£200-230** SBel

A circular epergne, makers' mark H/M, Birmingham, 1907. 13³/₈", 34.0 cm. overall height, 84 oz. 16 dwt; 2,631 gm. **£680-780** SBel

A Card case in silver. by Joseph Willmore, Birmingham 1841, cased. **£340-420** KC

A Pair of 18th C. Dutch Incense Burners, 7¼", 18.8 cm. high, by Maritinus Logerath, Amsterdam, apparently 1778, 30 oz. 16 dwt. **£700-1,000** SBS

A rare pair of George III silver spurs, London 1784, maker B.C. **£230-260** PK

A George I Censer, 8¾", 22 cm. high, marked on base and cover, by Anthony Nelme, London, 1722, 27 oz. 1 dwt. **£1,200-1,500** SBS

A German Bon-Bon Dish in the form of a rococo sleigh, 10", 25 cm. long, silver-coloured metal, marks rubbed, c.1900. 11 oz. 6 dwt; 351 gm. **£260-290** SBel

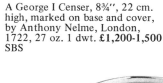

A Pair of George III Spurs, complete with buckles, maker's mark, T.S., Dublin, c.1770, 4 oz. 10 dwt (all in); **£720-820** SIre

A Silver articulated model of a fish with hinged head, 4¼", 10.5 cm. long. **£42-60** DHBN

470 A Continental silver metal bon-bon box in the form of a cats head, 2½″ 6.5 cm. high £100-140 HKC

A Continental Holy Water Stoup, of scallop form with hinged cover, oval back repousse decorated around and crucifixion representation, 11″ high, 28 cm. £310-350 PK

A Queen Anne Toilet Service, 3¾″, 9.5 cm. diam, by Robert Cooper, London, 1706, 81 oz., 12 dwt. (weight of casket and boxes). £7,500-8,200 SBS

A Large Silver-Mounted Blue Overlay Cut-Glass Scent Flask, 13¼″, 33.5 cm. long, English, c.1885, (case). £105-115 SBel

A Continental 18th C. smelling bottle with crown finial, hinged lid and lion supports. £240-270 PK

A George III 4 bottle decanter stand, by William Allen III, 4 engraved wine labels, London 1801. 10½″, 26.5 cm. £1,100-1,300 SBS

A Paul Storr silver centrepiece, London 1834. 9½″, 24.0 cm. diam. 9¼″, 23.5 cm. overall height, £900-1,000 KC

A George III cow creamer, the back with hinged flap applied with a fly and chased with flowers, by John Schuppe, 1764. 4 oz. 12 dwts. £2,800-3,000 CStJ

A James I seal top spoon, maker's mark C enclosing I, London, 1606. 6¾", 17.2 cm. long. **£500-600** PL

A Charles I unascribed provincial seal top spoon, the initials P.S.M. B. 1689, maker's mark TM, c.1630. 67/8", 17.4 cm. long. **£580-680** PL

A Charles I ascribed provincial seal top spoon, parcel-gilt, York marks, by Robert Harrington, 1638. 71/8", 18.2 cm. long. **£1,050-1,150** PL

An early Charles II seal top spoon, maker's mark I.I, London, 1665. 6¾", 17.2 cm. long. **£620-700** PL

An Elizabeth I hexagonal seal top spoon, silver gilt, London, 1577. 61/8", 15.5 cm. long. **£580-640** PL

A Charles I seal top spoon, initials and date W.C. 1646 M.B., maker's mark WC, London, 1640. 71/8", 18.0 cm. long. **£550-650** PL

A Commonwealth seal top spoon, maker's mark II, London, 1655. 71/8", 18.0 cm. long. **£850-950** PL

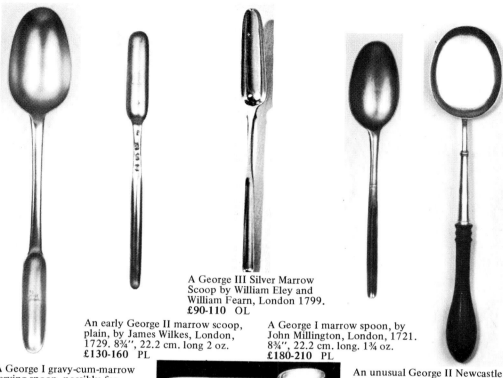

A George III Silver Marrow
Scoop by William Eley and
William Fearn, London 1799.
£90-110 OL

An early George II marrow scoop,
plain, by James Wilkes, London,
1729. 8¾", 22.2 cm. long 2 oz.
£130-160 PL

A George I marrow spoon, by
John Millington, London, 1721.
8¾", 22.2 cm. long. 1¾ oz.
£180-210 PL

A George I gravy-cum-marrow
serving spoon, possibly for
Meschach Godwin, London,
1724. 11⅛", 29.5 cm. long
3 oz. **£460-510** PL

A pair of Hester Bateman basting
spoons, London. **£150-180** AB

An unusual George II Newcastle
basting or serving spoon, by
Isaac Cookson, 1748. 14½",
37.7 cm. 4¾ oz. **£460-500** PL

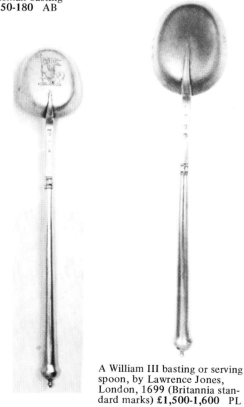

Pierre Platel heavy gauge basting
spoon, Britannia standard, London, c.1710. 13", 33.0 cm. long.
5½ oz. **£320-380** PL

A William III basting or serving
spoon, by Lawrence Jones,
London, 1699 (Britannia standard marks) **£1,500-1,600** PL

Pierre Platel heavy gauge basting
spoon, Britannia standard, London
1709. 13", 33.0 cm. long. 5½ oz.
£360-420 PL

A William and Mary basting or
serving spoon, by Lawrence
Jones, London, c.1690, 15",
38.0 cm. 4½ oz. **£850-950** PL

A rare Elizabeth I female draped figure terminal spoon, maker's mark I.S., c.1580., 6½", 14.2 cm. long. **£1,100-1,200** PL

A rare Charles I unascribed horse's hoof terminal spoon, maker's initials S.K., c.1640, initials I.H.D. 7⅛", 18.2 cm. long **£1,800-2,000** PL

A Charles I Buddha terminal spoon, with R. + C for Raleigh Clapham, Barnstaple, c.1635, 7¾", , 19.5 cm. long. **£1,000-1,200** PL

A Charles I naked female figure terminal spoon, mark for John Quycke of Barnstaple, c.1630, engraved on back of bowl with initials R.C. E.I. 1638. 7¾", 19.5 cm. long. **£1,900-2,100** PL

A rare William and Mary silver gilt marrow spoon, with crowned leopard's head and lion-passant marks, London, c.1690. 7¼", 18.5 cm. long. 1 oz. **£360-400** PL

A Hester Bateman mote spoon, fully hallmarked, London, 1785. 5½", 13.7 cm. long. **£160-180** PL

A George II mote spoon, of dessert size, by Edward Jennings, London, c.1730. 6½", 17.0 cm. long. **£85-95** PL

A George II cast mote spoon, c.1750. 5", 12.7 cm. long. **£130-160** PL

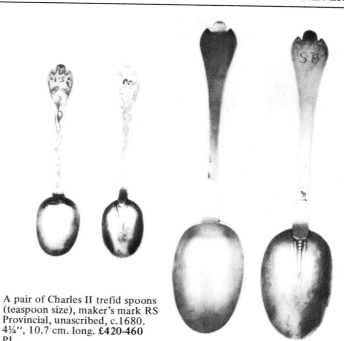

A pair of Charles II trefid spoons (teaspoon size), maker's mark RS Provincial, unascribed, c.1680. 4¼", 10.7 cm. long. **£420-460** PL

A William and Mary silver gilt matching trefid spoon and three-prong fork, maker's mark TD, London, 1694. 2½ oz. **£1,400-1,600** PL

A pair of William III trefid spoons, initials SB, by William Scarlett, London, 1699. 8", 20.0 cm. **£340-400** PL

A William and Mary trefid spoon, maker's mark I.S. London, 1690. 7½", 19.0 cm. long. **£190-220** PL

A Charles I apostle spoon, 'St. Andrew', bowl with prick-dot initials and dated maker's mark RC London, 1632. 7¼", 18.2 cm. long **£1,650-1,750** PL

A William III trefid lace back spoon, engraved I.S. D.S. 1701, maker's mark RS, probably for Richard Sweet of Chard, West Country, c.1700. 8", 20.0 cm. long. **£500-560** PL

A James I apostle spoon, 'St. Phillip', maker's mark I.F. London 1618. 7¼", 18.2 cm. long. **£1,800-2,000** PL

A Commonwealth unascribed apostle spoon, (possibly Scarborough?). 8", 20.3 cm. **£500-560** PL

A pair of James I provincial unascribed apostle spoons, 'The Master' and 'Another' (possibly St. Matthew), maker's mark RC, c.1620. 6¾", 17.2 cm. long. **£3,600-4,000** PL

A James I apostle spoon, 'St. James the Less', maker's mark MH conjoined, London, 1615. 7¼", 18.5 cm. long. **£2,200-2,500** PL

A rare provincial apostle spoon, 'St. Paul', with the initials and date AL IA 1651; mark of John Quycke, of Barnstaple, c.1630. 7½", 18.5 cm. long. **£1,850-2,100** PL

A very good James I apostle spoon, 'St. Simon Zealots', stem stamped Breadalbane with the initials K.M.E., maker's mark I.F., London, 1616. 7¹/₈", 18.0 cm. long. **£2,000-2,200** PL

A Charles I provincial apostle spoon, 'St. Phillip', with initials and date 1666, the Exeter assay mark, a Roman X crowned, c.1640. 7½", 18.5 cm. long **£950-1,050** PL

A Charles II provincial apostle spoon, 'St. Jude', maker's mark for Thomas Dare, c.1680. 7¾", 19.7 cm. long **£950-1,050** PL

A rare Commonwealth slip top spoon, with initials GD, and G.M.. maker's mark WC, London 1657. 5¾", 14.5 cm. long. **£780-880** PL

A Charles I slip top spoon, the initials NC, maker's mark D enclosing C, London, 1630. 6½", 16.5 cm. **£580-640** PL

A Charles II trefid spoon, plain, engraved on the back R.H., maker's mark IK, London, 1681. 8", 20.0 cm. long. **£340-390** PL

A Charles II trefid spoon, engraved on the back S.T.S. 1690, maker's mark IH, London, 1670. 7½", 19.0 cm. **£260-340** PL

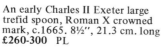

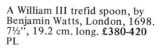

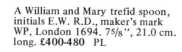

An early Charles II Exeter large trefid spoon, Roman X crowned mark, c.1665. 8½", 21.3 cm. long **£260-300** PL

A William III trefid spoon, by Benjamin Watts, London, 1698. 7½", 19.2 cm. long. **£380-420** PL

An early Charles II Exeter trefid spoon, engraved S.D. 63, stem with Roman X crowned mark, c.1663. 7¾", 19.7 cm. long. **£300-350** PL

A William and Mary trefid spoon, initials E.W. R.D., maker's mark WP, London 1694. 7⅝", 21.0 cm. long. **£400-480** PL

301

A rare Henry VI lion-sejant spoon, afronte, c.1450 (Provincial unascribed). 6½", 16.5 cm. **£2,600-2,800** PL

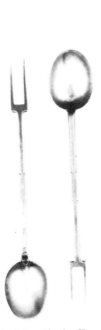

Two of a set of five Charles II sucket-spoon-forks, maker I.S. (probably for John Shepherd), London, c.1685. 2½ oz. **£1,900-2,000** PL

Hester Bateman gravy-straining spoon, London, 1775. 11¾", 29.8 cm. long. 4 oz. **£230-260** PL

A late Medieval English diamond point spoon, c.1425. 5⅞", 14.8 cm. **£980-1,050** PL

A set of six George III galleon picture back teaspoons, by William Cripps (probably), London, c.1775. 4½", 8", 11.7 cm. long 2 oz. **£540-620** PL

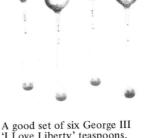

A good set of six George III 'I Love Liberty' teaspoons, London, c.1770. 4¾", 12.0 cm. long. 2 oz. **£440-500** PL

An early Charles II Puritan spoon, initials F.S.A, maker's mark IK, London, 1669. 7¼", 18.2 cm. **£680-780** PL

A pair of Commonwealth Puritan spoons, initials K.W.S., maker's mark I.I, London, 1656. 6¾", 17.0 cm. 3½ oz. **£1,050-1,150** PL

A George II medicine spoon, with Hanoverian turned up stem, by Paul Callard, London, c.1755, 3½", 9.0 cm. long. **£800-900** PL

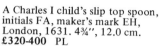

A Charles I child's slip top spoon, initials FA, maker's mark EH, London, 1631. 4¾", 12.0 cm. **£320-400** PL

A rare Charles I child's Puritan spoon, maker's mark II, London, 1646. 5½", 13.7 cm. **£460-500** PL

A rare Elizabeth I child's slip top spoon, maker's mark, London, 1595. 4¾", 12.0 cm. **£800-900** PL

A Charles II condiment spoon, maker's mark FG (for Francis Garthorne?), London, c.1680. 3¾", 9.5 cm. long. **£460-500** PL

A George III caddy spoon, plain die-struck, by John Sanders II, London, 1805. 2½", 6.5 cm. long. **£200-230** PL

Early Victorian silver gilt christening set, the spoon by Paul Storr, the fork and knife handle by W. Theobalds and R. Atkinson, all London, 1838, spoon and fork, 7", 17.5 cm. Knife 8½", 20.4 cm. 5.5 oz. **£1,200-1,400** PL

A Dutch marriage spoon with rustic bough handle. Inscription and date. **£90-110** AB

A Charles I stump top spoon, initials D.F.F., maker's mark (?) A (possibly IA), London 1630. 6⅛", 15.5 cm. long. **£950-1,050** PL

303

A George III Feather-edge Pattern Silver Punch Ladle, London 1805, by Eley and Fearn, 6 oz. **£120-150** KC

A pair of Art Noveau silver spoons by Liberty & Co., Birmingham, 1901. **£130-160** OL

A late Medieval English acorn knop spoon, with two chevron-like marks early 14th C. 5¾", 14.6 cm. long. **£1,250-1,400** PL

A Silver Toddy Ladle, with egg-shaped bowl and turned wood handle, London 1739, by Ben Saunders, overall length 13½", 34.5 cm. **£160-200** KC

Six Russian gilt and enamel tea spoons, St. Petersburg, c.1870, by Henrich Winstrom. (Later worked for Faberge). **£330-400** AB

A Set of Six Silver Berry Spoons with gilded bowl and engraved handles. Five London 1788 by Smith and Fearn, the other 1811 by Peter and William Bateman, total weight 6¼ oz. **£100-150** KC

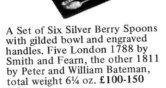

A good set of Henry Holland Parcel-Gilt Dessert Table Silver, 43 pieces, 64 oz., 17 dwt., 2,013 gm., London, 1869-1877, **£800-1,200** SBel

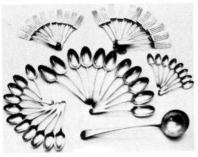

A Fine George III Silver part table service, in Old English pattern with bead edging, 52 pieces, all London hallmarked and made c.1795, weight 72 oz. **£700-800** KC

A James Deakin & Sons Ltd., Canteen, with initialled moulded reeded terminals, comprising 221 pieces (two maker's marks), within a mahogany cabinet 4' high 121 cm. **£2,600-2,800** SBel

A George III trowel, pierce – decorated with ornate scrollwork. Turned wood handle, by John Langford and John Sebille, 1763 – 5 oz. all in. **£110-140** PK

A Set of Four Silver Berry Spoons Embossed gilded bowl and engraved handle, London 1822, maker R.P., total weight 8 oz. **£140-200** KC

A pair of Hester Bateman game skewers, London. **£110-140** AB

A Three-Piece Berry Spoon Set. Two tablespoons and a sifter spoon, one spoon maker I.G., the other London 1775 maker W.I., the sifter spoon London 1810, total weight 5½ oz. **£90-110** KC

A Pair of Francis Higgins Fish Servers, maker's mark, London, 1865, 13 oz. 8 dwt; 415 gm. **£380-460** SBel

Former Assay Office Marks. Several of the larger provincial cities had Assay Offices which are now closed. Each had its distinctive mark, some of the more important of which are shown below. There is also an Assay Office in Dublin and marks struck there before 1st April 1923 are recognised as approved British hallmarks. The Dublin mark is a figure of Hibernia.

gold & Sterling silver

Britannia silver

London

Exeter   Glasgow   Newcastle   Chester   Dublin

1678	a	1712	1744	1780	e	1815	U	1850		1878	C	1904	i
1679	b	1713	1745	1781	f	1816	a	1851		1879	D	1905	k
1680	c	1714	1746	1782	g	1817	b	1852		1880	E	1906	l
1681	d	1715	1747	1783	h	1818	c	1853		1881	F	1907	m
1682	e	1716	A	1748	1784	i	1819	d	1854		1882	G	1908	n
1683	f	1717	B	1749	1785	k	1820	e	1855		1883	H	1909	o
1684	g	1718	C	1750	1786	l	1821	f	1856		1884	I	1910	p
1685	h	1719	D	1751	1786		1822	g	1857		1885	K	1911	q
1686	i	1720	E	1752	1787	m	1823	h	1858		1886	L	1912	r
1687	k	1721	F	1753	1788	n	1824	i	1859		1887	M	1913	s
1688	l	1722	G	1754	1789	o	1825	k	1860		1888	N	1914	t
1689	m	1723	H	1755	1790	p	1826	l	1861		1889	O	1915	u
1690	n	1724	I	1756	1791	q	1827	m	1862		1890	P		
1691	o	1725	K	1757	1792	r	1828	n	1863		1891	Q	1916	a
1692	p	1726	L	1758	1793	s	1829	o	1864		1892	R	1917	b
1693	q	1727	M	1759	1794	t	1830	p	1865		1893	S	1918	c
1694	r	1728	N	1760	1795	u	1831	q	1866		1894	T	1919	d
1695	s	1729	O	1761	1796	A	1832	r	1867		1895	U	1920	e
1696	t	1730	P	1762	1797	B	1833	s	1868		1896	a	1921	f
1697		1731	Q	1763	1798	C	1834	t	1869		1897	b	1922	g
1698		1732	R	1764	1799	D	1835	u	1870		1898	c	1923	h
1699		1733	S	1765	1800	E	1836		1871		1899	d	1924	i
1700		1734	T	1766	1801	F	1837		1872		1900	e	1925	k
1701	ff	1735	V	1767	1802	G	1838	C	1873		1901	f	1926	l
1702		1736	a	1768	1803	H	1839	D	1874		1902	g	1927	m
1703		1737	b	1769	1804	I	1840	E	1875		1903	h	1928	n
1704		1738	c	1770	1805	K	1841	F	1876	A			1929	o
1705		1739	d	1771	1806	L	1842	G	1877	B				
1706		1739	d	1772	1807	M	1843	H						
1707		1740	e	1773	1808	N	1844	J						
1708		1741	f	1774	1809	O	1845	K						
1709		1742	g	1775	1810	P	1846	L						
1710		1743	h	1776	1811	Q	1847	M						
1711				1777	1812	R	1848	N						
				1778	1813	S	1849	O						
				1779	1814	T								

Birmingham

1773	A	1778	F	1784	M
1774	B	1779	G	1785	N
1775	C	1780	H	1786	O
1776	D	1781	I	1787	P
1777	E	1782	K		
		1783	L		

Sterling silver Marked in England

 Marked in Scotland

 gold   silver

 gold   silver

Birmingham   Sheffield

Birmingham

Year	Letter	Year	Letter	Year	Letter	Year	Letter
1788	Q	1823	Z	1857	I	1893	t
1789	R	1824	a	1858	J	1894	u
1790	S	1825	B	1859	K	1895	v
1791	T	1826	C	1860	L	1896	w
1792	U	1827	D	1861	M	1897	x
1793	V	1828	E	1862	N	1898	y
1794	W	1829	f	1863	O	1899	z
1795	X	1830	G	1864	P	1900	a
1796	Y	1831	H	1865	Q	1901	b
1797	Z	1832	J	1866	R	1902	c
1798	a	1833	k	1867	S	1903	d
1799	b	1834	L	1868	T	1904	e
1800	c	1835	M	1869	U	1905	f
1801	d	1836	N	1870	V	1906	g
1802	e	1837	O	1871	W	1907	h
1803	f	1838	P	1872	X	1908	i
1804	g	1839	Q	1873	Y	1909	k
1805	h	1840	R	1874	Z	1910	l
1806	i	1841	S	1875	a	1911	m
1807	j	1842	T	1876	b	1912	n
1808	k	1843	U	1877	c	1913	o
1809	l	1844	V	1878	d	1914	p
1810	m	1845	W	1879	e	1915	q
1811	n	1846	X	1880	f	1916	r
1812	o	1847	Y	1881	g	1917	s
1813	p	1848	Z	1882	h	1918	t
1814	q	1849	A	1883	i	1919	u
1815	r	1850	B	1884	k	1920	v
1816	s	1851	C	1885	l	1921	w
1817	t	1852	D	1886	m	1922	x
1818	u	1853	E	1887	n	1923	y
1819	v	1854	F	1888	o	1924	z
1820	w	1855	G	1889	p	1925	A
1821	x	1856	H	1890	q	1926	B
1822	y			1891	r	1927	C
				1892	s	1928	D
						1929	E

Sheffield

Year	Letter	Year	Letter	Year	Letter	Year	Letter
1773	E	1807	S	1841	V	1877	K
1774	F	1808	P	1842	X	1878	L
1775	D	1809	K	1843	Z	1879	M
1776	R	1810	L	1844	A	1880	N
1777	h	1811	C	1845	B	1881	O
1778	S	1812	D	1846	C	1882	P
1779	A	1813	R	1847	D	1883	Q
1780	V	1814	W	1848	E	1884	R
1781	D	1815	O	1849	F	1885	S
1782	G	1816	T	1850	G	1886	T
1783	B	1817	X	1851	H	1887	U
1784	I	1818	I	1852	I	1888	V
1785	V	1819	V	1853	K	1889	W
1786	k	1820	Q	1854	L	1890	X
1787	T	1821	Y	1855	M	1891	Y
1788	m	1822	Z	1856	N	1892	Z
1789	M	1823	U	1857	O	1893	a
1790	L	1824	a	1858	P	1894	b
1791	P	1825	b	1859	R	1895	c
1792	U	1826	C	1860	S	1896	d
1793	Q	1827	d	1861	T	1897	e
1794	m	1828	e	1862	U	1898	f
1795	q	1829	f	1863	V	1899	g
1796	Z	1830	g	1864	W	1900	h
1797	X	1831	h	1865	X	1901	i
1798	V	1832	k	1866	Y	1902	k
1799	E	1833	l	1867	Z	1903	l
1800	N	1834	m	1868	A	1904	m
1801	H	1835	p	1869	B	1905	n
1802	M	1836	q	1870	C	1906	o
1803	F	1837	r	1871	D	1907	p
1804	G	1838	s	1872	E	1908	q
1805	B	1839	t	1873	F	1909	r
1806	A	1840	u	1874	G	1910	s
				1875	H	1911	t
				1876	J	1912	u

Duty Marks. Between 1784 and 1890 an excise duty on gold and silver articles was collected by the Assay Offices and a mark depicting the Sovereign's head was struck to show that it had been paid. These are two examples.

gold & silver

George III

Victoria

Edinburgh

Year		Year		Year		Year		Year		Year	
(castle)		1741	M	1777	X	1812	g	1847	Q	1884	c
1705	A	1742	N	1778	Z	1813	h	1848	R	1885	d
1706	B	1743	O	1779	Y	1814	i	1849	S	1886	e
1707	C	1744	P	1780	A	1815	j	1850	T	1887	f
1708	D	1745	Q	1781	B	1816	k	1851	U	1888	g
1709	E	1746	R	1782	C	1817	l	1852	V	1889	h
1710	F	1747	S	1783	D	1818	m	1853	W	1890	i
1711	G	1748	T	1784 (castle/thistle/head)	E	1819	n	1854 (castle/thistle)	X		
1712	H	1749	U	1785	F	1820	O	1855	Y	1891	k
1713	I	1750	V	1786 (castle/thistle/head)	G	1821	P	1856	Z	1892	l
1714	K	1751	W	1787	G	1822	q	1857	A	1893	m
1715	L	1752	X	1788	H	1823	r	1858	B	1894	n
1716	M	1753	Y	1789	IJ	1824	s	1859	C	1895	o
1717	N	1754	Z	1790	K	1825	t	1860	D	1896	p
1718	O	1755	A	1791	L	1826	u	1861	E	1897	q
1719	P	1756	B	1792	M	1827	v	1862	F	1898	r
1720	Q	1757	C	1793 (castle/thistle)	N	1828	w	1863	G	1899	s
1721	R	1758	D	1794	O	1829	x	1864	H	1900	t
1722	S	1759 (castle/thistle)	E	1795	P	1830	y	1865	I	1901	u
1723	T	1760	F	1796	Q	1831	z	1866	K	1902	w
1724	U	1761	G	1797	R	1832	A	1867	L	1903	r
1725	V	1762	H	1798	S	1833	B	1868	M	1904	v
1726	W	1763	I	1799	T	1834	C	1869	N	1905	3
1727	X	1764	K	1800	U	1835	D	1870	O	1906	A
1728	Y	1765	L	1801	V	1836	E	1871	P	1907	B
1729	Z	1766	M	1802	W	1837	F	1872	Q	1908	C
1730	A	1767	N	1803	X	1838	G	1873	R	1909	D
1731	B	1768	O	1804	Y	1839	H	1874	S	1910	E
1732	C	1769	P	1805 (castle/thistle/head)	Z	1840	I	1875	T	1911	F
1733	D	1770	Q	1806	a	1841 (castle/thistle/head)	K	1876	U	1912	G
1734	E	1771	R	1807	b	1842	L	1877 (castle/thistle/head)	V	1913	H
1735	F	1772	S	1808	c	1843	m	1878	W	1914	I
1736	G	1773	T	1809	d	1844	n	1879	X	1915	K
1737	H	1774	U	1810	e	1845	o	1880	Y	1916	L
1738	I	1775	V	1811	f	1846	P	1881	Z	1917	M
1739	K	1776	W					1882	a	1918	N
1740	L							1883	b	1919	O

307

A small Sheffield Plate epergne
£16-20   GA

Plated sauce boat. £15-20   GGA

Plated Sauce Boat, £10-15   GGA

A condiment frame with engraved
oil and vinegar bottles. £50-60
AB

A 5¾", 14.5 cm. high French
plated wax jack. £170-220 LJ

OLD SHEFFIELD PLATE

- a thin sheet of silver is
  fused on to a copper ingot
  by heat

- old Sheffield plate made
  from 1740's-1840's when
  it was replaced by electro-
  plating

- a problem arises over all
  electro-plating being called
  Sheffield Plate and hence
  the original plate should be
  notated **OLD** Sheffield
  Plate although frequently
  this title is omitted!

- electroplate always has a
  much whiter appearance
  than the mellow appearance
  of old Sheffield plate

- check for a seam on hollow
  ware as electroplate completely covers the piece

A silver-plated two-bottle cruet
stand, £100-130   KC

An early 19th C. Argyle, by J.
Watson & Son. £200-280   LJ

A Sheffield Wine Funnel by
D & S. £35-40   AB

A pair of unusual wood and
plated salts with matching spoons.
£20-25   GGA

A Victorian cut glass claret jug.
£85-95   AB

A Victorian engraved barrel.
£60-70   AB

A Silver-plated Wine and Cigar
Wagon, overall height 19½" x
16", 49.75 x 40.5 cm. across.
£500-590   KC

Old Sheffield Plate Pen and Ink
Stand. £100-120   KC

A Victorian embossed 2-division basket dish, 11″ x 7½″, 28 x 19 cm. £45-50 AB

A Sheffield Plate Tea Tray, 30¾″, 77.7 cm. English, c.1845. £260-290 SBel

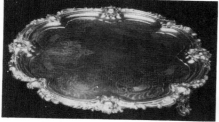

A Sheffield salver, 14″, 35.6 cm. diameter. £54-70 AB

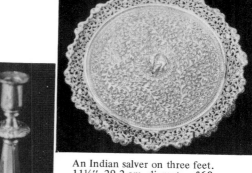

An Indian salver on three feet. 11½″, 29.2 cm. diameter. £60- AB

A Sheffield plate Tea Tray, 29¼″, 74 cm. English, c.1835, £240-280 SBel

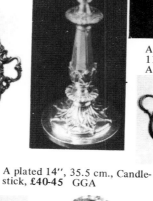

A plated 14″, 35.5 cm., Candlestick, £40-45 GGA

Old Sheffield plate Rectangular Tray. 22½″ x 17″, 57.25 cm. x 43 cm. £200-240 KC

A Sheffield tray 28″ x 20″, 71 cm. x 50 cm., £270-300 AB

A set of 6 Old Sheffield Plate Candlesticks, £340-400 KC

Sheffield plate Candlestick with snuffer. £30-40 MaH

A very small plated candle holder and snuffer. £30-40 TJC

A set of 4 W & G Sissons Sheffield Plate Table Candlesticks, 10¾″, 27.2 cm. high, makers' 'Bell' mark, c.1840, stamped 7908. £360-400 SBel

A Victorian engraved oval Teapot and a continental small bullet shaped teapot. £25-30 AB

Plated Teapot. £22-27 GA

A Mappin & Webb Sheffield plated tea service of three pieces, tea pot, sugar basin and cream jug, and a matching design Mappin & Webb Prince's plate hot water jug. £100-120 HKC

A Victorian pear shaped tea service. £120-150 HKC

A large Sheffield Tea Urn, c.1845, 17½", 44.5 cm. £310-350 LC

A Sheffield Coffee Pot, c.1775, 11¾", 30 cm. £100-125 LC

A Fine Pair of George III Old Sheffield Plate Entree Dishes, 29 cm. x 21.5 cm., 11½" x 8½", £170-200 KC

A Victorian Elkington plated engraved Coffee Pot. £16-20 AB

3 Sheffield Entree Dishes, 11½" x 8½", 29 x 21.5 cm. £240-290 AB

A Victorian engraved Tea and Coffee Service, 4-piece. £65-75 AB

A pair of Entree Dishes and Covers, 11¾", 30 cm. wide, c.1810. £200-230 SBS

An oval Entree Dish, 12" x 9½", 30.5 x 24 cm., £11-20 AB

A Sheffield Soup Tureen, c.1810, 13½", 34 cm. £440-500 LC

A Hukin and Heath electroplated Toast Rack, designed by Christopher Dresser, 5", 12.75 cm., 1880's. **£130-160** SBel

A Pair of Sheffield Candelabra, by Mathew Boulton, c.1795, 27½", 70 cm. **£760-840** LC

A Hukin and Heath Electroplated Picnic Set in box, by Christopher Dresser, 1880. **£240-280** SBel

A late Victorian E.P.B.M. tea set of spherical shape. **£50-60** HKC

An Electroplated 4 piece Tea and Coffee Set, makers' mark H & H c.1875. **£190-240** SBel

A Victorian Electroplated Decanter Stand, maker's mark Evans. **£200-250** LC

A pair of Sheffield Plate early 19th C. Candelabra 21", 53.5 cm. high, **£400-500**

An Electroplated 4-piece Tea and Coffee Set, with Tea Tray, English, c.1880. **£300-350** SBel

A Pair of Electroplated 4-light Candelabra, 24½", 62.5 cm. high, English, c.1865. **£240-270** SBel

A pair of 9½", 24 cm., telescopic candlesticks. **£30-40** AB

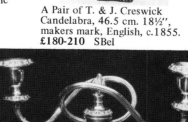

A Pair of T. & J. Creswick Candelabra, 46.5 cm. 18½", makers mark, English, c.1855. **£180-210** SBel

A Soho Plate Co. Electroplated 5-light Candelabrum, 25¾", 65.5 cm. high, 'Sun' mark struck twice, c.1845-50. **£400-460** SBel

A pair of twin branch squat table Candelabra 10½", wide 6" high, 26.5 cm. x 15 cm. **£25-30** AB

A Victorian Electroplated Centre Candelabrum, mark of Elkington & Co., c.1860, 29½", 75 cm. **£640-720** LC

311

A Continental Silver-Coloured Metal Oval Tea Caddy, French import mark. 9¾ oz. **£220-300** . KC

A silver-gilt Tazza, maker's mark of Robert Garrard II, London, 1838, engraved: 'Whistler/fecit/11 Strand London'. 11", 30.2 cm. diam., 31 oz. 6 dwt; 971 gm. **£280-340** SBel

Two Silver James I Apostle Spoons, St. Matthew and St. Bartholomew, with gilt terminal figures, the bowl backs pricked with initials I maker's mark indistinct, London, 1605. **£1,500-1,800** SBS

A George III oval soup tureen and cover, marked on base, cover and handles, by R. Emes and E. Barnard, London, 1811. 12½", 31.7 cm. wide, 71 oz. 19 dwt. **£1,900-2,200** SBS

A pair of George III silver-gilt meat dishes, by William Frisbee, London, 1803. 22", 55.9 cm. wide, 165 oz. **£2,100-2,400** SBS

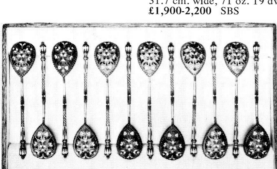

A Set of Russian Silver Gilt and Enamel Spoons. Russian standard marks of 1896-1898, assay master JK, the case labelled Mapuike, Kiev. Each spoon 5½", 14.3 cm., the case 11½", 32 cm. **£550-650** LC

A Silver-Gilt 62 piece Dessert Service, Fiddle Thread pattern, the dessert spoons and forks maker's mark P.B.L. the teaspoons maker's mark G.C.¨or G.O., all Paris, c.1800, 75 oz. 7 dwt. The Fruit Knives marked on blades and handles, by Eley and Fearn, London, 1822 (loaded). **£800-900** SBS

A William Cooper Silver-Gilt Taperstick with extinguisher and nozzle, 3", 7.2 cm., London, 1841, 3 oz., 4 dwt., 99 gm. **£250-300** SBel

A Silver-Gilt 72 piece Dessert Service, crested, maker's mark TWD in a hexagon, London, 1903, 85 oz. 5 dwt; 2,645 gm (of weighable silver) **£600-700** SBel

A William IV Silver-Gilt Casket, the interior lined with ivory, 6", 15 cm. wide, by Edward Farrell, London, 1835, Britannia Standard. **£2,200-2,500** SBS

GUIDE TO GRANDFATHER CLOCKS

- c.1660 – portico top to clock case
- c.1660 – appearance of minute hand
- c.1670 – flat top to clock case
- c.1670 – name of maker on dial plate
- c.1675 – appearance of seconds hand
- c.1675 – domed top to clock case
- c.1675 – Grinling Gibbons introduces crested top to clock case
- before 1720 – square brass dial
- after 1720 – arched brass dial
- c.1720 – top of doors became curved
- c.1720 – arched top to clock cases
- after 1750 – painted dials
- c.1760 – broken arch hood to clock cases
- c.1780 – round dials
- c.1790 – broken arch dial

A marquetry longcase clock, silvered chapter-ring signed Jones Barber at Rattclif Cross London, later movement with turned pillars, rack-strike and anchor escapement, the case late 17th C., 7'1", 216 cm., **£4,000-4,500** CStJ

A small walnut and laburnum wood parquetry longcase clock, signed Edw. Burgis London, 78", 198 cm., c.1675. **£5,200-5,800** SBS

A George III mahogany longcase clock, dial signed Thos. Barnes, Newport, rack-striking movement with anchor escapement, 7'8", 234 cm. **£2,200-2,400** CStJ

A walnut longcase clock, c.1710.
signed Tho. Baker, Portsmouth,
the 8-day anchor movement with
5 pillars, rack strike on bell.
84", 213 cm. high. £2,900-
3,200 KC

A George III Oak longcase clock,
signed Jno. Cleland Edinbr. 8-
day movement, 86", 218.5 cm.,
c.1780, with later twist-turned
columns £380-430 SBS

A lacquered longcase clock, plaque
signed Jno Baldwin, the eight day
anchor movement having internal
count wheel strike on bell. 8'1"
high, 246.5 cm. £680-780 HKC

A marquetry longcase clock,
c.1690, signed Tho. Baker,
Blandford, the 8-day 5 pillar
movement with heavy steel work,
78", 198 cm. high. £4,200-
4,600 KC

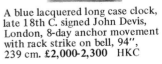

An Edmund Bullock, Ellesmere,
lacquered longcase clock, c.1740,
silvered chapter, 8-day anchor
movement, rack strike on bell.
108", 274 cm. £2,200-2,400 KC

A mahogany longcase clock,
c.1720, silvered brass dial, signed
Sam Cox, Long Acre, London,
the 8-day anchor movement with
rack strike on bell, 96", 243.5 cm
£1,800-2,100 KC

A fine Queen Anne three-month
going walnut longcase clock by
John Crucefix, London, 94",
238 cm. £4,800-5,300 CStJ

A blue lacquered long case clock,
late 18th C. signed John Devis,
London, 8-day anchor movement
with rack strike on bell, 94",
239 cm. £2,000-2,300 HKC

A fine Queen Anne ebonized longcase clock by Geo. Etherington, London, 12″, 30.5 cm. square dial with subsidiary seconds, signed silvered chapterring, outside countwheel strike and anchor escapement, 8′10″, 269 cm. £4,000-4,600 CStJ

An unusual mahogany longcase regulator by John Barnes, London, dead-beat escapement and steel-rod pendulum with large bob, 6′1″, 185 cm. £2,200-2,400 CStJ

A small oyster − veneered walnut marquetry month longcase clock, signed Tho. Dyde, Exchange Alley. 91″, 231 cm., c.1680. £4,000-5,000 SBS

An oak Longcase Clock signed Dan.1 Dickinson, Framlingham, 8-day movement, 79½″, 202 cm., case 18th C. c.1860. £370-450 SBel

A marquetry longcase clock, c.1720, case of walnut veneer, signed Esaye Fleureau, Londini, Fecit, 8-day recoil anchor movement, 84″, 213 cm. high. £2,800-3,200 KC

A month longcase clock, late 17th C. case of walnut veneer, signed Joseph Foster, Exchange Alley, movement with recoil anchor escapement, 84″, 213 cm. high. £4,000-5,000 KC

An early 19th C. mahogany longcase clock, inscribed Samuel Harper of Ayr. 94″, 239 cm. £1,150-1,250 HKC

A 17th C. Longcase Clock in a veneered walnut and marquetry case, signed Joseph Foster, Exchange Alley, 80½″, 204 cm. £4,800-5,300 PL

A walnut longcase clock c.1690, brass dial, signed John Gamell, Morefields, 8-day anchor movement, 86″, 218 cm. high. £1,600-1,800 KC

A George 11 burr-walnut month longcase clock, signed Benj. Gray, London, 94″, 234 cm. high, c.1750. £2,500-3,000 SBS

A mahogany long case clock and barometer, the 8-day movement rack striking, signed William Hart, Pelham St., Nottingham. Inset wheel barometer (defective) silvered 8″ dial, 101″, 256.6 cm. £1,350-1,500 LC

A William III Marquetry Longcase clock, walnut case, signed Jno. Gavell, London, 5 ringed-pillar movement with inside-countwheel strike and anchor escapement. 86″, 218 cm. high. £3,000-3,300 CStJ

A George III Mahogany longcase clock, signed Jno. Turnbull Harwick, 84″, 213 cm., c.1780. £1,100-1,300 SBS

A walnut marquetry longcase clock, signed Joseph Knibb, Londini, Fecit, 77½″, 197 cm. high. £3,600-4,000 SBS

James McCabe, Royal Exchange, London. A George III mahogany longcase clock, 8-day movement with anchor escapement, 78″, 198 cm. overall. £2,400-2,700 PL

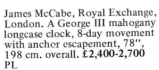

18th C. figured mahogany longcase clock, brass face engraved Jo Kirkwood, Melrose. The 8-day 4 pillar movement with striking action. 85″, 215.5 cm. £900-1,100 WBS

Green ground lacquered longcase clock, signed John Lush, London, the 8-day anchor movement having 5 pillars and rack strike on bell, mid 18th C. 92½", 235 cm. high. **£1,250-1,350** KC

A George III mahogany longcase clock, the dial signed John Mintern, London, rack striking movement with anchor escapement, 7'8", 235 cm. **£1,400-1,600** CStJ

William Newton, Lawson-le-Willows. A George III mahogany Longcase Clock, brass dial with silvered chapter ring, 3-train movement, 90", 229 cm. **£1,700-1,900** PL

Longcase clock well figured mahogany case, dial signed, John Philip, St. John's St., London. 8-day anchor movement, 96", 240 cm. high. **£3,900-4,300** KC

An important early 18th C. month going marquetry longcase clock, inscribed 'John Palmer, Portland Place, London'. 5 pillar movement with strike, with original brass bound weights. 80", 203 cm. high. **£3,500-4,000** B

Alexander Raitt, London. Late 17th C. marquetry month going longcase clock, with an ogee pediment, ebonised brass dial, month movement with bolt-and-shutter maintaining power, anchor escapement, 85", 215.5 cm. **£4,600-5,000** PL

A fine George III Mahogany longcase clock by Abel Panchaud, Oxford Street, signature arc in the matted centre, rack-striking movement with anchor escapement. – 96", 239 cm. high. **£2,500-2,800** CStJ

A late 18th C. mahogany Longcase clock, 8-day movement, by J. Ship, Long Melford, 85", 215.5 cm. high. **£530-620** OL

A mid 18th C. mahogany longcase clock, signed Wm. Rout, Enfield. The eight day movement of later date having quarter strike on eight bells and gong at hour. 8'1", 246.5 cm. £520-570 HKC

An early 19th C. longcase clock, signed Schwerer, Aberdare having eight day anchor movement with rack strike on bell. 7', 213 cm. £440-500 HKC

A mid-Georgian lacquered long-case clock, silvered chapter-ring signed Peter Selby, Wareham, rack-striking movement with anchor escapement, 7'2", 219 cm. £1,200-1,400 CStJ

A mid-Georgian grained walnut chiming longcase clock by Thomas Smith, Norwich, the dial, with calendar aperture, silvered chapter-ring, rack-striking movement chiming on 8-bells with anchor escapement. 96", 244 cm. high. £1,700-2,000 CStJ

A stained oak longcase clock, signed Stonehouse, Whitby, the movement with latched plated with 4 ringed pillars, 85", 216 cm., 18th C., carved c.1880. £920-1,100 SBel

Mahogany longcase clock, brass dial, silvered chapter ring, signed Thos. Sumart, London, 8-day anchor movement with strike on bell, late 18th C. 92½", 235 cm. high. £1,300-1,500 KC

A small walnut longcase clock, signed Francis Stamper, London, with part of a late 17th C. label. c.1690. £5,000-5,600 SBS

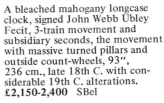

A bleached mahogany longcase clock, signed John Webb Ubley Fecit, 3-train movement and subsidiary seconds, the movement with massive turned pillars and outside count-wheels, 93", 236 cm., late 18th C. with considerable 19th C. alterations. £2,150-2,400 SBel

318

A late 18th C. longcase clock, veneered walnut case signed Edn. Vpjohn, Topham, 8-day recoil anchor movement, 78″, 198 cm. high. £2,500-2,700 KC

A Month Going Mahogany Longcase Clock by Wales and Mcculloch 56 Cheapside, London. 78″, 109 cm., 1910. £1,000-1,600 SBel

A green lacquered long case clock, 8-day five pillar movement rack striking, signed John Worsfold, Hampton Wick, 86½″, 219.5 cm. £950-1,100 LC

A burr-walnut longcase clock, signed J. Windmills London. 84″, high 213 cm., including later feet. £1,800-2,000 SBS

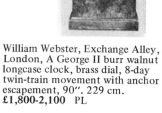

William Webster, Exchange Alley, London, A George II burr walnut longcase clock, brass dial, 8-day twin-train movement with anchor escapement, 90″. 229 cm. £1,800-2,100 PL

Mahogany longcase clock, with 8-day anchor movement rack strike on bell, mid 18th C. 97½″, 247 cm. high. £1,500-1,700 KC

An Arabesque marquetry longcase clock, signed Benj Willoughby, Bristol, c.1690. 85″, 216 cm. high. Plinth reduced. £2,500-2,800 SBS

An early Georgian longcase clock, the case with anchor escapement 98″, 254 cm. high, lacking calendar linkage. £1,600-1,800 CStJ

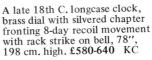

A figured mahogany long case
clock, 8-day movement rack striking, 91", 231.5 cm. **£2,000-
2,200** LC

An 18th C. longcase clock in oak
case, inscribed motto, striking
movement, by Agar York. **£750-
850** LJ

A fine quality 18th C. walnut
veneered longcase clock, brass
dial with silvered chapter ring,
inscribed. **£1,800-2,100** PWC

A late 18th C. longcase clock,
brass dial with silvered chapter
fronting 8-day recoil movement
with rack strike on bell, 78",
198 cm. high. **£580-640** KC

A good mahogany longcase clock,
the month movement chiming on
8-bells and 5 gongs, 101½",
258 cm., early 20th C. **£2,450-
2,600** SBel

A mahogany long case barometer
clock, 8-day movement rack
striking, 81¾", 207.5 cm. **£800-
900** LC

Early 19th C. mahogany French
long case regulator timepiece, the
single train movement of month
duration, with power maintaining,
dead beat escapement. 79½",
202 cm. **£4,600-5,300** LC

A small walnut marquetry longcase clock, dial with engraved
centre. 78", 198 cm. high.
£3,800-4,200 SBS

An oak long case clock, 30-hour movement with shaped rectangular plates and rope drive, 83½", 212 cm. **£420-500** LC

A large mahogany month going longcase clock, with 3 various chime related dials in arch, on 9 rod gongs. 112", 284.5 cm. Late 1890's. **£3,000-3,400** SBel

A mahogany longcase clock, the movement with 4 ringed pillars, 94", 239 cm., early 19th C. **£330-400** SBel

An Oak longcase clock, 89", 226 cm., c.1840. **£420-500** SBel

An ebonised Bracket Clock with a 7", dial , signed Joseph Alder London. 20", 50.5 cm., **£1,150-1,250** HKC

A late 19th C. Bracket Clock, signed Wilfrid Atlay of Hereford, with 8-day triple fusee movement 25", 63 cm. **£1,100-1,200** KC

An Ormolu-Mounted Boulle Bracket Clock, the movement signed Gustav Becker, Freiburg, 48", 122 cm. high. **£1,250-1,400** CStJ

A George III mahogany striking bracket clock, by Thos. Budgen, Croydon; movement with verge escapement, 18", 46 cm., **£2,600-2,900** CStJ

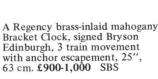

A Regency brass-inlaid mahogany Bracket Clock, signed Bryson Edinburgh, 3 train movement with anchor escapement, 25", 63 cm. **£900-1,000** SBS

A Louis XV ormolu mounted boulle bracket clock. 2 train movement with verge escapement, signed Bigand a Paris, 34″, 86.4 cm. **£1,350-1,500**   LC

A large oak Bracket Clock, signed Clerke 1, Royal Exchange London. 5062, 1903, 25½″, 65 cm., c.1900. **£580-680** SBel

A fine Queen Anne silver-mounted ebony striking bracket clock by Thomas Cattell, London; rack-striking movement with spring-suspended verge escapement, rise-and-fall regulation, signed Tho. Cattell, Londini Fecit, 35½″, 90.1 cm. **£11,000-12,000**   CStJ

A Victorian figured mahogany bracket clock, 3 train chain fusee movement with anchor escapement, signed Carter, London, 30¼″, 77 cm. **£1,200-1,400** LC

An early 18th C. ebony bracket clock, signed John Constantin Londini: Fecit; seven ringed-pillar movement, knife-edge verge escapement and quarter-repeat on a single bell operated by a three-tooth rack in the manner of Tompion, 15¾″, 40 cm., **£5,000-5,600** CStJ

A Louis XVI style brass Bracket Clock. marked Elekington & Co., French 8-day movement, 18½″, 47 cm. **£350-400** DHBN

A green-painted early 19th C. Alarum Bracket Clock and Bracket, signed Courvoisier et Compe., 2 train movement with pull alarum, narrow anchor escapement, 21″, 53.5 cm., Chaux-de-Fonds, **£1,200-1,400** SBS

Ellicott & Smith, London. Early 19th C. rosewood Bracket Clock, fusee movement with an anchor escapement, 11¾″, 30.0 cm. **£800-900** PL

A Fine George 11 Ebony Striking Bracket Clock signed Dan: Delander, London, 16½″, 42 cm., **£6,000-6,900** CStJ

A mahogany Bracket Clock by F.J. Dent, London. 18″, 46 cm., c.1840. £210-240 SBel

A late 17th C. tortoiseshell veneered bracket clock by John Ebsworth, verge escapement and engraved back-plate, also signed, with strike/silent lever, and outside set-up ratchets, contemporary style key, 12″, 30.5 cm. high. £4,000-4,500 CStJ

A lacquered quarter-striking bracket clock by Ralph Gout, London, movement quarter-striking on four bells with verge escapement, 21″, 53.5 cm. £1,600-1,800 CStJ

A George 111 mahogany striking bracket clock, signed 'Flashman, Fleet Street, London', 15½″, 39 cm. £900-1,000 CStJ

A George 11 Ebony Striking Bracket clock, signed Jno. Gordon, London, 16″, 41 cm., £1,000-1,100 CStJ

A George III mahogany striking bracket clock, the dial with silvered chapter disc, backplate signed Richard Griffiths, London, with anchor escapement, 16¼″, 41.0 cm. £1,800-2,000 CStJ

Victorian mahogany Bracket Clock, the 3 chain fusee movement with anchor escapement, signed Charles Frodsham, 18⅝″, 47.2 cm. £1,400-1,600 LC

An English Regency Bracket Clock, signed William Patrick Greenwick, 8-day anchor movement, with double fusee, 20″, 50 cm. £850-950 KC

An unusual early 18th C. German Bracket Clock, signed Elias Gunschy Neu Statt, 3 train movement, narrow anchor escapement, 19″, 48 cm. £700-1,000 SBS

An early 18th C. small ebony verge Bracket Clock by Benjamin Gray & Justin Vulliamy, 8-day 5 pillar movement with verge escapement, 12" high x 9" wide, 30.5 cm. x 23 cm. **£2,000-2,400** B

A small ebonised bracket clock, 2 train fusee movement with anchor escapement. Signed J. & H. Jump, London. 13", 33 cm. **£1,150-1,250** LC

A William IV mahogany cased musical Bracket Clock, by Keeling of Blackfriars Road. **£520-600** LE

An ebonised Bracket Clock, signed P. Hill, Edinburgh, 28", 71 cm., c.1880. **£340-400** SBel

Johnson, London. An ebonised 3-train Bracket Clock with brass dial, fusee movement with an anchor escapement, 14³/₈", 36.5 cm., **£1,000-1,100** PL

An early 19th C. French Boulle Bracket Clock, signed Lefort a Paris, 8-day movement, having anchor and count-wheel strike, 19", 48 cm., 14", 35.5 cm. **£600-670** KC

A French Bracket Clock, inscribed 'Hanet et G. a Paris'. 142 cm., 56", **£640-740** DHBN

A rare and early veneered ebony Bracket Clock, skeleton chapter ring, 2 train movement with latched plates, 5 ringed pillars and verge escapement. signed Joseph Knibb Londini Fecit, c.1675, 14", 35.5 cm. **£15,000-16,500** SBS

A George III mahogany Bracket Clock, signed Frederick Miller London, the 3 train movement with anchor escapement, 16", 41 cm. **£1,150-1,250** SBS

An attractive mid-18th C. Bracket Clock, signed Laur. Mace, London, 8-day anchor movement, having double fusee, 18¾", 47 cm., 13¾", 35 cm., **£850-950** KC

A George II ebonized Bracket Clock, signed Henry Neve London, 6 pillar movement and verge escapement with bob pendulum, 16", 41 cm. **£3,400-3,600** SBS

Payne, London. A small ebonised Bracket Clock, fusee movement with an anchor escapement, 16¼", 41 cm. **£600-700** PL

An oak Bracket Clock signed James Mc Cabe, repeating movement with anchor escapement, 14", 36 cm., c.1850. **£700-800** SBS

A George III ebonized striking bracket clock with alarm, signed in the arch John Pepys, London; separate alarum train and knife-edge escapement, 20", 51 cm. **£1,200-1,400** CStJ

A mahogany Bracket Clock, signed Paul Rimbault London, the movement with verge escapement, 16½", 42 cm., c.1780. **£1,200-1,400** SBS

A gilt-bronze Bracket Timepiece, by Josh. Penlington, Liverpool. 15¾", 40 cm., c.1830. **£200-300** SBel

An early 19th C. musical bracket clock by James McCabe. 3 train fusee movement with anchor escapement. New case and dial restored, 28", 71 cm. **£1,300-1,500** LC

An ebonized Bracket Clock, signed Thos. Pott London, the movement with verge escapement, 18½", 47 cm. **£850-950** SBS

A mahogany Bracket Clock, 8-day double fusee verge movement signed W. Robson, N.Shields, 18", 46 cm., **£500-600** KC

A small Regency Bracket Clock by Ross of Exeter, 8-day striking movement, 11½", 29 cm. £800-900   B

A George III ebonized striking bracket clock, the dial signed Smith & Son, London, strike/silent in the arch; movement with verge escapement, 19", 48 cm. £1,800-2,000   CStJ

A rare veneered ebony Bracket Clock, signed Tompion and Banger, London, Dutch striking and verge escapement, 17", 43 cm., c.1705. £14,000-15,000 SBS

A rare large 18th C. French Boulle Bracket Clock, anchor movement signed Roquelon a Paris 43", 108 cm., 40 cm., 16", £2,450-2,650   KC

A mahogany Bracket Clock, c.1780, signed Robt. Salmon, 8-day double fusee verge movement, 19", 48 cm., £800-1,000 KC

A mahogany Bracket Clock by Vine and Thompson, London, 21¾", 55 cm., early 20th C. £640-740   SBel

A George III Mahogany Striking Bracket clock signed John Scott, London, subsidiary regulation movement with verge escapement, 16", 40.5 cm., £2,400-2,700 CStJ

Frans. Thompson, London, A George II ebonised Bracket Clock. Fusee movement with an anchor escapement. 19¼", 49 cm. £720-820   PL

A George II ebonized quarter-striking bracket clock by William Webster, Exchange Alley, London, movement quarter-striking on six bells, now converted to anchor escapement, 18½", 47 cm. £3,500-3,900   CStJ

A George I ebonised alarum Bracket Clock. signed C. Wuenouault, London, the movement with pull alarum and verge escapement, c.1725, 13½", 34 cm. **£3,500-5,000** SBS

An Austrian 18th C. Bracket Clock, signed Kilian Geist Wienn, repeating movement with a chain fusee, 18½", 47 cm. **£700-1,000** SBS

A red Boulle Bracket Clock, 16", 41 cm. late 19th C. **£380-460** SBel

Wilkins, Soho. A Regency mahogany Bracket Clock, fusee movement with an anchor escapement, 16¼", 41 cm. **£400-500** PL

A Boulle Bracket Timepiece, 16¾", 42.5 cm., mid-19th C. **£350-400** SBel

An attractive early 19th C. Boulle Bracket Clock, verge movement with 5 baluster pillars, 35½", 89 cm. **£1,450-1,650** KC

A mahogany Bracket Clock, 8-day double fusee movement, verge with 'V' block, signed Rich. Ward, Winchester, c.1770, 18", 45 cm. **£1,900-2,200** KC

A red Boulle Bracket Clock, 16", 40.5 cm., c.1880. **£330-370** SBel

A large scarlet boulle bracket clock. 21¼", 54 cm wide, 19th C. **£2,300-2,500** CStJ

A Boulle Bracket Clock with half-hour striking, 17", 43 cm., c.1880, **£420-480** SBel

327

A red Boulle Bracket Clock, 16½", 42 cm., c.1870. **£360-390** SBel

A 19th C. French boulle bracket clock, stamped 'Fieffe Hgr De L'Observatoire, 8-day anchor movement, 26", 66 cm., **£1,300-1,500** HKC

An oak Bracket Clock, 15¾" 40 cm., c.1880. **£170-220** SBel

A red Boulle Bracket Clock, 17¾", 45 cm., c.1880. **£260-290** SBel

A Red Boulle Bracket Clock, 17¾", 45 cm., c.1900. **£590-680** SBel

A Regency Mahogany Bracket Clock, having 8-day double fusee anchor movement, 23", 58 cm. **£420-460** KC

A 19th C. French boulle bracket clock with ormolu mounts. 8-day anchor movement, 20", 50.5 cm., **£1,050-1,200** HKC

Gilt-metal mounted oak Bracket Clock. 21½", 54.5 cm., c.1890. **£250-400** SBel

A Regency mahogany Bracket Clock, with 8-day double fusee anchor movement, 22", 56 cm. **£400-450** KC

An oak Bracket Clock. 18", 46 cm., c.1900. **£500-700** SBel

An oak Bracket Clock, 21½", 54.5 cm., probably German, c.1890. **£410-480** SBel

A Rosewood and marquetry Bracket Clock, 20½", 52 cm., c.1900 **£400-600** SBel

19th C. rosewood Bracket Clock. 18″, 45 cm. **£280-360** PWC

A walnut Bracket Clock, 20¼″, 51.5 cm., late 19th C. **£550-620** SBel

An early multi-piece carriage clock, case of brass, signed Bolviller a Paris. **£1,200-1,300** KC

A miniature Gorge cased carriage clock, brass case, lever platform movement with 2-trains, 1 barrel signed J.J.L. Brevet, 3″, 7.5 cm. high. **£700-800** KC

A Chinese Bracket Clock, fusee and chain movement with verge escapement, 18½″, 47 cm., **£650-750** CStJ

A Gilt-Bronze-Mounted red tortoiseshell Bracket Clock, 20½″, 52 cm., late 19th C. **£420-500** SBel

An unusual carriage clock with an enamel dial signed Arnold and Lewis Manchester, lever movement with the stamp of Achille Brocot, 7″, 18 cm. high, **£1,150-1,300** SBS

French Louis XVI style Buhlwork Bracket Clock, **£500-550** RBB

A rare tortoiseshell musical Bracket Clock, with later anchor escapement, 24″, 61 cm., c.1760. dials replaced. **£4,000-4,500** SBS

A fine French porcelain-mounted gilt-metal carriage clock, the movement stamped D.C. with platform lever escapement, by Drocourt, 5½″, 14 cm. **£1,400-1,600** CStJ

329

A French grande sonnerie alarum carriage clock by P & A Drocourt in brass case, 5¾", 14.5 cm. **£2,400-2,700** GSP

A French gilt-metal oval striking carriage clock, the movement stamped D.C. 5¼", 13 cm. high by Drocourt. **£470-520** CStJ

An 8-day Drocourt Grande Sonnerie carriage clock fully jewelled lever escapement, gorge case and Grande/Petit/Silent lever in base, 6¾", 17 cm. **£1,650-1,850** GSP

A French Gilt brass porcelain mounted miniature carriage timepiece, the single train movement with lever escapement, compensated balance. 4", 10.5 cm. **£650-720** LC

A French brass Grande Sonnerie carriage clock signed Drugeon, Paris, lever movement, 6", 15.5 cm. high. **£720-810** PL

An unusual porcelain-mounted carriage clock, the dial signed Edward & Sons, stamp of Maurice et Cie, 6¼", 16 cm. high. **£1,250-1,500** SBS

A brass cased carriage timepiece of oval section. **£190-220** HKC

A gilt-brass time-piece, the dial stamped Harrods Made in Paris, 5¾", 14.5 cm., c.1900. **£50-70** SBel

A miniature French porcelain-mounted carriage clock time-piece, signed Le Roy & Fils, with platform lever escapement, by Drocourt, 3¼", 8.3 cm. **£1,100-1,200** CStJ

A brass-cased carriage clock, gorge case, 8-day lever platform movement stamped Aigile, Reveil Repasser Par, LeRoy et Fils, Paris Royal, 5¼", 13 cm. high. **£1,050-1,200** KC

An 'English' gilt-metal striking carriage clock, the movement with platform lever escapement, signed E.W. Streeter, 18, New Bond St., London W., 5¼'', 13.5 cm. £750-830 CStJ

An oval carriage clock, having grande and petite sonnerie, enamel dials, 8-day movement with lever platform. £2,700-2,900 KC

A brass-cased carriage clock, the 8-day platform lever movement, stamped by Francois Arsene Margine, 6'', 15 cm. high. £620-700 KC

A very unusual porcelain-mounted striking carriage clock, movement signed Moser a Paris, with platform lever escapement, 7'', 18 cm. £1,000-1,200 CStJ

A French brass striking carriage clock, the movement signed A*V with platform lever escapement, 7¼'', 18.5 cm. £460-500 CStJ

A French lacquered brass petite-sonnerie carriage clock, with platform lever escapement, 5¼'', 13.5 cm. high. £500-560 CStJ

A French gilt-metal striking carriage clock, the movement stamped A.H. Rodanet, Paris, with platform lever escapement, signed enamel dial, 8¼'', 21 cm. high. £600-680 CStJ

A gilt-brass repeating carriage clock, enamel dial stamped Wordley & Co., Paris, 6¼'', 16 cm., c.1880. £150-250 SBel

A gilt-brass centre-seconds alarum repeating carriage clock. 7'', 17.8 cm., c.1900. £400-450 SBel

A gilt-brass repeating carriage clock, 6½'', 16.5 cm., in travelling case, c.1890. £280-320 SBel

A French brass carriage clock, lever movement and push repeat, 8¼'', 21 cm. high. £500-590 PL

A gilt brass Carriage Clock in, 7'', 17.8 cm., c.1900. £230-260 SBel

A French brass Carriage Clock with lever movement, push repeat and alarm. 6¾'', 17 cm. high, in a case. £480-520 PL

A gilt-brass calendar carriage time-piece, 5¾'', 14.5 cm., early 20th C. £190-260 SBel

A small French silver-gilt and enamel carriage clock, with platform lever escapement, 3½'', 9 cm., £450-500 CStJ

A French brass Carriage Clock, with a lever movement, push repeat and alarm, 6'', 15.5 cm. high. £520-600 PL

A brass carriage clock with strike repeater movement and alarm dial. 7½'', 19 cm. high, with key. £400-460 DHBN

An engraved gilt-metal repeating carriage alarum clock, 8'', 20 cm., c.1850. £400-480 SBel

A French gilt-metal quarter striking carriage clock, with platform lever escapement, ivorine chapter-rings within gilt-metal surrounds, 4¼'', 12 cm. high. £650-720 CStJ

A mahogany mantel time-piece signed Barraud & Lund, Cornhill, London 1798; 9½ by 6½", 24 by 16.5 cm., c.1840. **£220-260** SBel

A gilt-brass and champleve enamel mantel dock, signed Chett & Co., c.1880. 19½", 49 cm. **£720-800** SBel

A red and black marble perpetual calendar mantel clock, signed Howell and James Paris, 17½", 44.5 cm., c.1860. **£450-520** SBel

A 19th C. brass calendar clock, signed Wm. Boore, London, 18", 46 cm. **£1,700-1,900** PL

A William Comyns Silver-mounted Tortoiseshell Mantel Clock with French movement, 5½", 14.1 cm., London, 1913. **£480-550** SBel

An unusual 'Tudric' pewter clock, attributed to Knox, 38 cm., **£820-920** PL

An ormolu-mounted marble and bronze mantel clock, c.1860, 24½", 67 cm. **£200-230** SBel

A mantel timepiece by Charles Frodsham, movement with chain fusee and English lever escapement, 10½", 26 cm. **£3,500-4,000** WW

A gilt-bronze and white marble mantel clock, signed Lemerle-Charpentier, mid 19th C., 25¾", 65 cm. **£500-600** SBel

A mid-19th C. porcelain mantel clock, 8-day drum movement, signed "Chaudin, Paris", 17½", 44.4 cm. **£250-350** KC

A gilt brass and champleve enamel mantel clock, 2 train movement with Brocot suspension, trade stamp of Japy Freres; 15½", 39.3 cm. **£850-950** LC

A gilt-bronze and alabaster mantel clock, signed Levy Freres a Paris, c.1870, 14", 35.5 cm. **£310-350** SBel

A gilt-bronze and alabaster mantel clock, signed Hry. Marc Paris, late 19th C., 15½", 39.5 cm. **£170-200** SBel

An English ormolu mantel clock, 2 train fusee movement with anchor escapement, signed John Peterkin, London; 13⅞", 35.2 cm. **£550-650** LC

A gilt-bronze and champleve enamel mantel clock stamped Staley & Co., 15", 38 cm., c.1900. **£680-780** SBel

A mid-19th C. mahogany regulator mantel clock, by Moore, London, 17", 43 cm. **£850-950** LE

A bronze and marble mantel clock, signed W.B. Promoli a Paris, mid 19th C. 21½ ', 55 cm. **£260-290** SBel

A French ebonised mantel clock in the Empire style, 2 train movement with anchor escapement, trade stamp of Vincenti & Cie. **£220-300** LC

A spelter mantel clock, signed A. Ouver, c.1910, 15½", 40 cm. **£100-140** SBel

A 19th C. rosewood travelling mantel clock, the 2 train chain fusee movement with power maintaining, platform lever escapement, signed Simmons; 11½", 29 cm. **£1,800-2,000** LC

A good 19th C. mantle clock. signed Viner, 8-day movement, 8", 20 cm. high. **£1,600-1,900** HKC

A second Empire gilt and bronze mantel clock, c.1860, 10", 25.5 cm. **£370-450** SBel

A carved walnut mantel clock 27½", 70 cm., Austrian, late 19th C. **£310-350** SBel

An Austrian Stained Burr-Maple Mantel Clock 18½", 47 cm. high, early 19th C. **£160-180** CStJ

A gilt-bronze mantel clock, mid 19th C., 11½", 29.2 cm. **£190-240** SBel

A Japanese brass clock, overall height 47¼", 90.5 cm. **£1,300-1,500** CStJ

A 19th C. French gilt brass mantel clock; 13¾", 35 cm. **£340-400** OL

French ormolu and ray skin cased easel clock, 9", 22.8 cm. **£210-240** RB

A rare miniature German gilt-metal tabernacle clock, the going train with steel fusee converted from balance wheel to short bob verge escapement, 6½", 16.5 cm. early 17th C. **£1,800-2,000** CStJ

A 'Louis XV' gilt-metal and porcelain timepiece, 1840's, 16", 40.5 cm. **£580-640** SBel

A 19th C. French porcelain painted mantel clock, 15", 38 cm. **£320-400** PL

A 19th C. French tortoiseshell veneered mantel clock; 15¾", 40.0 cm. **£220-260** OL

A late 19th C. French mantel timepiece, 8-day drum anchor movement, 13¼", 33 cm. **£550-650** KC

An Empire Ormolu Mantel Clock, 16", 40.5 cm. eide. **£850-930** CStJ

A French empire mantel clock, 8-day drum movement, 20", 50 cm. high. **£390-490** KC

335

A gilt-bronze mantel clock, French, late 19th C., 18½", 47 cm. **£170-200** SBel

A 19th C. French ormolu mantel clock, 13", 33 cm. wide. **£1,700-1,900** PL

A gilt and bronze mantel clock with outside count-wheel, c.1860, 29", 73.5 cm. **£400-460** SBel

A French porcelain-mounted gilt-bronze mantel clock, 2-train movement, mid-19th C., 13¼", 33.5 cm. **£450-550** SBel

A bronze and gilt-bronze mantel clock, c.1850, 13¾", 35 cm., **£150-250** SBel

A porcelain-mounted gilt-brass mantel clock, c.1860, 18", 45.7 cm. **£360-400** SBel

A musical mantel clock, with 2-train movement, French, 1860-1870, 21", 53 cm. **£330-400** SBel

A gilt-bronze mantel clock, c.1840, 16", 40.5 cm. **£250-300** SBel

A rosewood and parquetry mantel clock, c.1880, 19¾", 50 cm. **£130-160** SBel

A 19th C. French mantel clock with 8-day drum movement, 18", 45 cm. **£320-420** VC

A gilt-spelter and porcelain-mounted mantel clock, 1870's, 15½", 39.5 cm. **£240-290** SBel

A gilt-spelter and porcelain mantel clock, c.1860, 13½", 35 cm. **£150-180** SBel

A large gilt-brass and painted glass mantel clock, c.1880. 18¾", 47.5 cm. **£520-600** SBel

A fine early 19th C. French ormolu mantel clock, signed Asselin, Paris, 18¾'', 48 cm. £790-910 KC

A gilt-bronze mantel clock, signed Sykes Williams & Cullums, London, c.1880, 14½'', 37 cm. £250-300 SBel

A French porcelain-mounted gilt-bronze mantel clock, late 19th C., 14'', 36 cm. £450-600 SBel

A French gilt bronze sculptural mantel clock, 2 train movement with silk suspension, trade stamp of Raingo Freres; 20¾'', 52.6 cm. £450-550 LC

A French gilt-bronze sculptural mantel clock, mid 19th C., 16½'', 42 cm. £550-650 SBel

A gilt-brass and porcelain mantel clock, c.1880, 12½'', 32 cm. £310-400 SBel

A gilt-spelter and porcelain mantel clock, c.1890, 14¾'', 37.5 cm. £260-300 SBel

A 19th C. French ormolu mantel clock in inverted "T" form, with 8-day drum movement, 13'', 34 cm. high. £320-400 KC

A French gilt and patinated bronze sculptural mantel clock, mid 19th C., 22'', 56 cm. £400-500 SBel

A gilt-bronze and porcelain mantel clock, signed J.W. Benson, 1860's, 15½'', 39 cm. £480-560 SBel

A gilt-bronze and porcelain-mounted mantel clock, signed G. Wadham Bath, c.1870, 16'', 40.5 cm. £370-430 SBel

A gilt-spelter and 'Sevres' porcelain-mounted mantel clock, c.1870, 18'', 46 cm. £210-280 SBel

A gilt-spelter mantel clock, 1880's; 25'', 63.5 cm. **£500-900** SBel

A gilt-spelter and porcelain mantel clock, c.1890, 16½'', 42 cm., with urns, 10½'', 27 cm. **£450-500** SBel

A gilt-metal timepiece, mid 19th C. 11½'', 29 cm. **£200-250** SBel

An ebonised and gilt-bronze mantel clock, c.1850, 19¼'', 49 cm. **£180-220** SBel

An unusual early 19th C. musical calendar alarm clock with narrow anchor escapement, probably Austrian, distressed; 18'', 45 cm. **£1,300-1,600** SBS

A 19th C. 8-day black marble cased mantel clock; 11½'', 29.0 cm. **£20-25** WW

A gilt-bronze and porcelain mantel clock, c.1870, 19¼'', 49 cm. **£1,100-1,300** SBel

A gilt-metal and champleve enamel mantel clock, movement with Brocot's escapement; late 19th C. 21½'', 54.5 cm. **£1,300-1,600** CStJ

A gilt-bronze mantel clock, late 19th C., 23'', 58.5 cm. **£230-270** SBel

A bronze and marble mantel clock, 1860-80, 30'', 76 cm. **£500-800** SBel

Late 19th C. cast brass 8-day striking mantel clock; 17'', 43.0 cm. **£195-250** WW

A silvered brass and copper mantel timepiece, c.1900, 22'', 56 cm. **£150-250** SBel

An unusual mantel timepiece;
14", 35.5 cm. **£380-480** SBS

A rosewood and marquetry
mantel clock, c.1900, 11¾", 30
cm. **£210-270** SBel

A late 19th C. ebonised
mantel clock, 8-day anchor
movement, 28", 71 cm. **£720-
820** KC

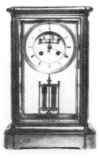

A gilt-brass mantel clock with
open Brocot escapement,
c.1900, 12½", 32 cm. **£240-280**
SBel

A gilt-metal and porcelain easel
timepiece, early 20th C., 13¼",
33.5 cm. **£390-450** SBel

A gilt-spelter and porcelain
mantel clock, late 19th C., 15½",
39.5 cm. **£250-350** SBel

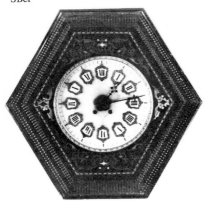

A Shell and Brass inlaid ebonised
wall clock, signed H. Ceyr Paris,
25½", 65 cm., late 19th C.,
£200-300 SBel

A fine 18th C. hooded wall clock
inscribed 'Robert Evens, Halstead',
anchor escapement. 33", 83 cm.
£510-580 B

A George II gilwood Cartel timepiece, signed Rich. Grove London
movement with verge escapement
and bob pendulum. 33", 84 cm.
high. **£1,500-1,800** SBS

An 18th C. Tavern or 'Act of
Parliament' clock by Goodyer,
London. 60", 152 cm. high.
£1,800-2,000 B

Regency period brass inlaid wall
clock by Hanson & Son, Windsor.
£275-310 PG

A mahogany wall timepiece,
signed Robt. Mack. Clerkenwell,
mid 19th C. 16", 40.5 cm.
£240-270 SBel

339

A Staartklok wall clock, late 19th C. White chapter ring, 30-hour anchor movement. 51½″, 130 cm. high. **£1,000-1,200** KC

An ormolu Cartel Clock signed Milleh a Paris; 33″, 84 cm. c.1890. **£300-500** SBel

An 18th C. Dutch Staartklok in oak case. Anchor escapement. 51½″, 130 cm. **£750-850** SBel

An early 19th C. Dutch oak Friesland Staartklok, brass pillared movement with 2 bells. 53″, 134 cm. high. **£1,200-1,600** B

Mahogany drop dial wall time-piece. 8 day anchor fusee movement. 12½″, 32 cm. high. **£260-300** KC

An 18th C. 30-hour wall or tavern clock, by Humphrey Sellon, London. 63″, 159.5 cm. high. **£400-500** OL

A mid-Georgian giltwood cartel clock with later movement. 27″, 68.5 cm. **£880-980** CStJ

An unusual alarum wall time-piece, signed Whitehurst, Derby, with plated movement with anchor escapement. 9″, 23 cm. high. **£600-700** SBS

Late Victorian walnut wall clock with 8 day movement. **£140-180** LE

A 19th C. postman's alarm wall clock. **£45-55** WW

A Rosewood Regulator, 39",
99 cm., late 19th C. £300-400
SBel

A Black Forest wall clock with
anchor escapement. 12", 30.5 cm.
dia. £280-340 B

A wall regulator, stamped Dent
Maker to the King, outside dead
beat escapement, Harrison's
maintaining power and high
count train, 84", 213 cm.
£7,000-8,000 HKC

A pewter-cased Wall Clock, 28",
72.5 cm., dated September 15th,
1926. £100-150 SBel

German marquetry wall timepiece. Gilt-metal skeleton chapter
ring, movement with narrow
plates and verge escapement.
16½", 41 cm. high. £1,200-
1,500 SBS

A skeleton Timepiece signed
Barrauds London 725, with
chain fusee and anchor escapement, 15", 38 cm. £600-700
SBS

A small gilt-metal telleruhr with
verge escapement. 8", 20 cm.
high. £1,100-1,200 SBS

Victorian brass gothic skeleton
clock with pierced painted dial.
14½", 37 cm. £46-56 WW

An important English astro-
nomical skeleton timepiece by
James Gorham, London, with
mean and sidereal time indication,
the detached lever escapement
with dead-beat 'scape wheel and
elaborate mercurial balance with
steel regulation crossbar, between
the globes a thermometer and
magnetic compass. 27", 68.5 cm.
£19,000-21,000 CStJ

Vaughan, Bristol. Brass skeleton
Timepiece of Gothic design.
silvered chapter ring, the fusee
movement with an anchor
escapement, 38 cm. high, £380-
430 PL

19th C. brass skeleton clock of Litchfield Cathedral design with pierced chapter ring, fusee movement with anchor escapement. 13½″, 35 cm. high on stand. £580-640 PL

A skeleton timepiece, brass structure, 8-day anchor fusee with skeletonised silvered dial. 14″, 35.5 cm. £200-230 HKC

Unusual early 19th C. Skeleton clock of 'Rafter' construction. £1,300-1,400 RBB

A 19th C. Skeleton clock, pierced silvered dial, 8-day double dead-beat movement, £620-700 KC

SKELETON CLOCKS

- c.1860
- very much an English fashion although style probably originated in France
- on the whole French clocks more valuable than English
- English clocks generally strike one stroke each hour
- often feature a typical English striking movement with rack and snail mechanism
- Fusees and barrels connected by chains instead of gut lines

---

A silvered brass skeleton timepiece, with anchor escapement and chain fusee 12½″, 32 cm., 19th C. £150-180 SBel

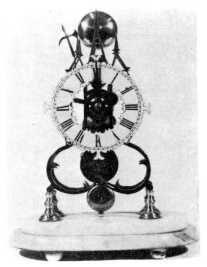

A brass skeleton clock. Movement with chain fusee and lever escapement, 15¼″, 38.8 cm., c.1890. £180-210 SBel

A brass Gothic skeleton clock on marble plinth with striking movement, under dome. £380-420 LJ

A repeating skeleton clock, the two train fusee movement with anchor escapement, marble base, under a glass dome, 19½″, 49.5 cm. £950-1,100 LC

A fine mahogany stick barometer, thermometer signed Dolland, London, 40", 102 cm. high. **£400-500**

A banjo barometer, thermometer above 13", 33 cm., silvered dial signed G. Rosse, Norwich, 45½", 115 cm. high. **£480-530** KC

A rare 'Royal' wheel barometer, dial signed J. Russell, Falkirk, Invt. Et Fecit, Watch-Maker to His R.H. The Prince of Wales, with thermometer (lacking tube), 42½", 108 cm. **£1,700-1,900** CStJ

A late Georgian mahogany wheel barometer, dial signed H. Westaway, Woolwich, 36", 91.5 cm. **£700-800** CStJ

A large mahogany clock barometer, verge escapement, signed William Terry, London, early 19th C. 3'7⅝", 111 cm. **£1,000-1,100** LC

A William and Mary walnut marquetry stick barometer with engraved brass face, 49", 125 cm., c.1880. **£900-1,000** SBel

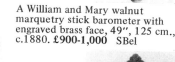

A mahogany stick barometer, with vernier scale, signed Joseph Somalivco, London, late 18th C., 38¼", 97.2 cm. **£450-500** LC

A mahogany stick barometer, with vernier scale, signed Henry Andrews, Royston, c.1790, 38¾", 38.5 cm. **£400-440** LC

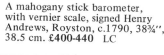

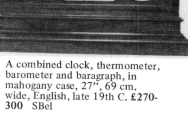

A late 17th C. stick barometer, 44", 111 cm. high. **£1,600-1,800** KC

A combined clock, thermometer, barometer and baragraph, in mahogany case, 27", 69 cm. wide, English, late 19th C. **£270-300** SBel

An oak barometer and timepiece, above a mercury thermometer and circular pressure dial, 44", 112 cm., 1880's. **£180-220** SBel

343

A mahogany stick barometer, the ivory register plate with vernier scale, signed W. Gardner, Glasgow, late 18th C., 37½", 95.3 cm. **£210-230** LC

A mother o'pearl inlaid rosewood barometer, signed Baker Horsham, c.1850, 40", 101.6 cm. **£130-160** LC

A mahogany wheel barometer, signed Josh. Ortaly, Fecit, London, early 19th C., 39½", 100.3 cm. **£360-390** LC

A mahogany wheel barometer inscribed P. Caminada Fecit, 38¼", 97.2 cm. **£240-260** LC

A French garniture de cheminee, c.1770, signed Causard Lyen du Roy, Paris, 14", 35.5 cm. high, with 2 candle holders, 12", 30.5 cm. **£1,200-1,400** KC

A gilt-bronze and alabaster composed clock garniture, signed L. Leroy & Co. Paris, 21½", 54.5 cm with urns, 12", 30.5 cm., c.1900. **£1,050-1,150** SBel

A gilt-spelter and porcelain clock garniture, stamped Hry. Marc. Paris, 14½", 37 cm., with urns, 11¾", 30 cm., c.1890. **£400-500** SBel

A gilt-bronze and porcelain composed clock garniture, signed H. Houdebine, 10", 25.5 cm., with candlesticks, 8¼", 21 cm., c.1880 **£700-800** SBel

A gilt-bronze and vernis martin clock garniture, by John Walker, 12", 30.5 cm. and vases, 11", 28 cm., early 20th C. **£320-390** SBel

An early 18th C. French garniture de cheminee, 8-day drum movement with count wheel, 13", 33 cm., with urns, 11", 27 cm. **£1,700-2,000** HKC

A gilt-spelter 'Sevres' mounted clock garniture, 1880's, 16″, 40.5 cm. **£360-400** SBel

An onyx champleve enamel and gilt-bronze mantel clock garniture, 12¾″, 32.5 cm., with urns, 11¾″, 30 cm., c.1890. **£880-980** SBel

A gilt-brass clock garniture, c.1890, 15″, 38 cm., with candlesticks, 10⅜″, 27 cm., **£340-400** SBel

A gilt-bronze and porcelain clock garniture, c.1890, 15¾″, 40 cm. **£340-400** SBel

A 19th C. garniture de cheminee, 20¼″, 52 cm. **£740-840** KC

A 19th C. garniture de cheminee, 8-day drum movement, 20¼″, 52 cm. high. **£920-1,050** KC

A Louis-Philippe ormolu and griotte marble clock-set, 20½″, 52 cm. **£500-600** CStJ

A gilt-spelter and 'Sevres' porcelain mounted clock garniture, 19″, 48 cm. with pair of urns and covers, late 19th C. **£360-400** SBel

A Gilt Spelter and Marble Clock Garniture, 12¾″, 32.5 cm., c.1900 **£200-240** SBel

A white marble and gilt-metal clock garniture, 13″, 33 cm., with candelabra, 9¼″, 23.5 cm., c.1900. **£230-300** SBel

A gilt-spelter and marble clock garniture, c.1900, 12½″, 32 cm., with urns, 9¾″, 25 cm. **£210-260** SBel

A spelter timepiece garniture, early 20th C., 29¾″, 76 cm. **£250-350** SBel

A Lantern Clock, signed Ed. Hemins Bisiter, the movement with anchor escapement, 1′2½″, 37 cm. high. **£1,500-1,700** SBS

A brass lantern clock dial signed John Ebsworth in New Cheap Side Londini Fecit, 12½″, 32 cm. high, with later bell. **£1,400-1,600** CStJ

An early 18th C. Lantern Clock, case of brass, signed Wm. Kipling, London 30 hour posted movement with verge and count-wheel 14¼″, 36 cm. high. **£900-1,000** KC

William Kipling, London, an 18th C. brass Lantern clock, pierced cresting pieces and a verge escapement, 18.5 cm. high. £800-900 PL

John Knibb Oxford, a small brass striking lantern clock, signed John Knibb, Oxon, the movement with verge escapement, 8½", 21.5 cm. high, £1,000-1,200 CStJ

A 17th C. brass Lantern Clock inscribed 'Tho. Wheeler, near Ye French Church', movement with anchor escapement, 16", 40 cm. high. £2,150-2,400 PL

A Hamilton 2-day marine chronometer, in gimbal mounts, mahogany case, 7", 18 cm. high, American, early 20th C. £250-500 SBel

Parkinson & Frodsham. 2-day Marine Chronometer, with an Earnshaw escapement, gimbal fitting, mahogany and brass case, 6¼", 16 cm. square. £780-880 PL

A rare gilt-metal cased falling ball clock, by J. Schlemmer of Schleswig. Movement with fusee, going barrel, 3-wheel train, 3³/₈", 9.3 cm. diam. £14,000-16,000 SBS

A brass 5-minute repeating keyless lever chronograph by Tiffany and Co. the visible movement with compensation balance. 1½", 3.9 cm., £200-300 SBel

A gilt bronze Desk Timepiece and Compass, stamped Rodrigues 42 Piccadilly, 4½", 11.5 cm., c.1860. £440-500 SBel

A William Comyns Silver-cased Boudoir Clock, 4½", 10.5 cm., makers' mark, London 1900. French Movement. £200-230 SBel

An Enamel Boudoir Clock, 4½",
11 cm., probably French, c.1885,
£480-560 SBel

A Polish gilt-metal table clock,
the bridge-cock verge movement
signed Antoni Barisch Fecit
Cracoviae, with resting barrel
for the passing quarter-strike and
fusee and chain for the gong,
3¼", 8.3 cm. diam. of dial,
c.1700. **£2,400-2,700** CStJ

A French tortoiseshell covered
travelling clock with brass mounts,
8", 20 cm. **£270-300** RB

An octagonal brass cased striking
centre seconds Japanese table
clock, fusee and chain for
verge escapement, 19th C., 3",
7.4 cm. **£4,500-5,000** SBS

A Japanese stick clock, balance
wheel with verge escapement, the
trunk with the chapter scales,
15¾", 40 cm. high, fitted box.
c.1870. **£900-1,000** CStJ

An onyx and gilt-bronze pedestal
clock, with half-hour striking,
49", 125 cm., c.1900. **£300-400**
SBel

19th C. French Kingwood and
Rosewood pedestal clock in Louis
XVI style, 8 day striking movement, 85", 215.5 cm. **£4,100-
4,500** MH

Brass time-piece suspended on
ivory tusks, **£300-360** JHR

A good japanese Pillar Timepiece.
Verge escapement, the trunk
containing the weight. 26½'',
67.5 cm. high. £780-880 PL

A gold 18 ct. good minute
repeating keyless lever watch
by Jos'h Penlington, Liverpool,
with three-quarter plate movement,
hallmarked 1873. 2'', 5.2 cm.
£1,650-1,850 SBel

A Japanese pillar clock, the weight
driven movement with verge
escapement. Hood incomplete.
15³⁄₈'', 39 cm. £400-440 LC

3

6:

6:

A lady's dress watch, with 18 ct.
gold case, key-wind cylinder
movement. £95-125 KC

A Swiss gold hunter-cased minute-
repeating keyless lever chronograph, signed J.M. Wendt, Adelaide,
& Mt. Gambler; 2¼'', 5.7 cm.
diam. £1,800-2,000 CStJ

A gold and enamel cylinder
watch by Bautte & Co. of
Geneva No. 64338, mid 19th C.
1½'', 3.8 dia. gold key set.
£500-800

A lady's dress watch, with
18 ct. gold case and key-wind
lever movement with fusee.
£160-200 KC

A gold pair cased cylinder watch,
brass escape wheel, signed Graham,
London, hall-marked 1727, 2'',
4.8 cm. dia. £1,200-1,400 SBS

A lady's dress watch, with 18 ct.
gold case, key-wind cylinder
movement. £110-150 KC

A lady's dress watch, with 18 ct.
gold case, keyless three-quarter
plate lever movement. £95-130
KC

A gold Hunter-cased cylinder watch. Gilt movement with balance cock with substantial diamond end-stone, escapement with steel 'scape wheel, signed Jno. Brockbanks, London, 2846, London, 1814, 2¼", 5.8 cm. dia. £800-900 CStJ

A French gold ruby cylinder quarter-repeating watch, the gilt movement quarter-repeating on two gongs, the gilt cuvette signed Hunliker a Paris, No.1342, 2¼", 6.0 cm. diam. £1,400-1,600 CStJ

A French gold quarter-repeating ruby cylinder watch, the cuvette signed Breguet A Paris, No. 1464, silver engine-turned dial numbered on the underside 3705 and signed Breguet et Fils; tipsy key, 2", 5.1 cm. diam. £2,800-3,100 CStJ

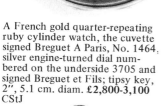

A gold cylinder watch and chatelaine by Leroy of Paris, 1½", 3.6 cm., 19th C. £600-800 SBS

A Swiss gold and enamel verge watch, the bridge-cock movement with eccentric chapter-ring, 1½", 4.0 cm. diam. £300-340 CStJ

A French gold quarter-repeating musical cylinder watch, the pin-barrel concealed beneath shaped plate. Inscribed Leroy a Paris, 2¼", 5.7 cm. dia. £2,100-2,300 CStJ

A gold quarter repeating cylinder watch by Moulinie Bautte of Moynier, 2", 5.1 cm. dia. c.1830. £580-680 SBel

A gold cylinder watch by Ate. Ame. Perrenoud of Chaux-de-Fonds, the Lepine calibre movement with plain three-armed balance, 1842, 2", 4.9 cm., £300-400 SBS

A Swiss gold and enamel hunter-cased cylinder watch, with cuvette signed Larroix & Falconner Geneve, 1½", 3.6 cm. long. £850-950 CStJ

A Swiss cylinder watch, the gilt movement with engine-turned dial, 1½", 3.6 cm. diam. £220-240 CStJ

A rare silver pair-cased mock pendulum watch with calendar, the verge movement signed Robert Anderton, London, 153, cases plain, 2¼", 5.8 cm. diam. **£2,100-2,400** CStJ

A gold quarter-repeating automaton verge watch, signed Breguet & Fils, c.1820. 2¼", 5.5 cm., **£2,000-2,200** SBS

An 18 ct. gold open-faced lever watch no. 529 by Jane Gardner, Coventry, Hallmarked, 1818, 1¾", 4.4 cm., **£230-260** SBel

A verge watch by Wm. Barrow, London, No. 1890, in silver pair cases, c.1725, 2¼", 5.3 cm., **£400-500** PL

A French gold quarter-repeating Jacquemart verge watch, the bridge-cock movement signed Breguet & Fils, No. 23593, 2¼", 5.6 cm. diam. **£1,500-1,700** CStJ

An 18th C. carved wood watch stand, damaged, containing a verge watch movement by Goret of Paris, 11¼", 28.5 cm., wormed. **£300-350** SBS

A continental silver verge watch, signed Abm. Blanchoi with cuvette signed Philipe Senechau, 2¾", 7.1 cm. dia. **£300-350** CStJ

An 18 ct. gold open-faced lever watch No. 7414 by Louis Bornand, Geneva, 2¼", 5.2 cm. dia. **£230-260** SBel

A gold and enamel pair-cased verge watch, signed Abraham Colomby, 1½", 4.2 cm. dia. **£1,100-1,200** CStJ

A gilt metal cased verge watch, early 17th C. the movement with turned baluster pillars, signed W.J. Kittson att Yorke. **£600-700** LC

A 'Pendulum' verge Watch, by Cornelius Manley, Norwich, the movement with Egyptian pillars, enamel dial, in silver pair cases, London 1740. 2¼", 5:7 cm. dia. **£460-520** PL

A gold repousse pair-cased verge watch, the movement signed John Pyke, London, shagreen protecting case, 1¾", 4.8 cm. diam. **£950-1,100** CStJ

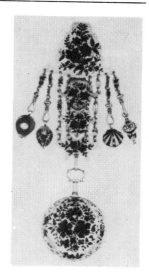

A gold half-quarter-repeating verge watch and chatelaine, No. 2982 by Roger Simpkinson of London, 2", 4.8 cm. dia. c.1790. **£7,500-8,500** SBS

A gold pair-cased repousse verge watch, the movement signed Saml. Northcote, Plymouth, inner case plain (London, 1756), 2", 4.8 cm. diam. **£1,200-1,400** CStJ

A quarter repeating verge Watch, with diamond endstone, the cap signed, c.1720, the dial and cases later, Daniel Quare, 2¼", 5.6 cm. dia. **£820-900** PL

Thomas Tompion and George Graham No. 4543. A gilt-metal verge watch, 2¼", 5.5 cm. dia. 1713. **£900-1,100** SBS

A gold quarter repeating hunting cased keyless lever watch, 2¼", 5.3 cm. dia. **£240-270** SBel

A gold and enamel rose-diamond set scarab watch, with cylinder escapement, c.1900, 2¼", 5.9 cm. **£1,200-1,600** SBS

A gold and enamel verge watch, by George Prior, London, with diamond endstone, 1½", 4 cm. **£1,800-2,000** CStJ

A 14 ct. gold hunting cased keyless lever watch No. 26198 1", 2.4 cm. dia. **£150-180** SBel

An 18 ct. gold hunting cased lever watch by Geo. Edward & Son, London and Glasgow. Hallmarked 1877, 2″, 5 cm. dia. **£305-380** SBel

An 18 ct. gold Hunting cased lever watch No. 88639 by Lebet, Geneve, with bar movement and compensation balance, 1¾″, 4.5 cm. **£350-400** SBel

A gold hunting cased keyless lever watch Appleton, Tracy and Co. of Waltham, Mass., 2¼″, 5.4 cm. dia. **£500-600** SBel

A Swiss gold hunter-cased minute-repeating keyless lever watch, movement signed A. Lecoultre, Geneve; 2″, 5.1 cm. diam. **£400-450** CStJ

A good gold half-hunting cased keyless level minute repeating watch No. 04797 by E.F. Ashley of Clerkenwell, hallmarked 1898, 2¼″, 5.5 cm. **£1,500-1,700** SBel

A Swiss gold and enamel hunter-cased keyless lever watch, the jewelled movement signed Victor Jeannot, Geneve, No. 30373, 2″, 5.2 cm. diam. **£400-600** CStJ

A French gold lever watch, the Lepine calibre movement signed on the cuvette Leroy & Fils, Hgrs. du Roi A Pairs; 1¾″, 4.5 cm diam. **£240-270** CStJ

A gold keyless lever watch by Jules Jurgensen, the nickel-finished movement, No. 14592, with signed enamel dial, and subsidiary seconds, 2″, 5.0 cm. diam. **£900-1,000** CStJ

An unusual silver-gilt cased watch, signed James Cole, London, No. SD. and with plain gold balance and lever escapement; case plain (London 1819), 2½″, 6.2 cm. diam. **£700-800** CStJ

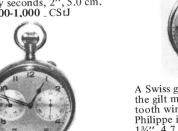

A Swiss gold keyless lever watch, the gilt movement with Wolf's tooth wind and signed Patek, Philippe i Spolka w Genewie, 1¾″, 4.7 cm. diam. **£400-600** CStJ

A German silver deck watch, the keyless lever movement signed A. Lange & Sohne, Glashutte i Sa, 2¼″, 5.9 cm. diam. **£950-1,050** CStJ

A gentleman's pocket watch, late 19th C. with button-wind Swiss lever movement. **£490-590** KC

A continental gold quarter-repeating and musical watch with virgule escapement, the gilt cuvette signed Decombaz No. 895, 2¼", 5.8 cm. diam. **£2,800-3,100** CStJ

A gold centre seconds Alarum watch, No. 15/586 by Terroux L'Aine of Geneva, alarum pulse piece, 2¼", 5.8 cm., c.1790. with gold chain. **£1,500-1,700** SBS

A Swiss gold and enamel watch, the gilt bridge-cock movement signed Chevalier & Compe., 3925, 2", 5.1 cm., enamel repaired. **£1,300-1,500** CStJ

A quality keyless wind watch 18 ct. gold full hunter case, signed Chas. Frodsham, AD Fmsz, hallmark 1888. **£7,500-8,300** KC

A Champleve enamel desk watch, 7½", 19 cm., c.1900. **£310-340** SBel

A silver-gilt and enamel duplex watch, the bridge movement signed Richardson, London, 571, with plain steel balance. 2¼", 5.5 cm. diam. **£2,000-2,500** CStJ

A pocket Chronometer by C.J. Cope, London No. 52280. Full plate movement with chrono-meter balance and segmented weights, helical spring, Earnshaw spring detent escapement, c.1825. 2¼", 5.5 cm., **£500-600** PK

A French enamel Fob watch, early 20th C. 2", 5.2 cm. long. **£600-660** SBel

An unusual Swiss hunter-cased double-dial calendar watch, with keyless movement with engine-turned dial, 2¼", 5.4 cm. diam. **£900-1,000** CStJ

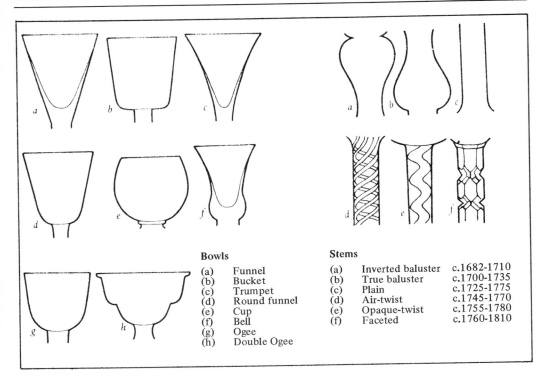

Bowls

(a) Funnel
(b) Bucket
(c) Trumpet
(d) Round funnel
(e) Cup
(f) Bell
(g) Ogee
(h) Double Ogee

Stems

(a) Inverted baluster   c.1682-1710
(b) True baluster   c.1700-1735
(c) Plain   c.1725-1775
(d) Air-twist   c.1745-1770
(e) Opaque-twist   c.1755-1780
(f) Faceted   c.1760-1810

A fine cut decanter of dark metal, probably Irish, diamond and sunburst cut with facet neck. c.1820. 10¼'' high, 26 cm. **£80-100** SA

A small Cork decanter. Engraved with vesica motif, inscribed T N H, 7¾'', 19.5 cm. c.1800. **£240-290** SIre

An early 19th C. heavily cut decanter, strawberry cut diamonds and cut neck rings. Matching stopper. 10¾'', 27 cm. **£70-90** SA

An engraved Cork decanter and stopper, the base impressed CORK GLASS CO., frilled target stopper, 8¾'', 22 cm. c.1800. **£330-370** SIre

A pair of tapered decanters with base fluting and facet cut neck, plain lozenge stoppers, c.1790. 11'' high, 28 cm. **£200-220** SA

A large decanter and spire stopper enamelled in blue and white, 20¼'', 56 cm. c.1850. **£900-1,000** SBel

Hog in the form of a decanter, amber glass eyes and opaque white teeth. £70-120

An 18th C. Bristol green decanter, three neck rings, lozenge stopper, c.1770. 11¾", 30 cm. £150-200 SA

A Large Green Glass Decanter and Spire Stopper, 20½", 52 cm, c.1850. £200-230 SBel

An early 19th C. decanter, band of strawberry cut diamonds, horizontally prism cut neck, matching stopper, c.1825. 9", 23 cm., £60-80 SA

A moulded cruciform decanter, 8¾", 22.2 cm, early 18th C. £50-60 LC

A tapered decanter, scale cut neck and band of engraving round body. Lozenge stopper. c.1770. 11¼" high, 28.5 cm. £170-200 SA

A mallet shaped decanter, with lunar cut lozenge stopper. c.1770. 11½", 29 cm. £200-240 SA

A Pair of Sunderland Bridge Decanters and Stoppers, 9½", 24 cm, c.1820. £440-500 SBS

An early 18th C. cruciform moulded decanter, with string ring round neck and loose fitting stopper. c.1740. 10¾", 27 cm. £100-120 SA

An 18th C. magnum decanter, c.1770. 12½" high, 33 cm. £400-450 SA

A Waterford decanter, the base impressed PENROSE WATER-FORD, wafer stopper, 8″, 20 cm. c.1800. **£320-360** SIre

A pair of George III Waterford glass decanters, with ribbed necks and two bands of etching, 19″ high, 48 cm. c.1780. **£3,000-3,500** SBS

George III Waterford Glass decanter cut with meandering feather band and stars, 20″ high, 51 cm. c.1780. **£2,200-2,400** SBS

An unusual pair of decanters and 'flame'-stoppers, 16½″, 41.9 cm. c.1840. **£120-140**

A small Rodney decanter, three diamond cut neck rings, bulls eye stopper, probably Irish, c.1810. 9¼″, 23.5 cm. **£100-120** SA

An Unusual Enamelled Flask with false handles, 5½″, 13.8 cm, 1875. **£220-250** SBel

A mid 18th C. two compartment decanter with folded foot and applied trailing around necks. 8¼″ high, 21 cm. c.1750. **£100-120** SA

A two compartment Gimmel flask of clear glass with trans-lucent red and white looping, c.1850. 9½″, 24 cm. **£60-80** SA

A small flask, signed 'Galle', iridescent colours 6½″, 16.5 cm. early 20th C. **£300-400** SA

A Central-European enamelled flask, metal mount. 5½″, 14 cm. c.1750. **£180-210** SBS

A Central-European enamelled flask, white, yellow, rust, blue and green, metal screw-cap, 6¾″, 17 cm. c.1750. **£110-140** SBS

A Central-European enamelled flask decorated, blue, yellow and rust, metal screw-cap, 7", 18 cm. c.1750. £520-600 SBS

A Rare Silver, Gilt and Bronzed Moon Flask in amber glass, 10", 25 cm, 1875. £200-230 SBel

A Central-European enamelled flask, metal screw mount. 4¾", 12 cm., c.1750. £170-190 SBS

An opaque white flask with translucent red looping, c.1860. 7¼", 18 cm. £60-80 SA

A clear glass Nailsea flask with opaque white looped decoration, c.1860. 10¾", 21.5 cm. £40-50 SA[

An opaque white flask with red, white and blue looping, probably Stourbridge. c.1860. 7½", 19 cm. £60-80 SA

An early bristol blue flask. c.1800. 6¾", 17 cm. £50-60 SA

A rare Pugh Brandy Bottle. 12½", 33 cm. Pugh Glass House, Dublin, c.1870. £900-1,000 SIre

A Central-European enamelled flask, white, rust, ochre-green and blue, metal screw-cap, 8½", 21.5 cm. c.1750. £210-240 SBS

An early Nailsea clear bottle with red and blue flecking, c.1790. 10¾", 22 cm. £250-300 SA

A pair of deep amethyst iced water bottles, probably Bristol, c.1780. 11¾", 29.5 cm. **£180-220** SA

A set of 3 Georgian spirit bottles and stoppers, c.1800. **£200-240** LC

A good Galle etched and enamelled Glass Bottle and Stopper, the body in green glass mottled with streaks of orange, 12", 30.5 cm. incised mark 'Cristallerie d'Emile Galle modele et decor deposes', 1890's. **£800-900** SBel

An early sealed wine bottle with a large 'wafer' seal inscribed 'R. Howe at Chedworth 1683', the metal of light-green tone but considerably pitted. 6", 15 cm. c.1683. **£750-850** SBS

A sealed Wine bottle, 8", 20 cm. c.1720. **£340-450** SBS

A German enamelled Pharmacy Bottle inscribed 'Fumal', 3¾", 9.5 cm. c.1740. **£240-270** SBS

A pair of 18th Century green glass Spirit Bottles, 11½", 29.2 cm. **£80-110** KC

A German enamelled Apothecary Bottle inscribed Sigil. Rubr. 3¾", 9.6 cm. c.1740. **£240-280** SBS

A Rare Commemorative Wine Glass. Solid base enclosing tear-shaped air bubble, 6½", 16.5 cm, c.1715. **£1,800-2,000** SBS

A Newcastle Wine Glass, Dutch wheel-engraved, 7½", 19 cm. **£500-550** GSP

A Newcastle Wine Glass, Dutch wheel-engraved, 7¾", 19.5 cm. **£190-210** GSP

A Pair of Jacobite Wine Glasses, 6", 15 cm, c.1750. **£600-660** SBS

A Newcastle Wine Glass, Dutch wheel-engraved, 7½", 19 cm. **£300-330** GSP

A Newcastle Wine Glass, Dutch wheel-engraved, 7¼", 18.5 cm. **£260-290** GSP

A Newcastle Wine Glass, Dutch wheel-engraved, 7", 17.5 cm. **£300-330** GSP

A Newcastle Wine Glass, Dutch wheel-engraved, 7¼", 18.5 cm. **£460-500** GSP

An engraved masonic wine glass, the ogee bowl with Masonic emblem and two leaf sprays, double series opaque-twist stem, conical foot. 6", 15 cm. c.1760. **£60-80** SIre

An engraved masonic wine glass, the round funnel bowl moulded at the base, engraved with a Masonic emblem, double series opaque-twist stem, conical foot, 6", 15 cm. c.1760. **£58-75** SIre

An unusual 'Facon de Venise' small wine glass. Hollow baluster stem with two serpentine 'wings' in blue glass and two blue glass rings attached by clear glass loops, on a wide foot with slight fold on one side, 6", 15.3 cm. probably German or Netherlands, early 17th Century. **£750-950** PL

A 'Facon de Venise" Serpent stem wine glass. Unusual octagonal faceted bowl, red and white coiled stem, edged in bright blue pincered work glass. 6¾", 17.2 cm. German or Netherlands, early 17th century. **£1,500-1,700** PL

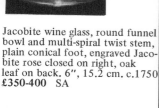

Jacobite wine glass, round funnel bowl and multi-spiral twist stem, plain conical foot, engraved Jacobite rose closed on right, oak leaf on back. 6", 15.2 cm. c.1750 **£350-400** SA

A wine glass with a round funnel bowl, multi-spiral air twist stem, plain domed foot, c.1735. 6", 15 cm. **£100-120** SA

A wine glass, the round-funnel bowl set on an unusually tightly-packed multi-spiral air-twist gauze, conical foot, 5¾", 14.5 cm. c.1750. **£75-95** SBS

Wine glass with round funnel bowl, moulded base, single series air twist stem with two spiralling cables and plain conical foot. c.1740. 6½", 16.7 cm. **£100-110** SA

Wine glass with round funnel bowl, multi-spiral air twist stem, shoulder knop, plain conical foot. Bowl engraved with band of fruiting vine. c.1760. **£120-140** SA

A wine glass with round funnel bowl and panel moulded at base. Double series opaque white twist stem and plain conical foot, c.1760. 5½", 14 cm. **£70-90** SA

A wine glass with round funnel bowl, engraved hops and barley, double series opaque white twist stem, plain conical foot, c.1760. 6¼", 16 cm. **£120-130** SA

A Lynn wine glass with round funnel bowl and five radially moulded rings. Double series opaque white twist thread and plain conical foot, c.1760. 5½", 14 cm. **£150-160** SA

One of a set of six wine glasses, round funnel bowl. Gilt bouquet of roses and floral sprigs, gilt band on rim. Double series opaque white twist stem, plain conical foot. c.1760. 5½", 14 cm. **£150-170** SA

A balustroid wine glass, the round funnel bowl, the plain stem set in to an inverted baluster knop with two rows of air tears, folded conical foot, c.1730. 7¼", 18 cm. **£100-120** SA

A heavy baluster wine glass, round funnel bowl with tear in base, set on cushion and inverted baluster knop stem, folded conical foot. c.1720. 6½", 16.5 cm. **£250-300** SA

A Newcastle wine glass, the round funnel bowl finely Dutch engraved with baroque scrolling, set on a typical Newcastle stem with inverted baluster knop containing two rows of air beads. Plain conical foot., c.1720. 7¼", 18 cm. **£480-520** SA

A late 17th C. wine glass with heavy baluster round funnel bowl with thick base and tear, set on inverted baluster stem, folded conical foot. c.1690. 5½", 14.2 cm. **£450-500** SA

A wine glass, the round funnel bowl set on a teared stem with shoulder cushion knop, folded conical foot, c.1750. 6½", 16.3 cm. **£70-90** SA

Wine glass with round funnel bowl engraved with stars and printies, conical folded foot, c.1750. 5¼", 13 cm. **£40-50** SA

A wine glass with round funnel bowl, with feint vertical and honeycomb moulding. Fine incised twist stem and plain conical foot, c.1750. 5½", 14.2 cm. **£120-140** SA

Wine glass with round funnel bowl, engraved band of baroque scrolling, stem with horizontal notching, folded conical foot, c.1770. 5¾", 14.2 cm. **£120-130** SA

A wine glass, the funnel bowl engraved with a band of fruiting vine, on a drawn stem with centre angular knop, high plain conical foot, c.1730. 6½", 16.5 cm. **£260-280** SA

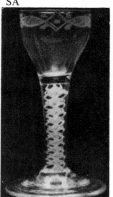

A Newcastle wine glass, the round funnel bowl engraved in Holland with house and tree scene, and the inscription 'Twelvaren van Vecht Stroom' — set on a multi-knop stem, domed conical foot, c.1720. 7¼", 18.7 cm. **£450-500** SA

A wine glass with flared funnel bowl set on a stem with an inverted baluster and base knop containing a central air tear, conical folded foot, probably Newcastle, c.1740. 6", 15.2 cm. **£130-150** SA

A wine glass with ogee bowl and engraved rim with hatched design, double series opaque white twist stem and plain conical foot, c.1760 5¼", 13.4 cm. **£70-90** SA

Wine glass with flared ogee bowl, band of stars and printies at edge. Double series opaque white twist thread stem, plain conical foot. c.1770. 5¼", 13.5 cm. **£70-80** SA

Belby wine glass with ogee bowl, band of opaque white fruiting vine, traces of enamel gilding at rim. Double series opaque white twist stem, plain conical foot. c.1765. 5¾", 14.8 cm. **£600-650** SA

Wine glass with ogee bowl, pan top. Multi-spiral air twist stem, shoulder and centre knop, plain conical foot. c.1750. 6", 15.3 cm. **£100-120** SA

A wine glass with ogee bowl and vertically moulded at base. Multi-spiral opaque white twist stem and centre swelling knop, with plain conical foot, c.1760. 5¾", 14.6 cm. **£80-90** SA

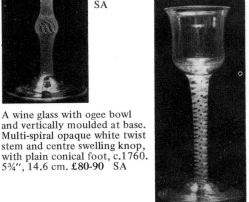

Wine glass with ogee bowl decorated with gilt fruiting vine and with gilt rim. Drawn plain stem, conical foot, c.1750. 5¾", 14.5 cm. **£150-170** SA

A wine glass with ogee bowl and everted rim stem with double series opaque twist thread, plain conical foot, c.1760. 6¼", 15.5 cm. **£70-80** SA

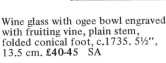

Wine glass with ogee bowl engraved with fruiting vine, plain stem, folded conical foot, c.1735. 5½", 13.5 cm. **£40-45** SA

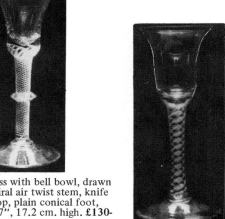

Wine glass with ogee pan topped bowl, drawn hexagon facet cut stem, thick conical foot. c.1770. 5¾", 14.5 cm. **£120-130** SA

Wine glass with bell bowl, drawn multi-spiral air twist stem, knife edge knop, plain conical foot, c.1750. 7", 17.2 cm. high. **£130-150** SA

Wine glass with bell bowl, multi spiral air twist stem with four knops. Plain domed foot, c.1740. 6½", 16.5 cm. **£450-500** SA

A colour twist wine glass, with bell bowl on stem, centre opaque cork screw with spiralling red, white and green threads, plain conical foot, c.1780. 7", 17.2 cm. **£580-550** SA

A mixed twist wine glass with bell bowl and central air twist gauze. Pair of opaque white spiralling threads on outside and plain conical foot, c.1760. 6¾", 17 cm. **£180-200** SA

A heavy baluster wine glass with a bell bowl and air tear in base, set on a teared acorn knop with inverted baluster and base below, domed folded foot, c.1720. 6½", 16.3 cm. **£700-800** SA

A wine glass with bell bowl and multi-spiral opaque white twist stem, shoulder and centre knops and plain conical foot, c.1770. 6¼", 15.6 cm. **£120-130** SA

A wine glass with bell bowl set on an acorn multi-knopped stem folded conical foot, c.1740. 6¼", 16 cm. **£180-200** SA

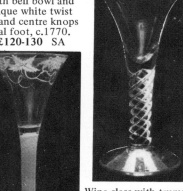

A wine glass with bell bowl, set on a six sided star-studded moulded Silesian stem, folded conical foot, c.1730. 7", 17.5 cm. **£100-120** SA

Wine glass with trumpet bowl, drawn stem with four multi-spiral air twist threads, plain conical foot, 6", 15.2 cm. c.1740. **£70-90** SA

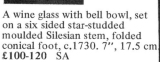

Belby wine glass with trumpet bowl, close multi-spiral opaque white twist thread stem, plain conical foot. Band of opaque white enamel fruiting vine with traces of gilding. c.1760. 7", 17.5 cm. **£600-650** SA

A wine glass with trumpet bowl engraved in diamond point around rim with animals and flowers, on a drawn plain stem containing air tear, conical folded foot. 6½", 16.6 cm. c.1720 **£80-100** SA

A Silesian wine glass with bucket bowl set on an eight sided moulded (or pedestal) stem, Plain conical foot. c.1730. 7¼", 18 cm. **£200-250** SA

A wine glass, the bucket bowl set on a stem with a shoulder cushion knop and base knop containing tears, folded conical foot, c.1745. 6", 15.2 cm. **£70-90** SA

Wine glass with bucket bowl engraved with hatched rose, plain stem, folded conical foot, c.1750. 5¾", 14.7 cm. **£50-70** SA

Wine glass with wasted bucket bowl, multi-spiral air twist stem, folded conical foot, 6", 15.2 cm. c.1750. **£100-110** SA

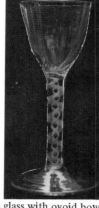

A colour twist wine glass with ovoid bowl, vertically moulded base stem with spiralling opaque white lace corkscrew and solid opaque tape edged in translucent blue, plain conical foot, c.1775. 6", 15 cm. **£500-550** SA

A wine glass with ovoid bowl and panel moulded. Double series opaque white twist stem, plain conical foot, c.1760. 7", 17.7 cm. **£100-110** SA

A wine glass with pan top bowl and vertically moulded at base. Double series opaque white twist stem and plain conical foot, c.1760. 6", 15.4 cm. **£90-100** SA

A deceptive wine glass with heavy conical bowl, set on a teared inverted baluster stem, folded conical foot. c.1720. 4¾", 12.2 cm. **£250-300** SA

An unusual wine glass, the conical flared bowl with wrythen moulded base, set on a double series air-twist stem and conical foot, 7", 17.5 cm. c.1750. **£140-170** SBS

A wine glass with pan top bowl, engraved band with fruiting vine and butterfly, multi-spiral air twist stem, swelling knop, with plain conical foot. c.1750. 6¼", 15.8 cm. **£120-130** SA

A tall goblet with funnel bowl well engraved with a stork in flight above bamboo and prunus blossom, set on a twisted stem and engraved folded foot. c.1880. 19", 47.5 cm. **£130-150** SBel

Goblet with funnel bowl, drawn plain stem with air tear, folded conical foot, c.1720. 8¾", 22.2 cm. high. **£70-80** SA

A Fine Baluster Goblet, 8¾", 22 cm, c.1700. **£550-600** SBS

A goblet with conical bowl, cut band of small diamonds above bridge cutting. Ball knop stem, conical foot, star cut underneath. c.1830. 5½", 13.6 cm. **£25-30** SA

A rummer with conical bowl, engraved view of Sunderland Bridge and ship in full sail. Words 'Sunderland Bridge' on reverse side and floral garlands and initials C.W.C. & M.A. in hexagonal cartouch, c.1820. 5½", 14 cm. **£150-160** SA

A Dutch engraved wine goblet, teared knopped stem, conical folded foot, 7", 17.5 cm. and an Engraved Cover with cup spire finial, c.1740. **£180-240** SBS

A coin goblet with bucket bowl engraved with hops and barley, and floral cartouche with initials W.M.M. On reverse side, the words 'George Morrell, born 27 November 1833, dies 7th February 1838' Hollow knopped stem containing a groat dated 1836, plain conical foot. c.1836, 7½", 19 cm. **£130-140** SA

A rare 'Facon de Venise' "Ice Glass" Goblet. Moulded to simulate ice, enriched at the sides with blue glass "C" scrolls edged with pincered clear glass, end 16th/17th Century. 6¼", 16.2 cm. **£950-1,100** PL

A rummer with tapered bowl engraved with Nelson's catafalque and words 'Trafalgar, Nile & Victory'. Plain stem, plain conical foot, c.1803. 5½", 13.8 cm. **£130-140** SA

A Masonic goblet with straight sided bowl, band of base flute cutting, engraved various masonic symbols with the initials J.B. in cartouche. Short stem and annulated knop, plain conical foot. c.1810. 6″, 15 cm. **£150-160** SA

A single flint goblet with teared funnel bowl set on a teared annulated base knop stem, domed and folded foot. c.1700. 7¼″, 18.7 cm. **£400-500** SA

A goblet with ogee bowl, engraved fruiting vine and bird in flight, single series opaque twist stem, two spiralling tapes, plain conical foot, c.1760. 7¼″, 18.5 cm. **£100-110** SA

Goblet with ogee bowl, bridge cut band of strawberry diamonds between horizontal prism cutting, band of narrow flute cuts above set on step with knife edge knop, plain conical foot, c.1820. 6¼″, 16 cm. **£50-60** SA

A Nuremberg goblet, engraved with a coat of arms inscribed "Vivat Josefus Romischer Kaiser" set on a hollow inverted baluster knop between mereses and a compressed knop below, on circular foot. 9″. 22.8 cm., c.1705 **£350-400** LC

A goblet with ovoid bowl, set on an eight-sided Silesian stem with base collar, domed conical foot, c.1750. 6¾″, 17 cm. **£80-100** SA

Rummer with ovoid bowl, engraved band of scrolling and darts. Initials H.T. outlined in gilt. Case of bowlflute cut, domed moulded square base. c.1800. 5½″, 14 cm. **£60-70** SA

A Rare Engraved Presentation Goblet, 9¾″, 24.5 cm, 1824. **£750-850** SBel

A Good Lobmeyr Goblet and Cover, 11″, 28 cm, c.1870. **£240-270** SBel

A Rare Bohemian Engraved Goblet, 4¼", 11 cm, c.1810. **£210-230** SBel

An Unusual Waldglas Goblet of bubbly green-tinted metal, 6", 15 cm, late 17th c. **£230-250** SBS

A Green-Tinted Roemer, 6½", 16.5 cm, Rhenish, late 17th C. **£450-500** SBS

A Dutch Goblet, c.1735. **£420-460** SBS

A Large Bohemian engraved Screw-Goblet, c.1735. **£420-460** SBS

A Fine Dutch-Engraved Newcastle Goblet, 7¼", 18.5 cm, c.1750. **£750-850** SBS

A Pair of Overlay Goblets, 7", 17.5 cm, c.1850. **£160-180** SBel

A very fine opaque white goblet with sunflowers in coloured enamels, gilt banding, probably Richardsons, Stourbridge, c.1850. 6¾", 16.9 cm. **£150-200** SA

A fine pair of red glass Bohemian goblets and covers, c.1814. 16½" high, 32 cm. **£76-90** KC

A Bohemian engraved Goblet and Cover. The whole overlaid in translucent red and finely carved with a continuous scene. 16¼", 41.2 cm. c.1850. **£400-500** SBS

A portrait goblet, the clear glass overlaid in white and carved with ·enamelled panel, the remainder carved with oak leaves and acorns above flutes, the details gilt, 5¾", 14.5 cm. c.1850. **£150-180** SBel

Jacobite wine cordial glass with trumpet bowl multi-spiral air twist stem, plain conical foot, c.1750. 6", 15 cms. **£400-450** SA

A rare two-handled coin goblet, the body with swelling base and everted lip, set on a hollow flattened knop containing a Queen Anne penny above a wide terraced foot, double applied loop handles. 5⅞", 15 cm., c.1710. **£380-450** SBS

A pair of cut goblets, the large conical bowl with a sun-and-star border, facet-cut round the base. c.1780. 6¼", 15.5 cm. **£200-240** SIre

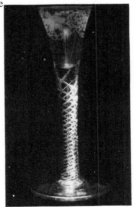

Cordial glass with trumpet bowl on drawn multi-spiral air twist stem. Plain conical foot, c.1750. 7", 17.5 cms. **£130-150** SA

A dram glass with cup shape bowl moulded at base and short drawn stem. Terraced conical foot, c.1750. 3¾", 9.5 cm. **£50-60** SA

A diamond point engraved 'Facon de Venise' Goblet. Bowl engraved with two birds. Hollow spirally fluted stem, wings in blue glass edged in pincered clear glass, foot with narrow fold and diamond point engraved with four leaves. 6¾", 17 cm. Netherlands, early 17th Century. **£1,800-2,000** PL

A Set of Six George II Cordial Glasses, c.1745. **£260-280** WW

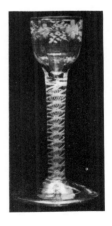

A cordial glass with ogee bowl, vertically moulded at base. Double series opaque white twist stem, plain conical foot, c.1760. 6¼", 15.8 cms. **£200-220** SA

A dram glass with round funnel bowl and vertically moulded at base. Thick double series opaque white twist stem and terraced conical foot, c.1760. 4¼", 10.8 cm. **£130-150** SA

A fine quality Stourbridge beaker, clear glass, translucent blue overlay on body and base of foot. 4¼", 10.5 cm. c.1840. **£60-80** SA

Conical shaped tumbler, with initials J.A.W. Base radially moulded. c.1810. 4½", 11 cm. **£60-70** SA

An unusual Spanish Tumbler decorated with the Royal Arms of Spain. 4¾", 12 cm. 18th C. **£440-500** SBS

A dram glass with ovoid bowl and plain drawn stem, over hung moulded foot, c.1750, 4", 10 cm. **£85-95** SA

A Victorian red glass beaker, inscribed 'A present from the Crystal Palace'. c.1851. 4¾", 12 cm. **£50-60** SA

Small tumbler with conical sided bowl, and base radially moulded. c.1800. 3¼", 8.3 cm. **£40-60** SA

A dram glass with trumpet bowl and thick firing foot. Bowl engraved with masonic symbols. c.1740. 3¾", 9.5 cm. **£60-70** SA

A German engraved armorial beaker. 4¾", 12 cm. c.1740 **£580-650** SBS

Tumbler with conical bowl, c.1780. 4½", 11 cm. **£50-70** SA

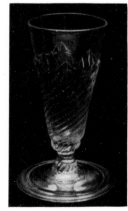

A dwarf ale glass with conical bowl and within flammiform moulding and a rudimentary stem. Folded conical foot. c.1720. 4¾", 12.0 cm. **£80-90** SA

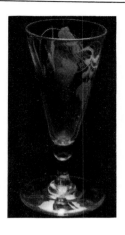

A dwarf ale glass with conical bowl with short drawn plain stem and folded conical foot. c.1780. 5½", 13.5 cm. **£25-30** SA

A dwarf ale glass with conical bowl, short stem with shoulder knop and plain conical foot. c.1790. 5½", 13.8 cm. **£25-30** SA

An Anglo-Venetian dwarf Ale Glass with conical bowl. Pinched lobe edge, short stem and shoulder and base knop. Folded conical foot. c.1700. 5½", 14 cm. **£300-350** SA

An ale glass, the deep funnel bowl, on a stem with shoulder and central cushioned knops, conical folded foot. 7½", 18.8 cm. c.1740. **£80-100** SA

A rare Anglo-Venetian ale glass, the funnel bowl teased fringe set on a marese above pincered wings and base knop, conical folded foot. c.1690. 5½", 14 cm. **£500-600** SA

An early Anglo-Venetian ale glass with conical bowl and a wrython moulded base on a stem with four pincered wings, base knop and folded conical foot. c.1690. 5½", 13.7 cm. **£400-500** SA

A fine amethyst rummer of cup shape and capstan stem, plain conical foot, c.1800. 5¼" high, 13.3 cm. **£60-80** SA

A set of twelve small Roemers, with yellow-green glass set above a printed. knop and ribbed foot, 5¼", 13 cm. 1920-1930's, fitted case. **£380-420** SBel

A green-tinted Roemer, the ovoid bowl tapering towards the rim, conical trailed foot, 5¼", 15.5 cm Rhenish, 17th/18th C. **£280-320** SBS

A fine jelly glass with ogee bowl with pan top. Overall diamond moulded with short incised knop stem and moulded domed foot. Applied handle, c.1740. 5½", 13.5 cm. **£90-100** SA

A sweet meat with double ogee bowl, dentil edge, knopped stem, multi-spiral opaque twist threads extending up bowl to dentil edge, radially moulded foot, c.1760. 3¾", 9.5 cm. **£130-140** SA

A sweet meat with double ogee ribbed bowl with everted rim, set on a stem with a shoulder unnulated knop, domed folded foot radially ribbed to match the bowl. c.1730. 5¾", 14.7 cm. **£250-270** SA

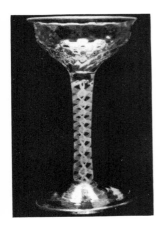

A sweet meat with double ogee bowl, double series opaque white twist stem and plain conical foot. c.1760. 6¾", 17.2 cm. **£180-190** SA

A sweet meat (possibly Irish) with ogee bowl, diamond facet cut stem, domed conical foot with sliced cutting, c.1770. 6¾", 17 cm. **£80-90** SA

A sweet meat with ogee bowl honeycomb moulded and everted rim, set on a stem with shoulder and base ball knops, plain conical foot, 4¼", 10.5 cm. c.1730. **£80-100** SA

A sweet meat with double ogee bowl, stem single series opaque twist corkscrew, radially moulded foot, c.1760. 2¾", 6.8 cm. **£120-130** SA

A sweet meat with double ogee bowl and dentil edge, with base moulding. Short stem with multi-spiral air twist thread and radially moulded foot. c.1760. 4", 10 cm. **£100-120** SA

A sweet meat with double ogee bowl set on a heavy inverted baluster stem with a tear, domed conical foot. c.1720. 4½", 11.7 cm. **£200-300** SA

A sweet meat with double ogee bowl with everted rim, set on a bobbin knop stem, domed conical foot, 5″, 12.3 cm. c.1720. **£200-250** SA

A sweet meat, with double ogee bowl, radially moulded plain dome foot. c.1740. 3½″, 8.6 cm. **£150-160** SA

An Anglo-Venetian sweet meat with everting bowl and folded rim, three knop stem, folded conical foot, c.1700. 3¼″, 8.2 cm. **£170-190** SA

A Dutch-engraved Newcastle glass, round-funnel bowl, set on a typical light-baluster stem and conical foot, 7¼″, 18.5 cm. c.1760. **£480-580** SBS

A stirrup cup with conical bowl. Thistle shape bowl with facet cut stem and diamond cut knop, 5½″, 14 cms. c.1820. **£25-30** SA

A toddy lifter, the shoulder facet cut with single plain neck ring, c.1810. 7¼″, 18 cms. **£25-30** SA

An engraved Ratafia, conical bowl tapering into a plain stem, conical foot, 6½″, 16.5 cms, c.1750. **£210-240** SBS

A mead glass with cup shaped gadrooned bowl set on a stem with an inverted baluster and base knop, folded conical foot. c.1700. 5¼″, 13 cms. **£600-800** SA

A set of six Flutes, each with conical bowl with everted lip, set on a double-series opaque-twist stem, conical foot, 7½″, 19 cms. c.1750. **£200-250** SBS

A large engraved Rummer, columnar stem, flanked by collars, conical foot. 7", 17.5 cm. c.1800. £60-75 SBS

A pair of nautical rummers, base collar and spreading stem with square lemon-squeezer base, 5³⁄₈", 13.5 cm. c.1800. £115-135 SBS

An unusual mould-blown rummer. 5³⁄₈", 13.5 cm. c.1820. Probably Irish. £55-65 SBS

An Unusual Hunting Overlay Tankard with silvered mounts, 6½", 16.5 cm, c.1850. £400-450 SBel

A 19th C. Continental glass tankard with pewter mounts, eagle finial, lid with opaque glass armorial panel. 8", 20 cm. £20-30 WW

A Central European Enamelled Tankard and Cover, 9½", 24 cm, c.1770. £550-600 SBS

A jelly glass with conical bowl and everted rim, horizontal prism cutting and lobe cut rim. Conical foot prism cut underneath. c.1810 4", 10 cm. £25-30 SA

A Large Humpen and Cover dated 1899, 19¼", 49 cm, late 19th C. £160-180 SBel

A jelly glass for syllabub with ogee bowl and pan top, star studded foot, c.1750. 4¼", 10.5 cm. £50-60 SA

A German Enamelled Humpen, with named armorial shields, 11¾", 30 cm, late 19th C. £180-220 SBel

A superb 'Nailsea' type ewer with red, white, blue and opaque looping, probably Stourbridge, c.1840. **£250-290** SA

A Glass Lemonade Jug with Electroplated Mounts, 9", 22.25 cm, 1880's. **£130-160** SBel

A small green bottle glass Cream Jug with brown/white marvered flecking, with opaque white stringing, c.1800. 3½", 8.8 cm. **£70-90** SA

A large jug with flared and sliced rim. 8¾", 22 cm. probably Cork or Dublin, c.1800. **£210-240** SIre

A Bohemian Gilt Drinking Set, of yellow-green glass, 6 Tumblers, 5½", 14 cm, and Jug 13¼", 33.5 cm, 19th C. **£160-190** SBel

A small light green bottle glass jug, heavily seeded, applied handle. c.1770. 5", 12.5 cm. **£60-80** SA

A small olive green glass Shropshire (Wrockwardine) jug, with white trailing and horizontal chain splashes round body. Applied strap handle; c.1800. 5¼", 13 cm. **£60-90** SA

A fine water Jug with flared and sliced rim, 8¾", 22 cm. probably Cork or Dublin, c.1790. **£520-600** SIre

A Pair of Silver-Gilt Mounted Glass Claret Jugs, 9¼", 23.5 cm high, maker's mark of George Fox, London, 1867, **£780-870** SBel

A Georgian claret jug, base fluting, facet and strawberry diamond and herringbone cutting, applied strap handle, 8⅞", 22.5 cm. **£130-160** SA .

An unusual Jug with bands of Strawberry diamonds bordered by prismatic cutting. 11½", 29 cm. c.1820. **£300-350** SIre

A large globular Jug, flanged base, 7½", 19 cm. probably Cork, c.1820. **£440-490** SIre

A Galle Bowl, 7½", 19 cm, diam. signed. **£600-660** PL

An unusual German spa decanter Jug and Stopper, stained in red, 12¹/₈", 30.8 cm. c.1850. **£250-300**

The Ailsa jug, an important Dobson & Pearce engraved Claret Jug, 13", 33 cm. 1862. **£410-490**

A Miniature Cameo Bowl in pink glass overlaid in white, 1½", 3.8 cm, 1880's. **£260-290** SBel

A Green Glass Bowl, Cover and Stand, 12¼", 31 cm, c.1850. **£650-730** SBel

A Large 'Pekin' Yellow Glass Bowl, 9½", 24 cm, c.1850. **£440-480** SBel

A Pair of Ruby-Glass Portrait-Overlay Footed Bowls, 10¼", 26 cm, c.1850. **£185-200** SBel

A boat-shaped Bowl cut with diamonds above a band of leaflets. 10¼", 26 cm. c.1790. **£500-560** SIre

A set of ten Victorian bubble glass double lipped finger bowls **£30-40** WW

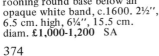

A fine early Venetian bowl with everted rim and moulded gadrooning round base below an opaque white band, c.1600. 2½", 6.5 cm. high, 6¼", 15.5 cm. diam. **£1,000-1,200** SA

A pair of unusual Bowls, the rim fan-cut, on a short sliced stem, circular foot, star-cut base, 5¼", 13 cm. c.1830, **£260-290** SIre

A Sugar Bowl with everted fan-cut rim above a band of strawberry diamonds, star-cut foot. 5¼'', 13 cm. possibly Waterford, c.1830. **£75-95** SIre

A good Galle 'Man in the Moon' dish, coloured with dark blue and pale blue streaks. 4¼'', 11 cm. diam., engraved mark 'Galle', c.1900. **£1,250-1,750** SBel

A Sugar Bowl, the ovoid bowl cut with a band of cubes with facets, 5¼'', 13 cm. c.1830, **£160-180** SIre

An unusual Bowl, cut with thirteen eight-pointed stars, the rim cut with short vertical blazes, 7½'', 19 cm. c.1820. **£290-330** SIre

A pair of 19th C. cut glass Honey Pots with covers having spiked finials, 14'', 35.5 cm. high. **£60-80** AB

3 Tiffany Glass Stemmed Dishes, 3½'', 9 cm, c.1910. **£300-340** SBel

A 9½'' dia., 24 cm. Lalique bowl, decorated with fish. Pressed mark LA, France. **£40-50** AB

A 'Man in the Moon' Dish, attributed to Galle, in pink tinted glass, 4¼'', 11 cm. diam., c.1900. **£75-95** SBel

A Daum pot and cover, in pink and orange glass, dense blue at base, 7.5 cm., 3'', engraved mark, "Daum Nancy", c.1905. **£180-220** SBel

A Celery Vase. Fan-cut rim cut
overall with strawberry diamonds.
7½", 19 cm. possibly Waterford,
c.1830. **£130-160** SIre

A Celery Vase. Scalloped rim and
base cut with strawberry diamonds
star-cut base, 10¾", 27 cm.
possibly Waterford, c.1820. **£170-190** SIre

A Celery Vase. Everted rim cut
with plain diamonds, serrated
rim cut with vertical prisms, 7¼",
18.5 cm. c.1820. **£140-160** SIre

A pair of opaline vases, in
opaque white transfer-printed
in sepia against a green ground,
10", 25 cm. mid-19th C. **£100-120** SBel

A Daum glass vase, in deep green
glass, 5¼", 13.25 cm., gilt mark
'Daum Nancy', c.1900. **£100-120**
SBel

Late Victorian glass vase, gold
floral decoration, 16", **£50-60**
40.5 cm. WW

A pair of olive green glass vases,
with white marvered flecking,
c.1800. 7⅛", 18 cm. **£150-180**
SA

A pair of fine quality pale lemon
opaline vases. c.1860. 14" high,
36 cm. **£500-700** SA

A pair of cream ground Victorian
glass vases, 14", 35.5 cm. **£20-30**
WW

Victorian green, lustre decorated
glass vase, 8", 20 cm. **£5-10** RB

A pair of amethyst glass Art
Nouveau vases with gilt decoration.
9", 23 cm. **£5-10** RB

Two green glass 'Mary Gregory'
vases, 9", 23 cm. and 7½", 19 cm
£15-20 AB

A pair of Bohemian overlay vases, with Ruby glass overlaid on the body, 13⅜", 34.6 cm. c.1850. **£300-380**

A Webb's Burmese-glass Vase, pink shading to yellow at base, 6¼", 15.9 cm., c.1890. **£160-200**

A Daum etched, gilded and frosted glass Vase, 7", 18 cm., 'Daum Nancy', c.1900. **£100-120** SBel

A Legras cameo glass Vase, in pale-blue glass overlaid in purple and green, 13", 33 cm. Cameo mark 'Legras', c.1900. **£260-290** SBel

A Bohemian opaline glass vase. 7½" high, 19 cm. **£470-55-** KC

A Galle cameo Glass vase, the grey body tinted yellow overlaid in clear cherry-red glass, 14.5 cm. 5¾", cameo mark 'Galle', c.1900. **£240-270** SBel

A Loetz iridescent glass vase, in pink/grey with feathered trails of pale peacock/gold iridescence. 6", 15.25 cm. c.1900. **£460-500** SBel

A rare Webb 'Ivory-Cameo' Persian-taste Vase with ivory-tinted body, 6¼", 15.9 cm. mark. c.1880. **£380-420**

A Galle cameo glass vase, the yellow/grey body overlaid in purple/brown, 6", 15.25 cm. Cameo mark 'Galle', c.1900. **£220-240** SBel

A Galle boat-shaped vase, the amber-coloured body in green and brown, signed Galle, 5⅛", 13.4 cm. high. **£210-240** KC

A Galle cameo glass vase, the grey glass body with salmon-pink, 6", 15.5 cm. cameo mark 'Galle', c.1900. **£360-400** SBel

An Art Nouveau glass vase by Emille Galle, Nancy, in overlay red signed, 5½", 14 cm. **£210-230** WW

377

A Pair of Overlay Vases, 12½",
31.4 cm, c.1850. **£200-250**   SBel

A Pair of Portrait Overlay Green-
Glass Vases, 13¼", 33.8 cm,
c.1850. **£220-240**   SBel

A Rare Lalique Scent Bottle with
frosted stopper, 3½", 9.25 cm.
£200-230   PL

A Pink and White Cameo Glass
Vase, 10", 25.5 cm, c.1880.
£700-770   SBel

A Ruby-Glass Overlay Vase, 21½"
54.5 cm, c.1850. **£290-330**   SBel

A Tall Overlay Vase, 15¾",
39.8 cm, c.1850. **£110-130**   SBel

Enamelled Satin-glass Vase.
Yellow glass shading. Rim with
blue foliate border, 8⅜", 21.3
cm. c.1880. **£200-250**

An unusual Galle cameo glass
Vase. Milky pale-green glass over-
laid in beige, 8", 20.5 cm. mark
'Galle', c.1900. **£420-480**   SBel

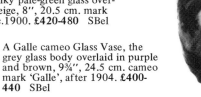

A German Vase by F. Zach, 8¾",
22 cm, c.1857. **£320-350**   SBel

A Galle cameo Glass Vase, the
grey glass body overlaid in purple
and brown, 9¾", 24.5 cm. cameo
mark 'Galle', after 1904. **£400-
440**   SBel

A Rousseau Engraved Smoked
Glass Vase, 7", 18 cm, c.1890.
£500-560 SBel

A Pair of Enamelled Vases in
opaque-white glass, 8", 20.5 cm,
1870's. £180-220 SBel

A Cameo Glass Vase, 9", 23 cm,
late 19th C. £900-1,000 SBel

A Pair of Large Enamelled Vases
with drop handles, 15", 37.8 cm,
late 19th C. £190-210 SBel

A Moser Glass Set, 7½", 19 cm,
rose bowl, 6¾", 17 cm, c.1900.
£500-560 SBel

An Unusual Pair of Vases, 9¾",
24.5 cm, c.1880. £500-550 SBel

A Pair of Pink-Ground Enamelled
Opaline Vases, 14¼", 36 cm,
c.1850. £150-180 SBel

A Good Lobmeyr 'Islamic'
Enamelled Vase, 5¼", 13.6 cm,
1870's. £230-260 SBel

A Pair of Burmese Vases, probably
by Webb, 4½", 11.6 cm, 1880's.
£290-320 SBel

A Pair of Enamelled 'Moonstone'
Vases, 11⅝", 29.5 cm, late
19th C. £180-210 SBel

A Tiffany Iridescent Glass Vase,
4¼", 10.5 cm, engraved mark,
1919. £280-320 SBel

A Pair of Overlay Vases in ruby
glass, 12", 30.8 cm, c.1850.
£280-320 SBel

An unusual Galle vase. The lower half with feathering in blue, the upper half in deep red glass, 10¾" 27 cm. mark 'Galle', c.1900. **£750-950** SBel

An unusual Galle cameo glass vase, in brown richly mottled with bright yellow, overlaid in dark brown, 5", 12.5 cm., cameo mark 'Galle', c.1900. **£600-900** SBel

A Galle enamelled glass vase, in deep green glass, 11", 27.75 cm. impressed mark 'Cristallerie de Galle Nancy.', 1890's. **£340-400** SBel

A small Galle glass vase, smoked glass body, 4½", 11.5 cm., mark 'E. Galle Nancy', 1880's. **£170-190** SBel

A pair of enamelled satin-glass vases, the exterior pink shading to white, with yellow and blue, 9¼", 23.5 cm. late 19th C. **£100-150** SBel

A pair of Stourbridge overlay vases, white on green, 10½", 26.7 cm., mid-19th C. **£300-340** LC

A pair of Pekin glass vases, overlaid with orange glass, 9¾", 24.5 cm. 20th C. **£160-180** SBel

An English opaque white vase in coloured enamels, Stourbridge, c.1850. 12½", 32 cm. **£100-150** SA

Pair of French glass vases on metal stands with handles, approx. 10" high, 25.5 cm. **£45-50** LBA

A pair of blue-glass vases, 15½", 39 cm. mid-19th C. **£120-140** SBel

A Pair of Overlay Lustres, 11¾",
29.6 cm, 1850. **£230-250** SBel

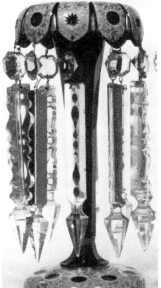

A pair of late 19th C. Bohemian
white overlay glass table lustres.
11" high, 28 cm. **£250-280** OL

An unusual pair of overlay
Lustres, with clear-glass lustres,
11¾", 29.8 cm. late 19th C.
£210-240 SBel

A pair of Bohemian overlay vases
of green glass, hung with clear-
glass lustres. 12", 30.5 cm. c.1850.
£270-300

A pair of gilt green-glass Lustres,
with clear glass lustres. 12",
31 cm. c.1850. **£210-240** SBel

A pair of Bohemian lustres in
clear red glass with white overlay
Icicle type lustres, c.1850. 12¾",
32.5 cm. **£700-800** SA

A pair of glass Lustres, the
bodies of pink crackled glass,
bases of pink and opaque white
overlay glass, 9½", 24 cm. **£190-
210** LC

An Attractive Tiffany Studios
Tulip Lamp, in pink and green
glass, 16¾", 42.5 cm, base
stamped, c.1900. **£2,600-2,900**
SBel

A Millefiori Lamp, fitted for
electricity, 16½", 41 cm. 20th C.
£100-130 SBel

A Cut-Glass Column, with faceted stem, 21½'', 54.5 cm, c.1900. **£210-250** SBel

A cut-glass Lamp, the shade, baluster stem and circular foot deeply cut with hobnail diamonds 17¼'', 43 cm. early 20th C. **£280-320** SBel

A moulded glass Chandelier, 32'', 81 cm. possibly Scandinavian, mid-19th C. **£195-220** SBel

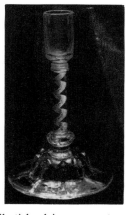

A pair of George III Irish cut-glass and gilt-metal Table Candelabra, 28½'', 72.5 cm. c.1785. **£950-1,200** SIre

Candlestick, plain sconce set on collar. Double series air twist section above beaded knop. Domed foot radially moulded, star bosses, c.1740. 8'', 20.5 cm. **£500-550** SA

A glass bell with an amethyst body and opaque white band round rim, clear moulded handle, c.1860/70. 10¾'', 27 cm. **£80-100** SA

A clear glass Nailsea bell, with opaque white looping, clear rings round red rim and translucent blue colour twist handle. c.1860. 12½'', 32 cm. **£80-90** SA

A small red glass bell, with opaque white band round rim, red, white and blue coloured spiral twist in handle. c.1880. 10¾'', 27 cm. **£70-80** SA

A clear glass Nailsea bell with brown and opaque white looping and colour twist in handle. c.1860/70. 10¼'', 26 cm. **£60-80** SA

A clear glass rolling pin with red and blue flecking. 14½", 37 cm. long, c.1840. **£30-40** SA

A heavy clear bottle glass rolling pin with translucent red looping, containing salt. 10", 25 cm. long, c.1840, **£40-50** SA

A dark blue rolling pin, gold enamel decoration, inscription 'Be True to Me Love'. 13¾", 35 cm. c.1855. **£40-50** SA

A St. Louis amber-flash posy Weight. Dome and sides cut with printies. 2½", 6.6 cm. **£180-220** SBS

A Baccarat primrose Weight. Five midnight-blue petals with white edges around star-dust stamens. Star-cut base. 3", 7.7 cm. **£400-500** SBS

A Baccarat double-clematis-and-garland Weight. Dome and sides cut with printies to reveal the flower; 3", 7.5 cm. **£400-450** SBS

A St Louis Mushroom Weight signed and dated SL 1953, 3", 7.6 cm, 1953. **£100-200** SBel

A green bottle glass door stop or 'dump', c.1870. 5¾", 14.5 cm. **£35-45** SA

A St. Louis double-clematis Weight; Dome with circular windows revealing the flower. Placed on a latticinio cushion. 3", 7.5 cm. **£460-500** SBS

A Baccarat 'thousand-petalled' Rose Weight. Many deep velvet-textured red petals, star-cut base. 2¾″, 7.1 cm. £850-950 SBS

A Baccarat Anemone Weight. Six ridged white petals outlined in blue. Star-cut base. 2¾″, 7.1 cm. £250-300 SBS

A Zodiac Weight depicting Pisces, 2¾″, 7 cm, 20th c. £60-80 SBel

A St Louis Pedestal Weight, 20th c. £70-100 SBel

A pair of unusual Punch or Custard cups, cut with border of stars. 3¼″, 8 cm. c.1790. £110-130 SIre

A church warden's pipe in clear amethyst glass, length 14½″, 37 cm., c.1860. £60-80 SA

A pair of tall Bristol blue wine glass coolers/rinsers, 4¼″, 11 cm. c.1800. £70-90 SA

A translucent red pipe with opaque white looping and finely shaped bowl, 1′6″, 46 cm. in length, c.1860. £70-90 SA

Mayer & Co. A Set of 6 Stained Glass Panels, 70½" by 24½", 179 cm by 62 cm, framed, c.1870. £600-700 SBel

A Pair of Stained Glass Panels, each 43¾" by 16½", 111 cm by 40.5 cm, c.1880. £310-340 SBel

William Wailes. A Set of Stained Glass Panels, 71" by 23", 180 cm by 59 cm, framed, c.1860. £460-500 SBel

A Stained Glass Panel of Saint Luke, framed, 74¼" by 26", 188.5 cm by 66 cm, late 19th C. £300-400 SBel

A Set of 9 Stained Glass Panels, 29½" by 30½", 75 cm by 77.5 cm, c.1900. £210-240 SBel

A Pair of Stained Glass Panels, probably by James Powell & Sons, dated 1892, each 72" by 20", 183 cm by 51 cm, framed. £440-500 SBel

A Large Stained Glass Panel, 34" by 34½", 86.5 cm by 87 cm, 1900-1920. £220-240 SBel

A Pair of Morris Studio Stained Glass Windows, 19¾", 50 cm. c.1876. £140-160 SBel

A Set of 3 Stained Glass Panels, possibly by J.W. Brown, each 28¾" by 24", 73 cm by 61 cm, framed, c.1889. £300-500 SBel

Stained Glass Window, 9'9" by 5'6", 297.5 cm by 168 cm. £1,700-2,000 MH

Mayer & Co. A Set of 3 Stained Glass Panels, each 64" by 23¾", 163 cm by 60 cm, framed , c.1870. **£210-240** SBel

A Set of 3 Stained Glass Panels, each 53½" by 24", 136 cm by 61 cm, c.1870. **£210-240** SBel

Mayer & Co. A Set of 3 Stained Glass Panels, each 71" by 24", 180 cm by 61 cm, c.1870. **£260-290** SBel

Mayer & Co. A Set of 3 Stained Glass Panels, each 71" by 24", 180 cm by 61 cm, framed, c.1870. **£260-290** SBel

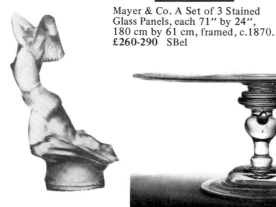

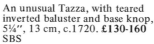
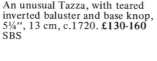

'Vitesse'. A Lalique Car Mascot, 7", 18 cm, metal radiator ring. **£620-680** PL

An unusual Tazza, with teared inverted baluster and base knop, 5¼", 13 cm, c.1720. **£130-160** SBS

A Set of 3 Stained Glass Tracery Lights, each 35½" by 23½", 90 cm by 60 cm, c.1880. **£200-300** SBel

A Glass Coffee Set, engraved and gilt, c.1900. **£400-450** SBel

Victorian translucent ornament. 12", 30.5 cm. high. **£26-30** RB

An unusual Galle Cameo Perfume Burner, 7", 17.50 cm. **£340-380** PL

POINTS TO NOTE WITH DRINKING GLASSES

- baluster glasses tend to have high value due to the relatively few made and that they are the oldest of the lead glasses

- when buying balustroid glasses the main criterion must be weight and proportion — there are a large number of inferior specimens

- original Newcastle Light Balusters are very scarce and valuable and hence there are many reproductions

- plain stem glasses were made in vast quantities and variable quality from the 18th century through the Victorian period

Yeh Chung-San the Younger: an interior-painted glass snuff bottle and apple-green jade stopper, signed and dated 1908, yin seal, 2⅞", 7.2 cm. £100-120 KC

A cameo glass scent bottle, the red glass overlaid in opaque white, the silver screw cap marked Birmingham, 1885, 5¼", 13 cm. 1885. £170-190 SBel

Cho Lo-Yuan: an interior-painted rock crystal snuff bottle and coral stopper, signed, 2¾", 7 cm. £110-150 KC

A multi-coloured overlay glass snuff bottle and banded orange agate stopper, 2¾", 7 cm. £120-140 KC

An interior-painted glass snuff bottle and stopper, £68-78 KC

A green overlay glass snuff bottle and rose quartz stopper, 2⅝", 6.6 cm. £60-70 KC

An overlay ruby-glass scent bottle and stopper overlaid in white, faceted stopper, 11", 27.5 cm. c.1850. £140-160 SBel

A Cameo Glass Scent Bottle with silver cover. 2½″, 6.2 cm, c.1884. **£190-210** SBel

An Enamelled Scent Bottle, cover by Sampson Mordan & Co., 1884. **£100-110** SBel

A Bohemian Ruby-Glass Scent Bottle and Stopper, 7″, 17.5 cm, c.1860. **£90-100** SBel

A Cameo Glass Scent Bottle. Silver hinged cover and mount, 4¼″, 10.5 cm. **£310-340** SBel

A Small Cameo Glass Scent Bottle. Silver screw cap, 2¼″, 5.5 cm, c.1884. **£195-215** SBel

A Cameo Scent Bottle. Silver screw cap marked Birmingham, 4¼″, 10.5 cm. 1884. **£200-230** SBel

A Bohemian Ruby-Glass Scent Bottle, 3¼″, 8.5 cm, c.1840. **£120-180** SBel

A Webb Ivory Cameo Glass Scent Bottle with silver screw cap 4⅜″, 11 cm. **£325-350** SBel

A gold and enamel-mounted scent bottle, the neck engraved: 'Emily', 3½″, 9 cm. unmarked, c.1895. **£170-190** SBel

An Art Deco yellow glass scent bottle and stopper with metal mounts. **£5-8** RB

Victorian blue glass and gilt scent bottle with flower stopper. **£22-26** WW

A Good German doll, by Kammer and Reinhardt, with wooden ball jointed limbs, 27½", 70 cm. **£230-260**   LC

An unusual bisque doll, possibly by Schmitt, 16", 41 cm. **£620-720**   SBel

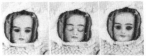

A bisque-headed three-faced doll, 13", 33 cm. **£500-560** CSK

A bisque-swivel-headed Parisienne doll, 16", 40.5 cm. **£280-310**   CSK

A brown Bisque-headed Bebe, 19", 38 cm. **£2,200-2,400**   CSK

A German doll, jointed kid body with bisque lower arms, hand damaged, 17", 43 cm. **£330-350**   LC

A bisque doll, 21½", 55 cm. **£1,200-1,800**   SBel

A Bisque-headed Bebe with fixed brown eyes. 20", 49 cm. high, **£1,400-1,600**   CSK

A Bisque swivel-headed Parisienne doll, 12½", 31.75 cm. high. **£380-460**   CSK

A German shoulder-bisque head c.1875. **£150-180**   SBel

A bisque-headed character baby doll, 16", 40.5 cm. **£360-400**   CSK

A bisque-headed Bebe with fixed blue eyes, 23", 58.5 cm. **£1,000-1,100**   CSK

A French doll with bisque head,
26", 66 cm. £975-1,100   LC

A Simon and Halbig doll, with
bisque head, dated 1909, German,
23", 58.5 cm. £150-180   LC

A German doll, with bisque head
18½", 47 cm. £80-90   LC

A 19th C. bisque-head mechanical
doll, 23.5 cm. 9¼", £120-170
KC

A French socketed bisque
fashion doll, 18", 45 cm. c.1860,
£1,800-2,000   SBel

A Schoenau & Hoffmeister
musical glass-eyed bisque-headed
doll. 12", 30.5 cm. German,
c.1900. £190-230   SBel

A bisque nonnet-character-
headed doll, 7½", 19 cm. high,
marked 22-13/o. £190-210   CSK

A bisque shoulder-headed doll,
13", 33 cm. £120-180   CSK

A fine French doll, by Jules
Nicholas Steiner, 1889, dressed
in original clothes, 14½", 37 cm.
£725-800   LC

A bisque swivel-headed Parisienne
doll, 17", 43 cm. £300-340   CSK

A bisque-headed portrait doll,
16", 40.5 cm. £300-330   CSK

A good FG bisque doll, 24",
61 cm. £420-460   SBel

A German 'Queen Louise' bisque head doll, 24¾", 63 cm. £85-95 PJ

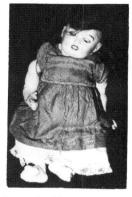

A Lantemier bisque head doll, 18½", 46 cm. £55-65 PJ

A Steiner bisque doll with kid body, 21", 48 cm. c.1880. £520-600 SBel

Part porcelain doll. £30-40 WW

China baby doll. £50-60 WW

A fine Victorian doll with porcelain head, £80-90 RB

A china shoulder-headed doll modelled as a boy, 13½", 34.5 cm. £150-200 CSK

A Victorian porcelain doll, £82-90 RB

A French porcelain headed doll with stuffed body, £80-90 WW

A china-headed doll, 16", 40.5 cm. £260-290 CSK

A china headed doll. £10-15 RB

A china shoulder-headed doll, 7½", 19 cm. high. £180-200 CSK

A china shoulder-headed doll, 13", 33 cm. **£260-290** CSK

K & R china pre-war doll. **£115-135** WW

Victorian wax doll top. **£50-60** WW

A poured wax Child doll, 23", 58.5 cm. stamped with Lucy Peck oval mark. **£300-350** CSK

An old German china doll with glass eyes. **£40-55** WW

A poured wax child doll, 14½", 37 cm. c.1860. **£170-190** CSK

A large boy doll or display figure with wax head, overall 38", 97 cm. **£165-185** LC

A good poured wax doll dressed in original costume, 18", 46 cm. **£100-110** LC

German china doll in lace dress. **£48-58** WW

A wax-over-composition-headed doll, 26½", 67.5 cm. **£140-160** CSK

A German doll with wax head, fabric body, c.1855, 13¾", 35 cm. **£35-45** LC

A carved wooden doll, wearing clogs, 9", 23 cm. high. **£5-10** PJ

A carved and turned painted wooden doll, 15″, 38 cm. c.1750. **£1,500-1,700** CSK

A German shoulder-papier-mache doll, 15″, 35 cm. c.1840. **£520-600** SBel

A painted felt portrait doll modelled as H.M. King Edward VIII, 14½″, 37 cm. **£75-95** CSK

A Carved and Painted Jointed Wooden Grodenthal Type Doll, 18″, 45 cm. c.1810, **£880-980** CSK

A brown leather doll with adult figure, 16″, 40.5 cm. c.1835. **£160-190** CSK

A Pair of Clockwork composition character busts of babies with nodding heads. 17″, 42.5 cm. **£210-240** CSK

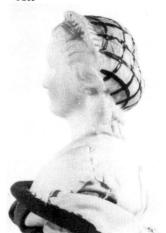

A Bisque Shoulder-Headed Doll. 13½″, 34.5 cm. c.1860. **£380-430** CSK

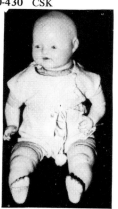

A Horsman composition doll, 19½″, 49 cm. **£10-15** PJ

A stuffed stockinette life-size model of a child, 42″, 106 cm. 3.6.43. **£210-240** CSK

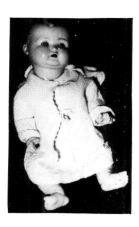

A German composition doll, 20½″, 51 cm. **£5-10** PJ

Automata became extremely popular in the 16th Century and clockmakers vied with one another to construct the most complicated and clever moving figures. They were certainly the playthings of the rich.

Automata became more widespread in the 18th Century when the most popular was the singing, moving bird in a cage. These are

now extremely rare and fetch high prices when they appear on the market.

The Victorians were very fond of automata but due to the high skill required by the craftsman these were gradually replaced by German clockwork toys, which could more easily be produced in quantity. These now also fetch some surprising prices, the early

20th Century examples being highly sought after, due to the scarcity of earlier pieces in good working order.

This is the main feature to watch for, an original mechanism in working order is a great find. It is extremely difficult and expensive to find a craftsman today who could repair and restore a damaged automata.

A monkey artist Automaton, probably by J. Phalivois, 20″, 51 cm. high, French, c.1884. **£1,700-1,900** SBel

A Musical Automaton of a Chinese laundry, providing nine movements, 19½″, 50 cm. **£800-900** CSK

A Negro accordion player musical Automaton, the figure with painted porcelain head, 11½″, 29 cm. high, French, late 19th C. **£300-350** SBel

A Piano-player musical Automaton, her head turns and her arms move across the piano keys accompanied by a tune, 12¾″, 32.5 cm. wide, French, late 19th C. **£260-320** SBel

A felt-covered model of a dog containing a musical movement operated by turning the tail, 9″, 23 cm. long. **£100-120** CSK

A large singing birds Automaton, the birds moving their tails, head and beak in time to the song, 20″, 51 cm. high, probably French, c.1900. **£700-800** SBel

A musical automaton rabbit in a cauliflower. **£420-470** CSK

A rare Nightingale singing bird Automaton, 17″, 43.5 cm. high, French, late 19th C. **£750-850** SBel

A rare 5¾", 14.5 cm. 'Pussies at Play' symphonion disc Automaton, 11½", 29 cm. high, German, c.1905. **£650-750** SBel

A Bingophone child's Gramophone, German, c.1925, **£140-160** SBel

A Louis Marx Donald Duck and Pluto tinplate 'Crazy Dancer'. 10½", 27 cm. high, American, c.1950. **£90-110** SBel

'Oh My,' a printed tinplate clockwork figure of a negro dancing a jig. 10", 25.5 cm. high, by Lehmann. **£230-260** CSK

A Louis Marx tinplate 'Ring-a-Ling' Circus, start/stop control and key at one side, 7½", 19.5 cm. diam. American, c.1930. **£48-58** SBel

A tinplate clockwork Mickey Mouse toy, lacking Minnie mouse 6¼", 16 cm. long, probably by Distler, German, c.1930. **£160-180** SBel

A good G.G. Kellermann tinplate clockwork Frog, 4¾", 12 cm. high, marked 'CKO' Made in Germany' c.1930. **£220-280** SBel

A Lehmann clockwork crawling Beetle, mechanism causing the wings to flap. 3¾", 9.5 cm. long, German, c.1915. **£90-110** SBel

A Phillip Vielmetter painted tin Clown, drawing pictures on paper on easel, 5½", 14 cm. high, German, c.1900. **£500-560** SBel

A Gunthermann tinplate Tramcar, the clockwork mechanism driving the twin rear wheels, 10", 25.5 cm. long, German, c.1925-30 **£120-150** SBel

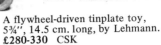

A Chad Valley tinplate Motor Bus, No.10005, 12″, 30.5 cm. long, with a Chad Valley Saloon Car, No: 10004, in original carboard boxes, 9¼″, 23.5 cm. long, English, c.1945-50 **£160-180** SBel

A flywheel-driven tinplate toy, 5¾″, 14.5 cm. long, by Lehmann. **£280-330** CSK

A Marklin tinplate clockwork sports car with leaf springs, rubber-tyred wheels and steering. 15″ long, 38 cm. **£220-250** CSK

A tinplate Battleship, possibly by Fleischmann, 12″, 30.5 cm. long, German, c.1925-30. **£90-110** SBel

A hand-enamelled tinplate clockwork Open Sedan, 14″, 35.5 cm. long, French, c.1904. **£150-170** SBel

A Bing Open Tourer, the tinplate vehicle with clockwork mechanism driving the rear wheels. 11½″, 29 cm. long, German, c.1918. **£200-230** SBel

A tinplate clockwork Limousine, with adjustable steering and brake, rubber tyred wheels. 14″ long, 35.5 cm. German. **£310-350** CSK

A clockwork Cat and Kitten, 14″, 35.5 cm. high, probably French, early 20th C. **£260-300** SBel

A walking Pussy, probably by Bontem. Clockwork mechanism. 13″, 33 cm. long, c.1920. **£55-65** SBel

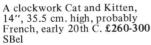

A 'Buzzie Lizzie' tinplate toy, possibly by H. Fischer. 6¾″, 17 cm. high, German, c.1920-23 **£105-120** SBel

A walking pig, the movement causing the legs and head to move backwards and forwards, 11½″, 29 cm long, probably French, c.1920 **£90-110** SBel

A Lehmann tinplate Rickshaw. 7″, 18 cm. wide. **£95-105** SBel

A Tea-party musical Automaton, the three bisque heads stamped 'Germany A15/OM' (Armand Marseille), 8¼" by 11½" by 12", 21 by 29 by 30.5 cm. German, c.1914. **£460-520** SBel

A Lehmann 'Wild West' Bucking Broncho tinplate toy, 6¼" cm. long, German. c.1930. **£170-190** SBel

A Magician Automaton, concealing sixteen varying tricks, the figure moves his eyes, mouth and head movement distressed, 21", 53 cm. high, probably French, c.1900. **£1,600-1,700** SBel

A Japanese McGregor battery-operated automaton figure, **£30-45** PJ

A Lionel Mickey Mouse handcar, No.1100, 11½", 29 cm. wide, American, c.1935. **£150-170** SBel

A tinplate man with clockwork mechanism, by Lehmann. 5½", 14 cm. **£80-90** CSK

A singing birds Automaton in brass cage, 10½", 27 cm. high, French, 1920-30. **£140-200** SBel

An early 20th C. papier mache automaton figure, the clockwork motor moving the head and glass eyes. 24", 61 cm. (not working.) **£210-230** LC

A Musical Automaton, 12½", 32 cm. long. **£400-600** CSK

A doll Automaton with bisque head and shoulders, the mechanism operating the head and hand movements, 26", 66 cm. high, French, 1860-1880. **£2,800-3,000**

A monkey music lesson musical Automaton, the coin-operated mechanism with seventeen movements, 27" by 28", 69 by 71 cm. French, c.1860. **£1,500-1,600** SBel

A 'Royal Trick' elephant tin-plate mechanical bank, marked 'Put a coin in the slot then you'll see something funny, Press my tail hard and I'll swallow the money' (lacking tail). 6″, 15.3 cm long, German, c.1920. £450-520 SBel

A rare tinplate push-along Drummer Boy, beats the drum. 5¾″, 14.5 cm. high, probably French, c.1890. £240-270 SBel

A Mickey Mouse tinplate Organ Grinder toy. Minnie dances on the top. 6¼″, 15.5 cm. wide, probably by Distler, German, c.1930. £950-1,100 SBel

A tinplate clockwork Uncle Wiggley Crazy Car, with eccentric steering. 9½″ long, 24 cm. German £160-180 CSK

A good Lehmann 'Naughty Nephew' tinplate toy, 5″, 12.5 c cm. long, German, c.1910. £280-330 SBel

A Bing tinplate Limousine, 12¼″, 31 cm. long, maker's mark, German, c.1908. £500-580 SBel

A Lehmann flywheel-driven Ostrich Cart. 7″, 18 cm. long, German, c.1906. £170-190 SBel

A tinplate Parrot on stand, with clockwork movement. 8″, 20 cm. high, £85-95 CSK

Jacko the Merry Organ Grinder, with clockwork musical movement. 6″, 15 cm. high, by Distler, c.1920. (monkey missing) £100-120 CSK

A Lehmann 'Tut-Tut' tinplate car, car drives erratically, 6¾″, 17 cm. long, German, c.1910. £280-340 SBel

A French tin-plate clockwork model of an early 1920's Renault touring car (possibly a 45) with steering, forward and reverse gears. Painted cream over green, by Automobiles Brevete SGDG Paris, 13¼″, 34 cm. long. £48-60 PJ

A rare Carette tinplate Limousine in dark green with red detailing, lined in black and gilt, with original key, 15¾″, 40 cm. long, German, c.1911. £1,000-1,100 SBel

A tinplate Money Box in the form of a cigarette vending machine, with drawer dispensing sweet cigarette. £70-80 CSK

A rare Leap-frog bank, by Shepard Hardware Co. 7½", 19 cm. wide, American, late 19th C. **£220-250** SBel

A collection of three amusing tinplate Money Boxes, Each 5", 12.7 cm. wide, probably German, c.1935-55. **£50-80** SBel

A tinplate 'Chocolat Menier' Dispenser Money Box. 10½", 26.7 cm. high, German, c.1920. **£30-40** SBel

A cast-iron mule and stable Money Bank, 8½", 21.5 cm. long, American, late 19th C. **£180-250** SBel

An Elephant and Howdah cast-iron Money Box, by Enterprise Man. Co., 6½", 16.5 cm. long, American, late 19th C. **£150-160** SBel

An owl cast-iron Money Bank, 7¾", 19.5 cm. high, American, late 19th C. **£160-180** SBel

A rare monkey and lion Money Bank, by Kyser & Rex, 9", 23 cm high, American, late 19th C. **£90-100** SBel

A late 19th C. French stained beech Dolls High Chair, 23¼", 59 cm. **£42-55** OL

A late 19th C. French burrwood veneered Dolls Wardrobe, 24", 61 cm. **£40-50** OL

A set of piano wire dolls house furniture. **£50-60** PJ

A printed paper-on-wood Doll's House, 20", 50.5 cm. **£130-160** CSK

A doll's wooden cradle, 18½", 46.5 cm. long. **£15-25** PJ

A tinplate trolley Bus, 11″, 28 cm. long, French, c.1905. **£170-190** SBel

A Lehmann 'Snick Snack' tinplate toy, 9½″, 24 cm. wide, German, c.1925-30 **£600-700** SBel

A tinplate clockwork 2-seater car, by Burnett, Birmingham. 7¾″. 19.5 cm. **£95-105** CSK

A Marx Merrymakers Mouse Orchestra, start/stop control to one side; 9″, 23 cm. wide, c.1945-50 **£260-290** SBel

A tinplate clockwork Open Sedan, probably by Tipp & Co., the mechanism wound through the radiator. 9″, 23 cm. long, German c.1925-30 **£240-270** SBel

A Lehmann 'Echo' tinplate Motorcycle and rider, 8½″, 21.5 cm. long, German, c.1912. **£400-460** SBel

A Lehmann 'Ampol' tinplate tricycle. 5″, 13 cm. long, German, c.1925. **£350-400** SBel

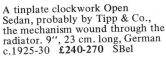

A 1½″, 4 cm. scale working model of a Burrell compound road engine. **£1,960-2,100** RB

A live steam spirit fired 2½″, 6.5 cm gauge model of the 4-4-0 locomotive number 192 'The Borderer', 27½″, 70 cm long. **£260-280** LC

4¼″, 10.5 cm. gauge brass and copper live steam coal-fired 2-2-2- engine, 19th C. **£260-280** SBel

3½″, 9 cm. gauge live steam coal-fired 0-4-0 'Tich' tank engine, 15½″, 39.4 cm. **£300-340** SBel

Model 4-2-2 working steam tender engine of brass, 23″, 57.5 cm. **£250-300** LE

A Bassett Lowke O-gauge electric 3-rail 4-6-2 locomotive and tender "Flying Scotsman". **£300-340** CSK

An S. Gunthermann tinplate carpet locomotive, German, c.1918, 13½″, 34 cm. **£42-50** SBel

A very good gauge 'Two' clockwork 0-6-2 tank locomotive. **£680-760** SBel

German 2½″, 6.5 cm. gauge 'Three' live steam spirit-fired 2-2-0 locomotive, 18″, 45.8 cm. **£310-340** SBel

A good early German gauge 'O' model railway collection. £120-140 SBel

A Bassett-Lowke gauge 'O' electric 4-6-2 locomotive, no. 4472 'Flying Scotsman', 20", 50.8 cm. £220-240 SBel

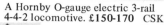

A Hornby O-gauge electric 3-rail 4-4-2 locomotive. £150-170 CSK

Carette gauge 'One' 8-wheeled electric railmotor, 16½", 42 cm., c.1910. £1,100-1,200 SBel

An O-gauge clockworked Midland 'Single' locomotive. £360-400 CSK

Hand-built gauge 'One' Drummond chairman's autocoach. £1,000-1,100 SBel

An almost mint Hornby gauge 'O' electric 4-4-0 locomotive, 'Eton', No. 900, 15", 38 cm. £280-300 SBel

Marklin gauge 'One' clockwork 0-6-4 tank locomotive, 17", 43 cm., c.1915. £620-680 SBel

A Carette guage 'One' live steam spirit-fired 2-2-0 locomotive, 15", 38 cm. 1905/10. £260-280 SBel

A rare Carette clockwork gauge 'One' 4-4-0 'Vauclain' locomotive. £850-950 SBel

Early Marklin gauge 'one' clockwork 2-2-0 locomotive. £450-500 SBel

A rare and early 'FV' tinplate carpet toy locomotive and carriages, French, 1880, 19", 48 cm. long. £250-280 SBel

Marklin gauge 'One' live steam spirit-fired 4-6-2 'The Great Bear' locomotive, c.1910-1913, 29", 73.5 cm. £2,500-2,800 SBel

Early gauge 3 Ernst Plank live steam boxed train set, c.1905. £260-280 SBel

A Carl Bub electric model railway, with 0-4-0 engine. £130-160 SBel

3½", 9 cm. gauge live steam coal-fired 4-6-0 locomotive 'Springbok', 46¼", 180 cm. £700-1,200 SBel

A Bing gauge 'One' clockwork 0-4-0 locomotive, c.1905, 13¼", 33.6 cm. £140-170 SBel

The Mountain/Artillery No: 28, with mules, gun barrels, wheels and attendants; Royal Field Artillery, complete gun team. £150-170 SBel

21st Empress of India's Lancers, five mounted figures with lances; £50-70 SBel

Britains Light Australian Horse (5), (B-C), one horse slightly damaged. £70-80 PL

Band of the Coldstream Guards — 23 pieces. £100-140   LJ

Britains South Australian Lancers, with officer (5), in a Britains box (A) £140-160   PL

A fireworks reward Amusement Machine, a free cigarette given for high score, 32", 81 cm. high, c.1933. £48-58   SBel

A Wonders 'Big Wheel' Amusement Machine, an Allwin-type penny-operated machine, 22", 89 cm. high, c.1950. £80-90 SBel

A conveyor Amusement Machine, penny-operated, 36", 91 cm. high, 1945-50. £55-65 SBel

A Bryans 'The Clock' Amusement Machine, penny operated 33", 84 cm. high, c.1952. £40-50 SBel

An Ahrems Test-your-Strength Machine with leather punchball, 79", 201 cm. high, English, c.1920. £320-400   SBel

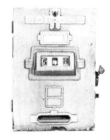

An Orion one-armed Bandit, 28", 71 cm. high, c.1960. £14-24 SBel

A trick pony cast-iron Money Bank, by Shepard Hardware Co., 7½", 19 cm. wide, American, late 19th C. £120-140   SBel

A 'Dark Town Battery' cast-iron Money Box, by James H. Bowen (repainted), 10", 25.5 cm. long, American, late 19th C. £140-160   SBel

An unusual musical tinplate Money Bank, 4", 10 cm. high, £28-38 SBel

An articulated wood model of a Dragon, the moveable limbs with flame collars. 43½", 111 cm. long, Japanese, 19th C. **£130-150** LC

An Edwardian Tricycle with solid-tyred wheels and fixed pedals. **£180-200** CSK

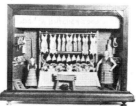

A good model Racing Stable, 37½", 95 cm. long, English, c.1920. **£260-300** SBel

A 19th C. working model of a muzzle loading bombardment mortar. **£230-260** PK

A good Bavarian Noah's Ark with 158 paired carved and painted wooden animals, unpaired animals and 6 figures, the boat 21", 53 cm. long, German, late 19th C. **£140-170** SBel

A model Butcher's Shop, painted sign within glazed oak frame, 23" by 17" by 7", 59 x 45.5 by 18 cm. English, c.1900. **£600-700** SBel

A Britains Nissen Hut, in original box No. 1733. **£220-240** PL

A carved and painted rocking horse, 84", 213 cm. long. English, c.1900. **£300-340** SBel

Argentine Infantry — 8 pieces (original box) **£50-65** LJ

Argentine Military Cadets — 8 pieces **£75-100** LJ

Machine Gun Section, sitting position — 4 pieces (original box) **£20-30** LJ

Mexico, Los Rurales de la Federacion — 8 pieces **£100-140** LJ

Canadian North West Mounted Police, on foot — 8 pieces (orginal box) **£50-60** LJ

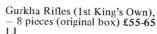

Turkish infantry, nine lying firing, five kneeling firing — 14 pieces. **£40-50** LJ

Zouaves charging — 3 pieces **£10-20** LJ

Seven Scots Guards Pipers (bag-pipes) — 7 pieces **£45-60** LJ

Gurkha Rifles (1st King's Own), — 8 pieces (original box) **£55-65** LJ

Early Bing live steam 'portable steam engine, c.1902-1906, 9½", 24 cm. **£220-240** SBel

A good vintage thistle open tourer pedal car, wood frame, 35½", 90 cm, c.1930. **£180-200** LC

A fine and detailed spirit fired model of a stationary steam engine, 15½", 39.4 cm. **£120-140** LC

Model of a stationary gas engine. Mounted in glazed beechwood case, 18", 45.8 cm., c.1900. **£250-450** SBel

Two Wells tinplate vehicles, comprising a Carter Paterson carrier van, and a BP motor spirit openbacked lorry. 6¼", 16 cm. long, English, c.1935. **£140-160** SBel

A twin-cylinder 'Duplex' horizontal steam engine, English, late 19th C., 29", 14 cm. **£130-160** SBel

A model of a steam Beam engine. **£240-260** PK

A Britains monoplane (blue), in original box no. 433. **£340-370** PL

A Bing vertical stationary steam plant, live steam spirit-fired, 14¼", 36.2 cm., c.1912. **£140-160** SBel

Unusual 19th C. model of a steam horseless carriage compound, 11½", 29.3 cm. **£950-1,050** SBel

A child's Galloper tricycle, 40" by 33½", 102 cm. by 85 cm. c.1870. **£120-140** SBel

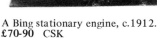

A Bing stationary engine, c.1912. **£70-90** CSK

Small vertical single cylinder stationary steam engine, 1920's. **£45-55** SBel

A Britains monoplane (green), in original box no. 433. **£550-630** PL

An Indian ivory set, stained green and brown, the kings and queens with fluted melon-shaped crowns, pointed baluster pawns (tiny chips to some finials) height of kings 4⅞", 12.4 cm., height of pawns, 1⅝", 4.2 cm., Delhi, 19th C. £450-500 CStJ

A German painted porcelain set, the kings and queens of 'bust' type, the rooks as towers with conical spires, picked out in gilt on a white ground and distinguished by black or orange finials, height of kings 3½", 8.8 cm., height of pawns, 2⅜", 6.1 cm., 19th C., probably Furstenburg. £1,200-1,300 CStJ

A metal set, the cast pieces silvered or gilt, with French and English Mediaeval monarchs, (4 weapons and bishop's crook missing ends), height of kings 4", 10 cm., height of pawns 2⅜", 6 cm., stamped Copyright, 1876 J. Lemon. £400-450 CStJ

An Indian silver and silver-gilt set, the kings as chiefs on elephants, queens as counsellors on horseback, bishops as camels, pawns as infantrymen, height of kings, 2½", 6.2 cm., height of pawns 1¾", 4.4 cm., c.1800, possibly Madras. £1,100-1,200 CStJ

A large Cantonese ivory set on puzzleball bases, natural and red stained, the rooks as turreted elephants with flags, pawns as mounted soldiers, (few details missing) height of kings 7½", 19 cm., height of pawns, 3⅞", 9.8 cm., 19th C. £1,200-1,300 CStJ

BRONZE

- alloy of copper and tin
- bronze first turns reddish-brown, then mid-brown and finally dark brown, however frequently a green surface forms

- because bronze is cast, new reproductions can be made from old moulds
- cannot always assume that when one buys a numbered piece from a limited edition

that only the fixed number exist as frequently moulds were not destroyed

A pair of bronze figures, signed Lalouette, 13½″, 35 cm., light-brown patination, c.1885. **£460-520** SBel

A bronze group, signed T. Campaiola, 24″, 61 cm., rubbed black patination, Italian, early 20th C. **£180-220** SBel

A large 19th C. bronze study, signed, P.J. Mene, 27½″, 70 cm., high. **£1,650-1,850** KC

A bronze figure of a Young Goddess, signed E. de Labroue, 20″, 51 cm., weathered patination, 1880's **£160-190** SBel

A bronze group of the Signing of the Magna Carta, stamped 3755, 13¾″, 35 cm., dark brown patination, mid 19th C. **£280-310** SBel

A 19th C. bronze study of a Classical Group, 16″, 41 cm., **£440-490** KC

A bronze figure of a young woman holding a writing board, 14″, 36 cm., on an ebonised plinth, light and dark brown patination, c 1870. **£190-220** SBel

A large sectional bronze group 18¼″, 46.5 cm., late 19th C. Japanese. **£360-400** LC

A 19th C. Italian classical bronze study, E. Guttkorn Hopfgarten, Roma 1872, 20″, 50 cm., **£180-240** KC

A pair of bronze models of
Temple Guardians, 26³/₈'',
67 cm., Tibetan. **£600-700** KC

A bronze figure of Jesus, signed
Raoul Larche Siot, 15¼'', 8.5 cm.,
c.1890. **£160-180** SBel

A pair of bronze Shepherdesses,
signed Detrier 24½'', 61 cm.,
brown/green patination, c.1870.
£1,350-1,500 SBel

Luca Madrassi. A bronze figure
of a Woman, 19½'', 50 cm.,
rubbed patination, c.1900. **£250-
290** SBel

A bronze figure of Napoleon,
8½'', 21.5 cm., dark brown
patination, mid 19th C. **£240-
280** SBel

Duchoiselle: A 19th C. 12'',
30.5 cm., bronze figure of
Terpsichore, **£220-250** RB

A pair of bronze figures after the
antique, one of Venus the other
of a reaper. Yellow marble plinth.
13'' high 33 cm. **£380-480** HKC

A bronze group, 13½'', 34 cm.,
black/brown patination, mid
19th C. **£310-350** SBel

A large bronze figure of a standing
warrior immortal, some damage.
32'', 81.5 cm., Ch'ing Dynasty.
£280-310 CStJ

Thai bronze figure c.1900. 14'',
35.5 cm., **£140-170** LBA

A bronze group signed J. J.
Jaquet, 32½'', 82.5 cm., black
patination, Belgian, c.1870.
£1,500-1,700   SBel

'Ne Bougeons Plus', Bronze
figure of a photographer,
by L. Raphael, 16'', 40.5 cm.,
late 19th C. £1,250-1,750   SBel

A bronze figure of a Knight in
Armour, stamped H, 14½'', 36 cm.
brown patination, c.1910. £100-
150   SBel

A bronze figure, signed A.
Boucher and F. Barbedienne
Founder, 21½'', 54.5 cm., c.1880.
£700-800   SBel

A weathered bronze figure of Lo
Spinario 2'7'', 78.5 cm. high
£350-430   HKC

A Bronze Group of a Baby and a
Goose, signed Dinee, on a marble
plinth, 14½''; 37 cm., rubbed
brown patination, c. 1890. £340-
400   SBel

A bronze figure of Wellington,
25¼'', 64 cm., black patination,
c.1860. £540-640   SBel

An 18th Century bronze group
after the antique of the captive
Hercules. 12½''; 31.75 cm. high,
now with a yellow marble plinth.
£3,000-3,500   HKC

A Franz Bergman Gold-Painted
bronze figure, stamped H. Schutzt,
15'', 12.7 cm., Austrian, c.1910.
£320-380   SBel

A bronze figure, signed S.
Kinsburger, 19½'', 49.5 cm.,
c.1890. £480-560   SBel

A bronze figure, signed J. Cavelier 278, 9½", 24 cm., brown patination, c.1870. £150-190 SBel

A pair of bronze figures, signed A. Carrier, 19½", 49.5 cm., rubbed brown/black patination, c.1880. £540-640 SBel

A bronze figure, signed E. Picault, 26", 66 cm., chocolate patination, c.1890. £720-820 SBel

After Emile Picault: A pair of bronze figures, 31", 79 cm., late 19th C. £850-950 LC

A pair of 19th C. bronze figures, 14½", 37 cm., high. £800-900 PL

Pair of bronze figures of Poseidon, signed J. Terre, 24", 61 cm., £975-1,150 MH

A bronze group, signed L. Tuaillon, Gladenbeck Berlin, 14½", 37 cm., dark brown patination, c.1900. £160-180 SBel

A bronze figure of a nude, signed F. Derwent Wood, 11⅞", 30.2 cm., dated 1904. £400-700 SBel

A 19th C. bronze study, after Carrier-Belleuse, 16½", 42 cm., £230-300 KC

A late 19th C. Italian bronze group, stamped 'Nell, Roma', 6½", 16.5 cm. high. £160-200 OL

A bronze figure of a Shepherd, 13¾", 32.5 cm., rich brown patination, c.1870. £125-150 SBel

A rare bronze Equestrian Group, signed E. Delabrierre, 13½" by 15", 34 by 38 cm., re-patinated, c.1870. £1,300-1,500 SBel

409

A pair of silvered bronze Greyhounds, signed E. Fremiet, 9½", 24 cm. high. **£310-390** MH

A pair of Japanese bronzes of elephants, 10", 25.5 wide. **£440-490** HKC

A bronze group of the Lion and Serpent, signed Barye, 9⁷/₈", 25 cm., c.1870. **£500-600** SBel

A Bronze group of a pair of horses with a Roman Chariot, after the antique. Yellow veined marble base, 16"; 40.5 cm. wide. **£300-350** HKC

A bronze figure, signed Rosa B, 6", 15 cm., rubbed black and light-brown patination, c.1860. **£210-240** SBel

A bronze figure, stamped P.J. Mene, 4⁷/₈", 12.5 cm., gold and brown rubbed patination, c.1870 **£140-190** SBel

A pair of late Ming bronze Cats, 11", 28 cm., 17th C. **£2,600-3,000** SBS

A bronze group of Two Deer, signed I. Bonheur, 5½", 14 cm., rich brown patination, c.1870. **£320-390** SBel

A pair of bronze groups of Marly Horses, signed Coustou, 15¾", 40 cm., c.1900. **£360-440** SBel

A pair of bronze groups of Marly Horses, 20", 51 cm. rich, light brown patination, c.1880. **£660-760** SBel

A bronze model, in a European style, 14½", 36 cm. incised mark? Shin-Dan-Saku, Japanese. **£150-190** LC

A bronze figure, signed P.J. Mene, 6½", 16.5 cm., c.1870. **£200-300** SBel

A bronze figure, signed E. Delabrierre, 8", 20 cm., rubbed black patination, c.1870. **£330-400** SBel

A bronze figure, signed P.J. Mene, 8", 20 cm., rubbed brown and gilt patination, c.1880. **£150-250** SBel

A bronze model of a Lion, 16", 41 cm., Japanese, c.1900. **£230-260** LC

A pair of bronze groups of
Marly Horses, signed Coustou,
14½", 37 cm., rubbed dark-brown
patination, c.1870. £460-520
SBel

A bronze group of Two Dogs,
signed Lalouette, 9", 23 cm.,
brown patination, c.1880. £150-
170 SBel

A cast bronze finish model
Greyhound. 6½", 16.5 cm.,
£30-40 WW

A bronze figure, signed P.J.
Mene, 4", 10 cm., re-patinated,
mid 19th C. £130-180 SBel

A bronze figure, signed Rosa B.
Comploir Francais d'art, 5½",
14 cm., rubbed dark-brown
patination, c.1860. £250-350
SBel

A Bronze Bust of Dionysius Myste
on yellow marble socle, 28";
71 cm., with well-chiselled hair
and beard, Italian, third quarter
of 19th century. £320-400 SBel

Francis Lamonaca. A Bronze
Portrait Bust signed La Monaca,
with foundry mark Cire perdue
A. Valsuani, 15¾"; 40 cm.,
Italian, early 20th century. £80-
120 SBel

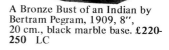

A Bronze Bust of an Indian by
Bertram Pegram, 1909, 8",
20 cm., black marble base. £220-
250 LC

A Bronze Bust, Tanagra and signed E. Villanis, stamped HP 4491, 24½'', 61.5 cm., dark-brown patination, c.1890. **£500-580** SBel

A Bronze Bust of Le Baiser Donne, signed Houdon, 19¾'', 50 cm., green and black patination, c.1880. **£620-690** SBel

A pair of French bronze Ewers, mid-19th C. 22½'', 57 cm. **£210-240** LC

A pair of archaistic bronze square baluster vases, slightly damaged, inscriptions on rims, 21'', 54 cm., **£500-600** CStJ

Two bronze Pitchers, one marked 'Aug. Moreau', the other 'Auguste Moreau', c.1900. 12½'', 31.5 cm. **£110-140** SBel

A Pair of Champleve and Bronze Vases, 8½'', 21.5 cm., late 19th C. **£120-180** SBel

A bronze arrow vase, Ming/early Ch'ing Dynasty, 15¾''., 40 cm., **£150-190** CStJ

A Bronze Vase, 11.5 cm., 4½'', stamped designer's monogram and 'Made in Austria, Hagenauser Wien Handmade', c.1910. **£170-190** SBel

A bronze tripod incense-burner and pierced domed cover, four-character hallmark 'Ch'eng Ssu T'ang chih', early 19th C., 8'', 20.5 cm., £280-320 CStJ

A Pair of Inlaid Bronze Vases, each decorated in gilt, silver and copper takazogan. 7¾''; 20 cm., late 19th century. £310-360 LC

A Pair of Bronze Masks of Pan, 18¾''; 47.5 cm., probably Italian, mid 19th century. £240-280 SBel

A Chinese bronze bell inscribed with verses, 21'' high, 53.5 cm. £290-320 HKC

A pair of second Empire bronze candelabra. 39'', 99 cm. £500-800 CStJ

A 19th Century bronze after the antique of Marcus Aurelrus, yellow marble plinth and black slate base, 20'', 50 cm. high overall. £400-490 HKC

A bronze bell with double-headed dragon handle, Ch'ing Dynasty, 15¾'', 40 cm., £550-600 CStJ

A Tiffany Studios Bronze Lamp Base, 22½'', 57.5 cm., c.1910. £620-700 SBel

A Pair of Marble and Bronze Candlesticks. 9¾''; 24.5 cm., c.1870. £70-90 SBel

A bronze Charger, signed J. Pearson, 2451, 24'', 61 cm. dia. dated 1899. £70-90 SBel

A Pair of Gilt-Bronze and Marble Occasional Tables. 28", 71 cm., 20th C. £580-640 SBel

A Splashed Gilt Bronze Incense Burner and Stand of Globular Ting Form, 6¾", 17 cm., overall, 4-character seal mark, Chinese, 18th C. £500-560 KC

A Pair of Gilt-Bronze Urns and Covers on a black marble socle, 20"; 51 cm., c. 1880. £190-230 SBel

A Gilt-Bronze and Marble Occasional Table, 25", by 16½", 64 cm. by 42 cm., late 19th C. top modern. £460-520 SBel

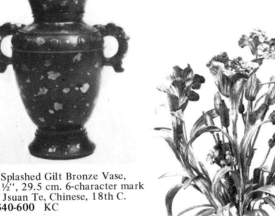

A Gilt-Bronze Table Display Cabinet, 11½", 29 cm., c.1880. £180-200 SBel

James Andrey. A Gilt-Bronze Figure of a Lioness, 11"; 28 cm., c. 1920. £160-190 SBel

A Splashed Gilt Bronze Vase, 11½", 29.5 cm. 6-character mark of Jsuan Te, Chinese, 18th C. £540-600 KC

A pair of gilt bronze wall lights, each with five floral nozzles, 19½"; 50 cm., early 20th century. £210-240 SBel

A Gilt-Bronze and Ivory Group, signed, 10¾", 27.3 cm., c.1910. £370-420 SBel

'La Cothurne.' A Small Gilt Bronze Figure of a Dancer, after a biscuit porcelain model by Agathon Leonard, 27 cm., 10¾"; signed in the maquette 'A. Leon Leonard Scl', impressed founders' mark for Susse Freres, c. 1900. £1,700-2,000 SBel

A Nuremberg bronze Tap, dark
brown patination, 11", 28.0 cm.,
long by 7¾", 19.5 cm. high,
c.1550. £580-670 LC

A fine Japanese bronze Koro
and Cover, cast three character
mark, mid 19th C. 15", 38 cm.
high. £310-340 LC

A Pair of Bronze and Ormolu
Chenets, each with a putto lean-
ing forward to warm his hands
besides a flambeau, 12½"; 32 cm.,
c. 1880. £460-560 SBel

After J. Causse. A Gilt-Bronze
and Marble Figure of a Young
Woman, writing on a marble
tablet, 20"; 56 cm., late 19th
Century. £190-220 SBel

A Pair of Gilt-Bronze and Glass
Vases, supported by a framework
cast with acanthus, base cast with
scrolling leaves and berries 11";
28 cm., c. 1880. £150-170 SBel

A Pair of Porcelain and Gilt
Bronze Urns, 17¼", 44 cm.,
c.1880. £400-440 SBel

A Pair of Gilt-Bronze Candelabra,
25½", 65 cm., c.1870. £170-190
SBel

A George IV Bronze and Gilt-
Metal Candelabrum, 2'2",
66 cm., c.1825. £350-380 SBS

415

Ivory has always enjoyed much favour with craftsmen for small pieces of carving and sculpture. It is not always an ideal medium due to its inherent hardness. However both the Chinese and Japanese craftsmen produced vast quantities of decorative items, including okimono, netsuke and inro. The Japanese have always stained ivory to make it appear older. Again any signed pieces by the leading craftsmen from any of the famous schools such as Tomotada, Masanao of Kyoto, Okatomo, Kaigyokusai, Mitsuhiro and Gyokuzan.

A Walrus ivory Gamma Sennin supporting two frogs, end of staff missing, 5¼''; 13 cm., signed, c.1900. wood stand. £90-120 SBel

A Sea ivory Girl, chips, 13''; 33 cm., c.1900. wood stand. £400-450 SBel

A Walrus ivory Girl in heavy flowing gown, her black hair swept back, 5½''; 14 cm., last quarter of the 19th century. £120-150 SBel

A sectional carved ivory figure of a Fisherman, 9½''; 24 cm., signed Japanese, c.1900. £280-320 LC

An ivory Lohan, 10''; 25.5 cm., engraved four character seal mark of Ch'ien Lung, 20th century. £130-160 SBel

A carved ivory figure of a Man 7½''; 19 cm., Japanese, Tokyo school, early 20th century. £180-200 LC

An ivory Kuan Yin, 7"; 18 cm., late 19th century. £200-240 SBel

An ivory Hare naturalistically carved 2¾"; 7 cm., c.1900. £260-290 SBel

A Good Eishin Ivory Basket-Maker, twine cracked, signed Eishin, c.1900. 4", 10 cm. £720-800 SBel

A Kozan ivory Armourer forming a helmet on a box of drawers, beside various equipment, 3¼"; 8 cm., engraved Kozan, c.1900. £120-150 SBel

An Okawa ivory Group of a woman, details engraved and filled in brown, black and red, end of bale of cloth under geta missing, 5½"; 14 cm., signed Okawa on a reserve, c.1900. £400-450 SBel

A Shugyoku ivory Jurogin, 6¼"; 16 cm., engraved Shugyoku, c.1900. £130-150 SBel

A large Masamitsu ivory Kwannon an image of Buddha on her head, 21¾"; 55.5 cm., signed Masamitsu on a lacquer reserve, c.1900. £1,700-1,900 SBel

An ivory Peasant, the ivory of white colour, lacks signature reserve, 6¾"; 17 cm., c.1900. £200-240 SBel

A large Tamayuki Sea ivory Fisherman slight sepia details, 12½"; 31.5 cm., engraved red Tamayuki, c.1900. £540-600 SBel

A carved sectional ivory figure of a Musician Singer, 4"; 10 cm., signed Keigu, Japanese, late 19th century. £320-360 LC

Miniature carving in ivory. £140-160 LBA

417

A well-carved Shitsu ivory Bear, the fur boldly carved and with mother-of-pearl inlaid eyes, three claws chipped, 3"; 7.5 cm., relief Shitsu, c.1900. **£130-150** SBel

A carved figure of a Falconer, Japanese, late 19th C., signed, 5¾" high, 14.5 cm. **£230-260** HKC

A carved ivory figure of Amida Buddha, 5"; 12.5 cm., signed in oval reserve, late 19th century. **£160-180** KC

A well carved ivory Group of Shao Lao, internal crack, 8¼" 21 cm., third quarter of the 19th century, wood stand. **£270-300** SBel

An Isshi Sea ivory Group of fishermen, 9¾"; 24.5 cm., engraved Isshi, c.1900. **£320-350** SBel

A Sea ivory Carving of monkeys playing on and under a camel, the fur engraved and with slight sepia stain, 3¾"; 9.5 cm., signed, c.1900. **£130-150**   SBel

A carved figure of a farmer, Japanese, late 19th C. 6¼" high, 16 cm. **£200-250** HKC

A Tamayuki ivory Group of two men playing the samisen and the drum, a boy beside them, small pieces missing, 6½"; 16.5 cm., engraved red Tamayuki, c.1900. **£380-420** SBel

A Sea ivory Group of two peasants black engraved detail, 9½"; 24 cm. signed, c.1900. **£350-390** SBel

An ivory Netsuke, the ivory with some wear, 1½"; 4 cm., late 19th century. £50-80 SBel

An ivory Netsuke, signs of wear, toe and hand missing, 1½"; 3.8 cm., signed, first half of the 19th century. £60-80 SBel

An ivory Netsuke of Jurogin teasing a minogame with a gourd, 1½"; 3.8 cm., signed late 19th century. £140-160 SBel

A Seigyoku ivory Netsuke, 1½"; 4 cm., engraved Seigyoku, c.1900. £95-120 SBel

An ivory Netsuke, deep sepia stained, 1³/₈"; 3.5 cm., last quarter of the 19th century. £160-190 SBel

An ivory Netsuke of Kwan Ti, 2½". 6.5 cm., third quarter of the 19th century. £240-280 SBel

A Jomin ivory Netsuke of a girl, her obi and details of her gown coloured or inlaid green and coral, 1½"; 3.5 cm., signed Jomin on a green reserve, c.1900. £380-450 SBel

A coloured ivory Netsuke of Ebisu his hair black and with pink tunic and gold details, toes chipped, 1½"; 3.8 cm., relief black signature, c.1900. £90-120 SBel

A Yoshitusuki ivory Netsuke 2"; 5 cm., engraved Yoshitusuki, late 19th century. £120-150 SBel

An ivory Netsuke of a Sage, black engraved detail, 1½"; 3.8 cm., late 19th century. £130-160 SBel

An ivory Netsuke, details in black, oval base, 1½"; 4 cm., signed third quarter of the 19th century. £130-160 SBel

An ivory Netsuke of Two Oni sepia stain, foot and sword damaged, 2½"; 6.2 cm., signed, c.1900. £150-190 SBel

A Carved Ivory Netsuke of a small Dog, the himotoshi formed by gaps between the hind legs and the ball, 1³/₈"; 3.5 cm. unsigned, Japanese, 18th century. £210-250 LC

A good Ivory Ball formed of numerous monkeys, the fur finely engraved, 2"; 5 cm., late 19th century. **£350-400** SBel

A Koshin ivory Group, pegs missing, 3"; 7.8 cm., engraved red Koshin, c.1900. **£140-170** SBel

A Sea ivory Group of a fisherman 12½"; 32 cm., c.1900. **£340-400** SBel

An ivory Okimono of an Immortal holding a shrine, sepia stained, 2½"; 6.5 cm., late 19th century. **£50-80** SBel

An ivory Okimono of Ebishu and Diakoku, sepia stained, minute chip, 2½"; 6 cm., last quarter of the 19th century. **£180-210** SBel

An ivory Okimono of Handaka Sonja holding a smoking censer, sepia stained, 2"; 5 cm., late 19th century. **£70-90** SBel

A Good Ivory Okimono, deep sepia stained, signed Masahiro, mid 19th C. 2½", 6.5 cm. **£310-340** SBel

A Shuko ivory Okimono, 3¼"; 8 cm., engraved Shuko, last quarter of the 19th century, wood stand. **£160-190** SBel

An ivory Okimono of the priest Kinko the ivory white with engraved black detail, 4¾"; 12 cm., signed, late 19th century. **£380-420** SBel

A good Chika ivory Okimono of a fight between a dog and a monkey, the details well engraved and the eyes inlaid in mother-of-pearl, 2½''; 6.5 cm., relief Chika, c.1900. **£360-400** SBel

An ivory Okimono of Kiyomasa, ends of sword replaced, end of spear missing, 2''; 5 cm., last quarter of the 19th century. **£220-250** SBel

A well-carved ivory Okimono of a girl with monkey, the details black filled, 3½''; 9 cm., signed, last quarter of the 19th century. **£230-260** SBel

An ivory Okimono of Kwannon handle missing, 4''; 10 cm., signed on a mother-of-pearl reserve, c.1900. **£170-200** SBel

An ivory fan, the paper mount painted, 11½'' long, 29 cm. probably Flemish, c.1830. **£120-150** SBel

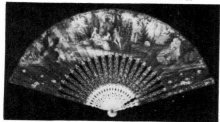

A French ivory fan, the paper mount painted 10'', 25.5 cm., c.1750, **£160-180** SBel

An unusual fan, Blanchard and Versailles balloons depicted on paper, within ivory mounts, radius 10¾'', 27.5 cm., French, late 19th C. **£200-230** SBel

A German carved ivory fan, the paper mount painted, 11½'', 29 cm., c.1760, **£95-105** SBel

A Chinese ivory fan, the paper mount painted, 10⅞'', 27.5 cm., c.1780. **£160-180** SBel

A small ivory Vase and Cover, carved in the form of a dense group of playful baboons, 3¼"; 9.5 cm., Japanese, c.1900. **£260-300** LC

A pair of ivory Spill Vases, one base slight damage, 7"; 17.5 cm., last quarter of the 19th century. **£170-200** SBel

A carved ivory Tusk Vase 7"; 18 cm., Japanese, late 19th century (fitted lacquered stand). **£220-250** KC

A pair of ivory Tusk Vases, the sides carved in elaborate detailed high relief, the details minutely engraved, 10"; 25.5 cm., fitted lacquered wood stands (both vases repaired). Japanese, late 19th century. **£300-350** LC

A pair of ivory Buddhist Lion Vases, 6½"; 16.5 cm., 20th century. **£160-200** SBel

A large lacquered ivory Tusk Vase, decorated in gold, black and red hiramakie and kirikane flakes, 10"; 25.5 cm., Japanese, late 19th century (fixed lacquered wood stand). **£540-620** KC

A well-carved Kosai ivory Raft Group, the son playing with a terrapin, end of pole chipped, rope cracked, 8¼"; 21 cm. engraved Kosai and kakihan, late 19th century. **£680-750** SBel

An ivory Workbox, deeply carved, the interior with fitted tray and various sewing materials slightly distressed, the cover cracked, 6¾"; by 10¾"; by 4¼"; 17 cm., by 27.5 cm. by 10.5 cm., third quarter of the 19th century. **£480-550** SBel

An ivory Box and Cover 3¼"; 8 cm., c.1900. **£150-180** SBel

A good and unusual Ivory Box and Cover, 4¼"; 10.5 cm., c.1900 **£520-600** SBel

An ivory Box and Cover, the squat section of tusk carved in relief, foot rim missing, knop replaced, 5½"; 14 cm., seal mark, c.1900. **£190-220** SBel

An ivory Box and Cover of rectangular section carved in low relief, hammered metal mounts, distressed, one edge missing, 9"; 23 cm., late 19th century. **£290-350** SBel

A carved ivory 'Hunting' Box on lion supports, velvet lined, 6"; 15.3 cm., long, German, mid 19th century, one foot detached. **£360-400** SBel

An ivory Card Case, carved with ladies and gentlemen, the sides with dragons, bats and phoenixes, 4¼"; 10.5 cm., mid 19th century. **£170-190** SBel

An ivory Card Case with a named view of Napoleon's House and his Tomb, slight cracks, 3¾"; 9.5 cm. c.1870. **£100-130** SBel

An ivory Card Case carved with birds and plants, the ivory of yellow colour, 4¼"; 10.5 cm., mid 19th century. **£120-140** SBel

A small ivory Card Case carved with immortals, the sides with bats and birds, 3¼"; 8.2 cm., third quarter of the 19th century. **£65-85** SBel

An ivory Card Case carved each side with a cross enclosing figures and trees, cracks, 4½"; 11.5 cm., late 19th century. **£48-58** SBel

An ivory Card Case carved with shaped borders 4¼"; 10.5 cm., late 19th century. **£65-85** SBel

An ivory Card Case, one inlay missing, some wear, 4½"; 11.5 cm., c.1900. **£130-160** SBel

A Three-Case Shibayama and Lacquered ivory Inro, a double-gourd form, the sides decorated in inlaid mother-of-pearl hard-stones and gold takamakie and kirikane flakes, 4''; 10 cm., long, signed in oval mother-of-pearl reserve, late 19th century. **£500-600** KC

A Three-Case Lacquered ivory Inro, decorated in gold and red takamakie and kirikane flakes, 3½''; 9 cm., 19th century. **£340-400** KC

A Four-Case lacquer and ivory Inro of lenticular shape, 3¼''; 8.25 cm., signed Shomosai, 19th century. **£340-400** KC

A carved ivory Chess Set, rendered in European taste, 2¾'' to 5½''; 7 cm. to 14 cm., Chinese, late 19th century. **£400-500** KC

A mid-18th C. gentleman's gold topped chased walking cane, 40½'' long, 102 cm., **£80-90** PK

An inlaid ivory Cabinet, the ivory case bound in brass and inlaid in stained horn and ivory and mother-of-pearl, back panel cracked, some brass missing, 3''; by 3½''; by 2½''; 7.5 cm by 9 cm. by 6 cm. c.1900. **£200-250** SBel

A rare ivory Snuff Horn cracked and chipped, 4''; 10 cm., c.1830. **£130-150** SBel

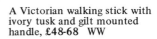

A Victorian walking stick with ivory tusk and gilt mounted handle, **£48-68** WW

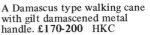

A Damascus type walking cane with gilt damascened metal handle. **£170-200** HKC

A carved sandalwood, ivory and bone Chess Set, carved box forming chess board, the interior with a backgammon board, 3½''; by 17½''; 9 cm., by 44.5 cm., closed, c.1890. **£300-350** SBel

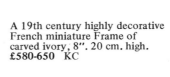

A 19th century highly decorative French miniature Frame of carved ivory, 8''. 20 cm. high. **£580-650** KC

424

Ivory Bust of Queen Victoria signed Chantry Fec. Cheverton Sc, 12", 30.5 cm. **£280-340** PL

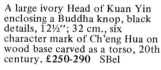

A large ivory Head of Kuan Yin enclosing a Buddha knop, black details, 12½"; 32 cm., six character mark of Ch'eng Hua on wood base carved as a torso, 20th century. **£250-290** SBel

An ivory Basket and Cover of lozenge form, several panels split, 15½"; 39.5 cm., third quarter of the 19th century, box. **£300-350** SBel

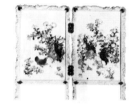

A masayuki Shibayama and Joun ivory Two-Fold Screen, two panels inlaid in mother-of-pearl, tortoise-shell and stained ivory, metal mounts, considerable inlay missing, lacks two panels at base, 10¾" by 12¼"; 27.3 cm. by 31 cm., signed Masayuki on a lacquer reserve and engraved Joun and seal, c.1900 **£800-900** SBel

A Tomonobu Shibayama Card Tray, the centre set with a heart-shaped ivory panel inlaid, the bamboo-form handle of ivory, 11½"; 29 cm. long, signed in oval mother-of-pearl reserve, Japanese, c.1900. **£500-550** KC

An Enamelled Silver and Shibay-ama Vase and Cover, seal marks, c.1900. 8¼"; 21 cm. **£760-850** KC

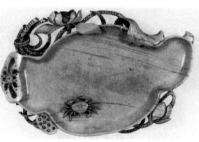

An ivory Tray lightly coloured, 7½"; 19 cm., last quarter of the 19th century. **£300-350** SBel

A sectional carved ivory model of a Straw Thatched Dwelling and summerhouse, 10⁵/₈"; 27 cm. wide, Japanese, c.1900, (fitted wood stand). **£110-140** SBel

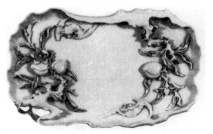

An ivory Tray 7¼"; 18.5 cm., last quarter of the 19th century. **£320-370** SBel

WOOD

Bone and Wood Model of a
French Man-of-War. Applied
overall with green and brown
inscribed decoration, 12" by 10";
30.5 cm. by 25.5 cm., French,
early 19th century. **£1,300-1,500**
SBel

An early 19th century Bone
Prisoner-of-War Work Watch-
stand of Architectural Shape,
with drawer to base, 11½";
29 cm. high. **£150-180** KC

French Prisoner-of-War Work.
An elaborate bone model of the
Guillotine, 24" wide by 16" high,
61 cm. by 41 cm., circa 1800.
£1,100-1,300 SBel

A Prisoner-of-War Bone of a
Frigate, 11½" by 13"; 29 cm. by
33 cm., mounted on ebonised
base, French, early 19th century.
£650-1,200 SBel

A good early 19th century
French Prisoner-of-War Work
Spinning Jenny. Fully articulated movement, complete with
spinning wheel and mechanism
below, 4¼"; 10.5 cm. high.
£150-180 KC

An English bone fan, 10¾",
27 cm. **£75-85** SBel

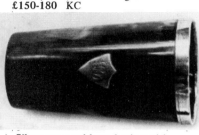

Silver mounted horn beaker with
monogram. **£19-25** LBA

Whale's Tooth Scrimshaw, basket
of flowers design, 7½"; 19 cm.
high. English, late 19th century.
£80-150 SBel

An American Scrimshaw Whale's
tooth, with portrait of Napoleon,
signed J.A., 19th C., 6¾", 17 cm.
£100-150 CStJ

A good Dolphin Jaw Scrimshaw
with portraits of ladies, 1'4½";
42 cm. long, English, third
quarter of the 19th century.
£200-300 SBel

Whale's-Tooth Scrimshaw, inscribed on one side only with
full-length portrait of a young
woman, 7¼"; 18.5 cm. high
overall, English, late 19th century. **£80-120** SBel

Curved Ram's Horn Snuff Mull.
Silver-coloured metal neck and
hinged cover, which is inset with
a stone. Cover also inscribed
"George Scott Thornley", c.1800
£90-120 KC

Decorated Whale's Tooth, inscribed with a portrait entitled
'William III' and reverse with a
vessel entitled 'The Olympic',
7½"; 19 cm., long, **£100-200**
SBel

Curved Ram's Horn Snuff Mull.
Silver-coloured metal mount to
neck and hinged cover. c.1800.
£32-45 KC

NETSUKE

- came into use in 16th C.
- small carved toggle
- used to fasten the inro to the sash
- mainly carved in human, mythological and animal forms

- by mid 18th C. schools for carvers at Echigo, Wakayama, Edo, Yamada, Osaka, Kyoto and Nagoyo
- Netsuke must be compact, show skill of carving and for high prices be carved by one of the top craftsmen

- watch out for late 19th and early 20th C. fakes, easiest way was to bore holes through small ornaments — these lack the quality and fine detail of good netsuke

Takeshimo wood Netsuke of Hotei, 3¼", 8 cm., late 19th C., **£210-240** SBel

Carved wood Netsuke of Riujin, 4¼", 10.5 cm., unsigned, c.1900 (foot repaired). **£600-680** KC

Carved wood Netsuke of Okame, 2½", 6.5 cm., unsigned, 18th C. **£180-200** KC

A 'Tomotada' wood netsuke, lip chip, 4 cm., 1½", c.1900, **£95-115** SBel

Four-Case Inro, in black and gold takamakie and kirikane flakes, 3½", 9 cm., c.1870. **£520-570** KC

A Four-Case Lacquer Inro, the sides decorated in gold, red and silver takamakie, 3⅛", 8 cm. long, signed, Japanese, 19th C. **£800-900** LC

Yamada School: A carved wood Netsuke, signed Masanao, mid-19th C. 1½", 4.25 cm. **£180-210** KC

Four-Case Lacquer Inro, decorated in gold takamakie and kirikane flakes, 2¾", 7 cm., 19th C. **£440-500** KC

A wood brush-pot, carved with the 'Three Friends', pine, prunus and bamboo, cracked, 18th/19th C., 5½", 14 cm., **£190-220** CStJ

17th C. carved Oak Panel with panels of rules for servants with punishments and fines, 19¾", by 6'6", 50 cm., by 200 cm. **£220-300** KC

An oak ships wheel, stamped Brown Bros. & Co., Edinburgh, 72" dia., 183 cm. **£270-300** HKC

Shuzan wood Group of Rats, 6¾", 17 cm., late 19th C. **£230-260** SBel

A rare early limewood carving of Adam and Eve, 16" x 15½", 40.5 x 39.5 cm. **£1,400-1,600** HKC

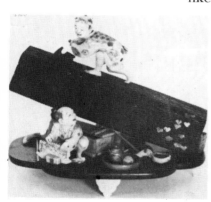

A Norwegian sycamore treen tankard, 8¾" high, 22 cm., early 19th C. **£250-280** CStJ

Wood and ivory Group of Two Sawyers, minute pieces missing, 6¾", 17 cm., c.1900. **£1,000-1,200** SBel

A Large Carved Oak 'Gothick' Torchere, 77", 195.5 cm. 1840's. **£150-190** SBel

A good mid-19th C. Scandinavian painted pine butter tub and cover, named and dated 1849. **£180-200** PK

A late 19th C. Swiss carved umbrella stand. **£250-300** KC

A Walnut Torchere, Italian, late 19th C. 36", 91.5 cm. **£200-350** SBel

Tosen Toshishige bamboo Brush Pot, inlaid in various metals including gold, 4½'', 11.5 cm., Rakusai (West Kyoto), late 19th C. **£120-140** SBel

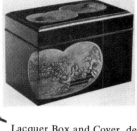

Lacquer Box and Cover, decorated with gold and silver takamakie, 6¼'' by 3¼'' by 4¼'', 16 cm. by 9.5 cm. by 11 cm., Japanese, 19th C. **£325-400** LC

Lacquer Box, in tones of gold lacquer, 5¾'', 14.5 cm., mid 19th C. **£480-560** SBel

Lacquer Sage Jubako, decorated in gold leaf, gold and silver hiramakie with a ro-iro ground. 9½'', 24 cm. wide. 19th C. (repaired). **£200-230** KC

Miniature Lacquer Incense Ceremony Cabinet (Kodansu), in gold takamakie and hiramakie, 5⅛'' by 3⅞'' by 3⅛'', 13 cm. by 10 cm. by 8 cm., Japanese, 19th C. **£1,020-1,200** LC

Lacquer Box and Cover, 8'', 20 cm. long. Japanese, 19th C. **£550-600** LC

Setsudo bamboo and ivory Box, 10¼'', 26 cm., signed Setsudo, late 19th C. **£160-180** SBel

Persian lacquer Qalamdan (Pen Box), 8½'', 21.5 cm. c.1835. **£510-600** KC

Elaborate Egg-Shell Lacquer Cabinet, lacquered in red, gold and black, 9½'', 24 cm., late 19th C. **£270-300** SBel

Circular Jadeite Screen, inlaid in malachite, lapis lazuli, coral and quartz, 11½'', 29 cm., Chinese, 19th C. **£410-460** KC

Lacquer Suzuribako, decorated in red and green hiramakie and gold takamakie, 10'' by 9¼'', 25.5 cm., by 23.5 cm., 19th C. **£400-450** KC

Pair of polychrome wood carvings, c.1600. **£935-1,150** CAL

Pair of 16th C. relief carved panels. **£300-330** CAL

Wood Plaque, the red wood ground lacquered in gold and silver, 25¼", 64 cm., c.1900. **£360-420** SBel

Pair of wood carvings of a man and a woman. **£30-40** WW

A pair of Italian walnut Caryatids, c.1480. **£1,425-1,600** CAL

Inlaid wood and ivory Musician, small pieces replaced, 5", 12.5 cm., late 19th C. **£450-550** SBel

Carving of St. John (?) c.1500, Kleefs Gelders Sch. **£2,200-2,400** CAL

Pair of antique carved wood Pilasters of Putti holding Cornucopia. **£30-40** WW

Flemish carved wood figure of St. Catherine, c.1480. **£3,600-3,900** CAL

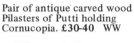

Well-carved English figure, c.1600 **£315-345** CAL

Carved wood figure of a saint in walnut, c.1420. **£3,950-4,250** CAL

A Pair of Continental Pinewood Figures, each 27", 68.5 cm. high, blazoning defective. **£600-700** LC

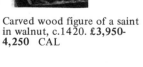

16th C. wood carving. **£165-185** BA

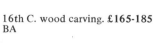

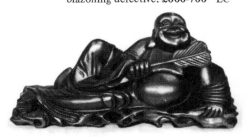

A pair of Gothic carved fragments. **£120-150** CAL

Carved and gilded study of a reclining Buddha. **£21-30** RB

PEWTER

Pewter is an alloy of tin with lead, copper, zinc, antimony or bismuth in varying combinations and quantities. It looks silvery when new but soon shades to a dull grey with aging. The Guild of Pewterers was formed in 1348 to maintain the standard of the metal as too much lead was being added.

- 1503 – maker's touch marks became compulsory, these were often initials

- 1509 – quality marks added (lilypot and portcullis marks)

- 1540's – Fleur-de-lys mark replaced lilypot mark. Rose and crown mark showed good quality

- 1671 – rose and crown mark on export wares

- 1690 – rose and crown mark in general use

A Liberty & Co. 'Tudric' Pewter Tea and coffee Service, c.1910. **£240-270** SBel

A Set of 3 French Late 18th C. Graduated Pewter Lidded Measures from Lille, **£700-800** KC

A selection of Pewter Measures. **£5-10 each** PG

Victorian Pewter quart Tankard. **£75-85** PG

A fine George I tankard, by John Spicer, London (Cotterell 4455), 7″ high, 18 cm., **£680-740** CStJ

A North German Krug inscribed D. G. A. H., 1659, 8¼″, 21 cm., 17th C. **£510-570** CStJ

An antique Pewter quart Mug, touch marked 7″, 17.5 cm. **£50-60** RB

Victorian pewter pedestal Mug, 4½″, 11.5 cm. **£12-20** RB

A rare English lidless tankard of squat proportions, late 17th C., 4½″, 11.5 cm., **£350-390** CStJ

A Cromwellian flagon with scroll handle inscribed A.P.P., 9¼″, 23.5 cm., touch T.C., possibly Thomas Cooper (Cotterell 1111) **£920-1,100** CStJ

An English pear-shaped tankard. 7½″, 19 cm. second half 18th C. **£140-160** CStJ

A 7″, 17.5 cm., Shaped Pewter Tea Pot (dented). **£13-20** RB

A WMF Pewter Candlestick, 10½″, 26.25 cm., c.1900. **£340-370** SBel

Pewter Tea Pot with seed pod knop. **£3-10** RB

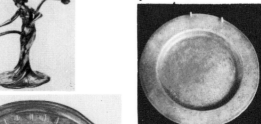

Pair of early Pewter Plates. **£85-95** LBA

A Pewter Chamberstick and Snuffer, stamped James Dixon & Sons, Sheffield. **£16-20** RB

A 6″, 15 cm., Teapot Stand. **£10-20** RB

A Continental Pewter Cistern, crowned X, 21″, 53.5 cm. late 18th early 19th C. **£660-720** LC

A set of six octagonal plates by Thomas Philips, London (Cotterell 3650), 18th C., 9½″, 24 cm. diam., **£1,050-1,100** CStJ

A Liberty & Co. 'Tudric' Pewter Stand with Clutha Glass Liner. 6½″, 16.5 cm., c.1905. **£150-170** SBel

A Silver-Coloured Metal Tea Urn, gross weight 92 oz. **£650-750** KC

A 19th C. French Silver-coloured Metal Teapot. Height 10½″, 26.5 cm. gross weight 30½ oz. **£420-500** KC

A Chinese Silver-Coloured-Metal Tea Set, 3 items, 10 cm., 4″, stamped marks, c.1900, 34 oz. 8 dwt., 1,061 gm. **£230-300** SBel

A WMF Silvered Metal Dish. 7″, 17.5 cm., height, c.1900. **£160-200** SBel

A Silver-Coloured-Metal Dressing-Table Set, 9 items, 12¼″, 31 cm., stamped mark, 20th C. fitted case. **£160-220** SBel

COPPER AND BRASS

Both metals have been used greatly for both utility and decorative wares.

Copper wares in particular have become extremely popular in recent years with collectors. This had led to an absolute glut on the market of reproduction kettles, warming pans, coal-scuttles, etc. This can be distinguished by their lighter quality and the thinner feel of the metal. Don't be taken in by dents and signs of age — they are easily applied!

Old copper wares were formed by hammering a flat sheet of metal over a shaped block. The edges had a row of dovetials cut in which were joined by brazing. Handles were riveted. Genuine coal scuttles were dated from the late 18th C. but most to be found in 'junk' shops are of much more modern production.

Brass production in England began in earnest in the late 17th C. There was also a large import business for continental brass and copper which on the whole tends to be heavily decorated, whereas English wares tend to be plain.

A Dinanderie circular brass alms dish, 19¾" diam., 50 cm., 16th C., £400-450 CStJ

A George III brass footman, 16" wide, 40.5 cm., possibly Welsh. £260-300 CStJ

A pair of late 18th C. brass candlesticks, 7", 18 cm. £65-75 LC

Brass preserving pan. £26-30 CFA

A pair of neo-classic brass candlesticks, c.1780. 9½", 24 cm. £45-50 LC

A brass chandelier, 19¼", 49 cm., 17th C., Dutch or German. £2,200-2,500 CStJ

A marble brass stewpan with iron handle 9", 23 cm. dia. £8-10 WW

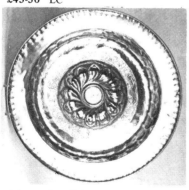

A brass alms dish. 18½" diam., 47 cm., 16th C. £650-720 CStJ

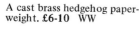

A Dutch brass cream pail, iron hinges and handle, late 18th/early 19th C., 12", 30.5 cm. £160-180 LC

A cast brass hedgehog paper-weight. £6-10 WW

A pair of brass table candlesticks, 12" high, 30.5 cm. £45-55 HKC

A brass lacemaker's lamp. £55-65 HKC

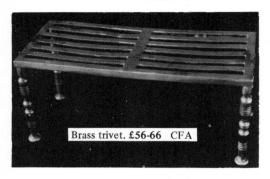

Brass trivet. **£56-66** CFA

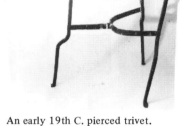

An early 19th C. pierced trivet. **£16-20** AB

A heavy brass mortar and pestle, **£34-40** TJC

A 19th C. lyre kettle hob stand. **£18-24** AB

A China and brass metal mounted Oil Lamp with glass chimney, 21½″, 54 cm. **£18-24** WW

A square brass coal box and cover **£31-40** RB

A brass log bin, 17″, 43 cm. high, first half 19th C. **£260-290** LC

A gilt-brass neo-classical design frame gauge spark guard. **£68-78** WW

A Large Brass Chandelier, 33″, 84 cm., diam. Dutch, c.1900. **£260-300** SBel

Old Brass Hanging Oil Lamp. **£20-30** PG

A Brass Night Clock with key and shade. **£10-15** RB

Oak and brass fire bellows. **£18-22** GGA

Brass coal scuttle. **£49-60** CFA

Brass inkstand. **£25-30** GGA

A two handled brass vessel, 14″, 35.5 cm. overall. £32-40 WW

Pair of Oriental brass vases. 6½″, 16.5 cm. £24-30 WW

A George III Copper and Brass tea urn, height 20″, 51 cm., £130-180 LC

Pair of Victorian brass letter scales and some weights. £20-25 RB

A heavy brass incense burner and cover in the oriental style. £55-65 RB

Brass double lipped jug. £28-34 TJC

Brass inkstand with pen rest. £42-48 CFA

A persian brass Travellers Sundial, incorporating a compass, 4⅝″, 12 cm., dia. 19th C. £200-280 KC

A small brass jug approx 9″, 23 cm. high. £22-30 TJC

Late 19th C. brass and copper banded water jug 10¾″, 27 cm., £15-25

A pair of 9½″, 24 cm. fluted column brass candlesticks on bronze bases. £28-35 AB

Embossed brass kettle on spirit stand. £68-75 TJC

Heavy brass nuremburg alms dish c.1600. £470-520 CAL

A pair of brass Queen Anne candlesticks. £65-75 JWB

435

Pair of 5″, 12.5 cm. brass candle-sticks. £23-28 GGA

Victorian rococo cast gilt brass and iron doorstop. £44-50 WW

An interesting set of 3 antique Syrian brass water jugs, £34-40 RB

Heavy Georgian brass candlestick stand £50-60 PG

Pair of 19th C. Victorian Gothick brass candelabra, 38″ high, 96 cm., £200-250

Antique copper coal scuttle. £75-80 PG

Two gallon copper jack, 14½″, 37 cm. £100-110 WW

Antique copper 4 gallon jug £110-120 ORM

Copper preserving pan with pouring lip. £70-80 CFA

A Syrian antique copper water vessel. £14-18 RB

Copper water bottle £12-15

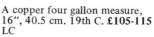

A copper four gallon measure, 17¾″, 45 cm. 19th C. £80-90 LC

A copper four gallon measure, 16″, 40.5 cm. 19th C. £105-115 LC

A two gallon copper measure, 14½″, 37 cm., 19th C. £75-85 LC

A one gallon copper measure, 12″, 30.5 cm. 19th C. £50-60 LC

An unusual copper jug with hinged lid. £34-40 TJC

A Brass mounted fire basket Overall 26", 66 cm. x 29", 74 cm. high, late 18th C. **£350-400** LC

A brass fire grate, and Fire Screen, 38", 96.5 cm. last quarter of 19th C. **£480-520** SBel

A brass trivet with pierced unicorn circular top, 8¼", 21 cm., **£21-30** WW

A Serpentine fronted brass and iron fire basket in the Adam style. 27¼", 69 cm. across front, late 19th C. **£300-380** LC

Pair of brass andirons in dragon design. **£45-55** PG

A lacquered brass pierced fender, 40", 101 cm. **£38-48** WW

Early 19th C. brass fender. **470-80** MPA

Fine Regency period brass and cast iron fireplace. 118 cm. wide, 3'10¾", with matching fender. **£660-760** KC

An antique brass fender with neo-classical frieze, 54", 137 cm. **£130-150** WW

A small antique brass pierced fender. 30", 76 cm., **£26-36** WW

Small Edwardian brass serpentine front fender. **£45-55** GGA

A brass Lectern, c.1868. **£750-850** SBel

Two Eastern copper vessels, 10½"
to 11", 26.5 cm. to 28 cm. £26-
30 WW

Late 19th C. copper jug, 10",
25.5 cm. high, £25-35 DG

A Copper-Coated Table Lamp
on a marble socle, 30", 76 cm.,
1880's. £230-260 SBel

Small copper kettle £49-55 CFA

A large Tibetan copper tea pot
and cover, with inlaid turquoise
stones. 16¼", 41.5 cm., £150-170
LC

A Copper-Coated Group of Two
Wrestlers, 16", 41 cm. German,
c.1900. £620-680 SBel

A large copper kettle, 19th C.,
13", 33 cm. £75-85 LC

Early Victorian Copper Campana
shape tea urn with brass tap. 18",
45 cm. £130-150 WW

A Copper-Coated Figure, signed
Th. Gentile, 40½", 103 cm.
Italian, c.1885. £800-900 SBel

A Pair of Copper Chandeliers,
56", 142 cm. c.1900. £400-600
SBel

A 19th C. copper tea urn with
brass tap. £90-100 WW

Two copper ring jelly moulds.
£50-65 HKC

Copper log bin. £56-62 MH

A copper helmet coal scuttle.
£56-62 WW

A copper fire-engine's paraffin
lantern with brass mounts. **£100-
120** HKC

An old bell metal stewpan with
brass base and iron handle 13",
33 cm. dia. **£12-20** WW

Copper saucepan and lid. **£65-70**
MPA

An 18", 45 cm., rococo jardiniere,
inset with six copper panels.
£150-170 RB

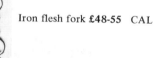

Iron flesh fork **£48-55** CAL

An iron fire front, 40", 102 cm.
x 32", 81 cm., late 18th C. **£120-
160** LC

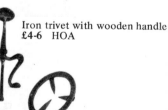

Iron trivet with wooden handle
£4-6 HOA

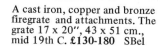

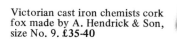

A cast iron, copper and bronze
firegrate and attachments. The
grate 17 x 20", 43 x 51 cm.,
mid 19th C. **£130-180** SBel

Victorian cast iron chemists cork
fox made by A. Hendrick & Son,
size No. 9. **£35-40**

The cast-iron stove of circular section finished in blacked-lead and black vitreous enamel. 15½" diam. by 42"; 39.5 by 108 cm., marked 'S. Demoulin Brevete', Belgian, c.1890. **£950-1,050** SBel

The free-standing cast-iron sectional stove of circular section. 20" by 55"; 51 by 140 cm., by STR Franco Americaine de Chauffage, A Reveilhac Uppot & Cie, French, c.1880. **£880-980** SBel

The free-standing cast-iron pot stove of circular section finished in black-leading. 17½" by 28"; 44.5 by 71 cm., Augie Maison, French, c.1890. **£100-120** SBel

The cast-iron stove of circular section finished in chocolate-brown vitreous enamel with nickel-plated details. 11" diam. by 34", 28 by 86.5 cm., marked 'S219' below hot plate, Belgian, c.1930. **£240-270** SBel

The cast-iron pot stove of circular section. 11¾" diam. by 29"; 30 by 74 cm., marked '17' under hot plate, Belgian, c. 1910. **£250-300** SBel

The cast-iron open fire cooker finished in black-painted cast-iron. 17" by 28" by 24", 43 by 71 by 61 cm., marked 'No. 2 PT 10' on top, English, c.1900. **£180-200** SBel

The free-standing closed stove finished in black-leaded cast-iron. 16½" by 30" by 12", 42 by 76 by 30.5 cm., No. 5 by The Cosy Stove Co., English, c.1920. **£170-200** SBel

The cast-iron stove of square section, in mid-green vitreous enamel, 14¼" by 43" by 14"; 36 by 109 by 35.5 cm., German, c.1920. **£400-500** SBel

The free-standing cast-iron cooking stove of rectangular section. 23½"by 32" by 16½"; 60 by 81 by 42 cm., by Sougland Brevet SGDG, French, c.1900. **£240-270** SBel

The free-standing cast-rion stove of rectangular section, finished in violet vitreous enamel. 17½" by 29" by 14"; 44.5 by 73.5 by 35.5 cm., French, c.1910. **£750-850** SBel

The black-leaded cast-iron pot stove of elliptical section. 14½" by 30" by 12"; 37 by 76 by 30.5 cm., French, c.1850. £260-290 SBel

The cast-iron closed stove finished in electric-blue vitreous enamel. 14" by 25" by 13", 35.5 by 63.5 by 33 cm., marked 'Godin 136' under lid and '136 2120' inside front door, French, c.1925. £220-250 SBel

The free-standing cast-iron stove of hexagonal section finished in mid-green vitreous enamel. 17" by 33½"; 43 by 85 cm., by Deville & Cie, French, c.1910. £350-380 SBel

The cast-iron stove of square section finished in tan and buff vitreous enamel with black-leaded details; 12" square by 30"; 30.5 by 76 cm., marked 'Ancne Maison Godin & Cie a Guise' on fuel-loading door and ash flap, French, c.1900. £240-270 SBel

The free-standing open fire finished in delicate black-leaded cast-iron filigree. 17" by 23" by 14"; 43 by 58.5 by 35.5 cm., No. 67, by Godin & Cie, French, c.1900. £250-300 SBel

The freestanding cast-iron and enamel pot stove of circular section finished in black enamel with nickel-plated details. 15" by 39" diam., 38 by 99 cm., by Brevet SGDG, French, c.1900 £320-380 SBel

The free standing closed stove finished in dove-grey vitreous enamel. 24" by 30" by 18"; 61 by 76 by 46 cm., French, c.1900. £450-500 SBel

The cast-iron stove of rectangular section finished in undecorated silver paint. 13¼" by 22" by 14½", 33.5 by 56 by 37 cm., marked '0-1-2-3' on front door, French, c.1930. £40-50 SBel

Free-standing vitreous enamelled stove. 17½" by 14", 44.5 by 71 by 35.5 cm., French, c.1910-15. £400-450 SBel

The black-leaded cast-iron stove of circular section, fuel loading at the top, 14½" diam. by 27"; 37 by 69 cm., with incorrect lid, marked '4120 Godin Guise (Aisne)', French, c.1890. £150-170 SBel

The free-standing closed stove of square section, in black-leaded cast-iron. 12" square by 36"; 30.5 by 91.5 cm., Scandinavian, c.1910. £160-180 SBel

The cast-iron stove of square section finished in mid-green vitreous enamel with nickel-plated corners and fittings. 14" square by 34", 35.5 by 86 cm., marked '361 362' under lid, 'Balkan Pied-Selle Ne 362', French, c.1920. £500-560 SBel

The free-standing pot stove of circular section, finished in cast-iron with enamelled and nickel-plated details. 20" by 30"; 76 by 51 cm., by Societe Choubersky 20B Monmartre Paris, French, c.1870. £3,200-3,500 SBel

A black-leaded cast-iron closed stove of square section. 17" square by 26"; 43 by 66 cm., marked '489 Fonderies de Sougland Aisne', under lid, French, c.1875; £280-310 SBel

The free-standing stove of circular section, in black-leaded cast-iron. 10½" diam by 28"; 26.5 by 71 cm., No. 1277, Charleville, French, c.1920. £80-150 SBel

The free-standing black vitreous enamel pot stove of circular section, with hot plate at the top. 15" by 36"; 38 by 91.5 cm., Maison Bemothe & Golseals, French, c.1890. £300-350 SBel

The free-standing bow-fronted stove finished in mid-green vitreous enamel. 18½" by 24" by 14½", 47 by 61 by 35.5 cm., German, c.1900 £370-420 SBel

The free-standing stove finished in mid-brown vitreous enamel. 13¾" by 31½" by 13½", 35 by 79 by 34 cm., No. 10A 37 Br Magenta Paris, Niederbronn, Alsace, French, c.1920. £280-310 SBel

A Pair of Marble and Ormolu
Urn Candelabra, 37½'', 95.3 cm.,
late 19th C. **£620-700** SBel

A Champleve and Bronze Lantern,
13½'', 34 cm., late 19th C.
£520-570 SBel

A Pair of Empire ormolu and
bronze candelabra, 2'6'', 76 cm.
£1,000-1,200 PJ

A Large Champleve Vase, 15½'',
39 cm., cast seal, late 19th C.
£150-200 SBel

A Pair of 19th C. Ormolu
Candelabra, 1'3½'', 41 cm.,
£200-230 KC

A Pair of Ormolu Candelabra,
16½'', 42 cm., late 19th C.
£120-160 SBel

An Empire ormolu Tazza.
£350-400 JWB

A French Ormolu Bust, on
marble socle, 10¾'', 27.5 cm.,
early 19th C. **£70-80** LC

A Pair of Ormolu and Onyx
Candelabra, 25'', 63.5 cm.,
c.1870. **£260-290** SBel

A Pair of Ormolu Candelabra
22¼'', 56.5 cm., c.1860. **£340-
400** SBel

A Louis Philippe bronze ormolu and white marble clock-set. 27½", 71 cm. including glass shades. **£1,900-2,100** CStJ

A Pair of Ormolu Candelabra of Louis XVI design, 16½", 42 cm., mid-19th C. **£400-460** CStJ

A Pair of Ormolu-Mounted Verde Antico Marble Urns of Louis XVI design, 14½", 37 cm. high. **£300-340** CStJ

A Louis-Philippe Ormolu and Griotte Marble Clock-Set, 22", 56 cm. high. **£500-555** CStJ

A Massive Louis-Philippe Ormolu and Porcelain Candelabrum, 43", 109 cm. high. **£380-420** CStJ

An Ormolu-Mounted Blue-John Urn, Derbyshire spar body, 1'7", 48 cm. English, c.1800. **£850-950** SBS

A Pair of Ormolu-Mounted Breche Violette Urns and Covers, 14½", 37 cm., marble tops damaged, 1870's, **£400-450** SBel

19th C. steel fire hob. **£80-90**

A pair of Ormolu Candlesticks. **£550-660** BL

A steel firegrate in George III style, 33", 84 cm. wide. **£350-420** SBS

18th C. corkscrew with pincers for cutting wire on champagne bottles and a brush for dusting the cork. **£25-30** HOA

A pair of late 17th C. Dutch pricket candlesticks, later prickets, 9¾", 25 cm. **£325-345** LC

A WMF Silvered Metal Stemmed Dish, 10½", 26.25 cm., c.1900. **£200-250** SBel

An Indian Silver-Coloured-Metal Boat, 23½", 59.7 cm., overall, stamped, early 20th C. **£310-350** SBel

A WMF Silvered Metal Mirror Frame, 14½", 37 cm., c.1900. **£460-500** SBel

A German Silver-Coloured Metal and Ivory Oval Tankard and Cover, probably of South German origin, c.1725, overall 8¾", 22 cm. **£1,800-2,000** KC

A Chinese Silver-Coloured Metal Mug, engraved 'TJH', 4¼", 10.5 cm., stamped mark, early 20th C. 10 oz. 10 dwt., 325 gm. **£100-150** SBel

A Pair of Spelter Horsemen, c.1880. **£140-170** SBel

Inlaid Silver Metal Vase Cover and Liner, 4½", 12 cm., Japanese, c.1900. **£1,000-1,100** LC

A Pair of Spelter Assyrian Horsemen, 18", 45.7 cm. c.1900. **£50-60** SBel

A Spelter Figure with mirror, 15", 38 cm. **£7-10** RB

A Pair of Cold-Painted Spelter Figures, 14½", 37 cm., and 15½", 38 cm., late 19th C. **£55-75** SBel

A Pair of Spelter Equestrian Knights, 11", 28 cm. **£40-50** RB

A Pair of Spelter Figures of Elizabethan Sea Dogs, 11", 28 cm. **£24-30** WW

A pair of onyx and metal baluster vases 9″, 23 cm. high. £7-10   RB

Letter Scales with five weights £45-50   PG

A Strong Box in sheet steel, the hinged lid enclosing a seven lock mechanism 18½″ high by 26″ wide, 47 cm. by 66 cm., c.1680. Flemish. £900-1,000   SBS

A set of cylindrical bell-metal grain measures of sizes ranging from 'Imperial Bushel' to 'Imperial Gallon', inscribed 'East Sussex', stamped with marks from William IV to Elizabeth II; largest 19½″, 49.5 cm. diam, smallest 7¾″, 19.5 cm. diam., £1,800-2,000 CStJ

Pair (almost) of early 17th C. Italian candlesticks £355-400 CAL

An embosser by Alfred H. Atkins. £9-15   GGA

An unusually large early sealed wine bottle, of dark green metal, inscribed BEN.JENNIN GS 1728, 10″, 25.5 cm. c.1728. £580-640 SBS

Pair of mid 18th C. bell metal square based candlesticks c.1760. £200-250

Victorian letter scales. £45-50 TJC

17th C. Persian Oil Lamp. £265-285   CAL

METAL

A fine pair of 18th C. ships 6 lb. Carronades by Carron. & Co. Cast-iron barrels, with wooden trucks. 42", 107 cm. long x 3½", 9 cm. int. dia. **£600-700** B

A Cast-Iron Group of 3 Dogs, 7½", 19 cm. c.1880. **£120-150** SBel

Victorian cast iron gilded lion mask claw doorstop. **£28-34** WW

A small iron snuffer **£10-15** CAL

A Cast-Iron Group, 9½", 22 cm., signed, dated 1847. **£480-560** SBel

19th C. Cast Iron Statuette of Sir Walter Scott, 9½", 24 cm. **£12-20** WW

A white metal square seal surmounted by a large mythical tortoise, its head raised. 5½", 14 cm., 4", 10 cm., square. Ch'ing Dynasty. **£300-350** CStJ

An old pair of painted metal Carriage Lamps with glass panels (cracked). **£20-30** WW

A Painted Metal Birdcage, giltwood handle, 2'1½", 65 cm., high by 1'4", 41 cm., mid-19th C. **£220-230** SBS

Early Victorian letter scales. **£37-40** TJC

A George III Bell-metal footman on cabriole legs, 17" wide, 43 cm., **£360-400** CStJ

An old sheep bell. **£8-12** FA

A Spanish Damascened Steel Amphora and Stand, 11¾", 19.8 cm., c.1890, foot bent. **£140-180** SBel

A Pair of Spelter Figures, 36½",
93 cm., fitted for electricity,
c.1900. **£450-500** SBel

A Pair of Spelter Urns on marble
bases, 12¼", 31 cm., c.1870.
£120-180 SBel

A Pair of Glass and Gilt-Brass
Candelabra, 19¾", 50 cm.,
Venetian, c.1880. **£410-460**
SBel

A Spelter Figure, stamped, 36½",
92.8 cm., lacking arm and sword,
c.1900. **£95-115** SBel

A Spelter Lamp, with alternate
blue and amber plaques, 16", 41 cm.,
1920's. **£400-440** SBel

A Pair of Gilt-Brass Chandeliers,
27", 68.5 cm., **£260-300** SBel

A Madurell Gilt-Metal Casket,
Silk lined, 15", 37.5 cm., c.1900.
£250-400 SBel

A Spelter Figure of Don Cesar,
stamped, 40½", 103 cm., with
electrical fittings, c.1880. **£440-
520** SBel

A Pair of Gilt-Brass Candelabra
26½", 67 cm., early 20th C.
£320-340 SBel

A Pair of Gilt-Metal Candelabra,
37", 94 cm., c.1880. **£250-350**
SBel

A Pair of George III White Marble, Gilt and Patinated Bronze Casseolettes, 9¾", 25 cm., c.1795. £600-700 SBS

A parcel-gilt bronze seated figure of Shou Lao, minor damage, Ch'ing Dynasty, 18¾", 47.5 cm., £300-350 CStJ

A Pair of Gilt-Bronze Wall Lights, 22", 56 cm., c.1870. £300-340 SBel

A parcel-gilt bronze standing figure of an immortal, late Ming/Ch'ing Dynasty, minor damage, 12¾", 32.5 cm., £450-500 CStJ

A gilt-lacquered bronze figure of a standing warrior immortal, Ch'ing Dynasty, 9½", 25 cm., £140-170 CStJ

A gilt bronze seated figure of a Taoist immortal, Ch'ing Dynasty, 10¼", 26 cm., £550-600 CStJ

A Pair of Gilt and Bronze Figures, 14½", 37 cm., and 13½", 34.5 cm., late 19th C. £380-450 SBel

A Gilt-Bronze and Marble Bust, 13¾", 35 cm., signed, 1890's. £290-340 SBel

A pair of gilt-bronze 3-branch candelabra. 14½", 37 cm. mid-18th C, possibly Dutch. £1,050-1,150 CStJ

A Gilt-Bronze and Ivory Figure 17", 43 cm., c.1905. £720-800 SBel

A Gilt-Bronze Group, 9½", 24 cm. late 19th C. £450-520 SBel

449

A Gilt-Metal and Enamel Singing Bird Box, 3¾″, 9.6 cm., c.1910, fitted case, no key. **£420-500** SBel

A Komai Inlaid Iron Box and Cover, 3¼″, 8.2 cm., c.1900. **£270-300** SBel

A Pair of Gilt-Metal Candelabra, 35½″, 90 cm., c.1880. **£1,200-1,400** SBel

A Gilt-Metal Singing Bird Box, French, c.1885 (case). **£500-560** SBel

A Fine Chippendale Revival Gilt-metal 8 light Chandelier, 2′5″, high by 2′7″, 74 cm. by 79 cm., c.1830. **£5,000-5,500** SBS

A 16th C. iron Armada Chest, Three hinged lid with workings of seven bolt lock, 34″, 86 cm. wide. **£500-600** B

A good 16th C. Gothic Iron strongbox, 25½″ wide, 64 cm., x 13″, 33 cm. high, x 11″, 28 cm. deep. **£900-1,000** B

A Pair of George III Gilt-Metal Wall Lanterns, 58 cm., 1′11″, c.1790. **£2,900-3,200** SBS

A George III Gilt Metal and White Marble Table Candelabrum in the manner of Matthew Boulton, 12″, 31 cm., c.1790. **£750-850** SBS

A French Gilt-Metal Jewel Casket, set with 7 carved shell cameos with key, 7″, 17.6 cm. long, c.1870. **£320-380** SBel

A Komai inlaid iron cabinet. c.1900. 8¼″, 21 cm. **£2,400-2,700** SBel

A wrought iron gate, the locking plate with a twist-turned handle, 78″ by 40″, 200 cm. by 102 cm., 1860's. **£420-500** SBel

A Brussels 'Teniers' Tapestry, 11'
by 10'6", 3 m. 35 cm. by 3 m.
20 cm., early 18th C. £4,200-
4,700   CStJ

A Louis XV Gobelin Rectangular
Tapestry Panel, 6'11" by 5'9",
2 m. 11 cm. by 1 m. 75 cm.
£1,300-1,450   CStJ

A Louis XV Gobelin Tapestry
woven after la Fontaine, 8'8"
by 7'10", 2 m. 64 cm. by 2 m.
38 cm. £2,000-2,200   CStJ

A Brussels Tapestry, 8'4" by
8'7", 2 m. 53 cm. by 2 m. 61 cm.,
second half, 16th C. (some re-
weaving). £1,900-2,100   CStJ

A Flemish Tapestry woven in
verdure colours, 7'10" by 5'6",
2 m. 38 cm. by 1 m. 68 cm., early
18th C. £3,600-3,900   CStJ

A Verdure Tapestry, 9'3" by
11'6", 2 m. 81 cm. by 3 m. 50 cm.,
early 18th C., possibly Aubusson.
£1,500-1,600   CStJ

A Rectangular Tapestry Panel in
verdure tones, 7'9" by 6'4",
2 m. 36 cm. by 1 m. 93 cm., early
18th C., probably Aubusson.
£1,200-1.300   CStJ

A Flemish Verdure Tapestry,
8'10" by 12'6", 2 m. 68 cm. by
3 m. 82 cm., early 18th C. (some
re-weaving). £1,500-1,600   CStJ

A Genji Kazak rug, with indigo
field, 8' by 3'2", 244 cm. by
97 cm. c.1880, condition: fair.
£850-950   SBS

A fine Belouchistan rug in tones of red, ivory and green with Killim borders, 5'8" x 3'4", 173 cm. x 101 cm. **£130-160** HKC

A Rectangular Tapestry Panel in verdure tones, 9'2" by 4'6", 2 m. 79 cm. by 1 m. 93 cm., early 18th C., probably Aubusson. **£650-720** CStJ

A pair of Ispahan rugs. 7' x 4'7", 213 cm. x 139.5 cm. **£320-380** HKC

A Kazak prayer rug with a blue mihrab on a tomato field. 4'3" x 3'4", 129.5 cm. x 101 cm. **£1,050-1,200** HKC

A fine silk Kashan rug in shades of rose, tan, green, blue, turquoise, ivory, gold and magenta. 5' x 3'5", 152 x 103.5 cm. **£3,700-4,000** HKC

A Malayer rug in tones of rose, blue, ivory, beige, gold and green. 6'5" x 4'2", 195.5 cm. x 127 cm. **£1,050-1,200** HKC

A Senneh-Killim rug in shades of green, gold, red, ivory, blue and rust. 6'7" x 4', 200.5 x 122 cm. **£420-480** HKC

A Turkoman rug in shades of rust and blue, old gold, green, and ivory on a wine field. 6'10" x 3'10", 208.5 x 116.5 cm. **£320-370** HKC

A Yomud chuval in shades of ivory, midnight and blue. 2'6" x 4', 76 cm. x 122 cm. **£70-90** HKC

A Yomud hatchli rug in tones of red, ivory, blue and brown. 5'4" x 4', 162 cm. x 122 cm. **£120-140** HKC

A fine Isfahan rug, with tan and red-brown border between blue floral stripes, 5'3" x 3'2", 160 x 96;6 cm., **£850-930** CStJ

A Brussels Tapestry woven in mainly verdure tones, brown selvedge with Brussels townmark, 7'11" by 12'5", 2 m. 71 cm. by 3 m. 79 cm., early 18th C. **£3,200-3,500** CStJ

MUSICAL BOXES

The cylinder musical boxes of the 19th century grew out of the watch movements of the 18th century. Hence Switzerland tended to lead the field. These vary much in quality and complexity; many playing up to 12 tunes and being contained in ROSEWOOD boxes. Among the most collectable are those made by Nicole Freres. When buying it is worth remembering that it is extremely difficult to repair a damaged comb or cylinder. The actual movement can be repaired by a skilled watchmaker but this will be generally quite expensive.

Disc musical boxes became popular around 1880 and enjoyed favour up to the First World War.

They were completely overtaken by the advent of the gramaphone. It is essential to find one with suitable discs. Coin-fed machines tend to add to the value, as do highly decorative and well made boxes. Rarity of the type of musical box does not automatically mean it will fetch more, as if no suitable discs can be found the value drops considerably.

The final type in the group is the large mechanical musical box, such as the barrel organ and the Symphonion 'penny in the slot' machine. Again one of the most important features is a good working mechanism. The cases of such pieces are of secondary importance.

A Bremond 'Hidden Drums and Bells' cylinder musical box, rosewood-veneered case, Swiss, c.1870, 21", 53 cm wide.
£550-630 SBel

A 'Bells in Sight' interchangeable cylinder musical box on stand, ebonised case with pewter banding, 29", 74 cm wide, Swiss, late 19th C. £1,700-1,800 SBel

A cylinder musical box, the 15 3/8", 39 cm., cylinder playing 10 airs, 25½", 65 cm., £500-580 LC

A key-wound cylinder musical box in rosewood case, Swiss, mid-19th C., 15", 38 cm wide. £260-280 SBel

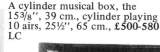

A mandolin cylinder musical box in burr-walnut veneered case, Swiss, late 19th C., 21", 53 cm wide. £580-640 SBel

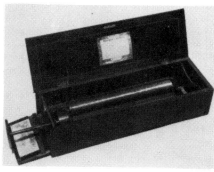

A Nicole Freres Key-wound cylinder box No. 29799, 51 cm. wide, Swiss, c.1848. £700-800 SBel

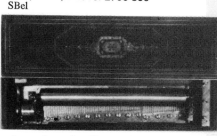

A rare Lecoultre Freres pianoforte cylinder musical box, in rosewood-veneered case, Swiss, c.1860, 24", 66 cm wide.
£1,400-1,500 SBel

A polyphon disc musical box, 15½", 39.5 cm, with 19 metal discs, German, early 20th C. £550-620 SBel

A good polyphon disc musical box, 19¾", 50 cm, coin-operated mechanism, in rosewood case, 36", 92 cm, metal discs, German, late 19th C. £1,450-1,550 LC

A Euphonika Atlas organette, zinc discs, ebonised case, German, late 19th C., 14″, 36 cm wide. £320-360 SBel

A B.H. Abrahams Britannia disc musical box, 11¾″, 29 cm, with 10 discs, Swiss, late 19th C. £750-830 SBel

A late 19th C. Swiss musical box, 6 airs, Nicole Freres, 18″, 45 cm. wide. £450-550 OL

A symphonion disc musical box, 10″, 25.5 cm, in beechwood-veneered case, 13″, 33 cm wide, with 10 metal discs, German, early 20th C. £350-380 SBel

An 11¾″, 30 cm. Symphonion disc musical box with one disc. £750-830 CSK

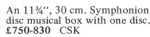

A late 19th C. Swiss musical box, 11¾″, 30 cm., 10 airs, by Nicole Freres, 24″, 61 cm. wide, £560-640 OL

A Mandolin Piccolo Interchangeable-Cylinder musical box, the table 47¼″, 120 cm. wide, the cylinders 13″, 33 cm. the lock stamped Mojon, Manger, c.1900. £2,800-3,100 CSK

A good 'Hidden Bells and Drum' cylinder musical box, the 9″, 23 cm., cylinder playing 4 airs, 16½″, 42 cm. £350-420 LC

A rare Kalliope Panorama automat disc musical box on stand, 25″, 63.5 cm, in rosewood case, 94″, 239 cm high, with 20 metal discs, German, c.1903. £2,600-2,800 SBel

A late 19th C. Swiss cylinder musical box by Nicole Freres, in rosewood case, 24″, 61 cm. £560-620 OL

A rare polyphon 'Bells in Sight' disc musical box, 8", 20 cm, simulated rosewood case, with 13 metal discs, German, early 20th C., 10½", 26 cm wide. **£380-450** SBel

A good Hicks Dulcimer in walnut case with brass handle, English, mid-19th C., 34", 87 cm. **£900-1,000** SBel

A polyphon disc musical box, 15½", 39.5 cm, with 40 metal discs, original carrying case, German, late 19th C. **£950-1,050** SBel

A Mignon paper roll organette in ebonised case, German, late 19th C., 20", 51 cm wide. **£450-520** SBel

A Rare Kalliston 28-key organette with eight bands, 17½", 44.5 cm. **£450-510** CSK

A Small 22-key Barrel Piano by George Hicks, 4½", 11.5 cm. high. **£950-1,050** CSK

A Chant-Du-Rossignol Box in burr walnut case with decorative crossbanding, 7", 18 cm. square. **£280-320** CSK

A mahogany cased organ Celeste musical box, the 6 air movement having 15 reeds and two combs, 9½", 24.0 cm. long barrel, **£360-430** KC

A rosewood-cased musical box, movement with 8 airs on 6", 15 cm., long barrel and three bells, ratchet wind, single comb, **£360-440** KC

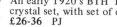

An early 1920's BTH 'Radiola' crystal set, with set of earphones. **£26-36** PJ

A mahogany cased musical box, the 14½", 37 cm., barrel playing 6 airs on single comb with Parachute Mermod for large spring barrel. **£460-520 KC**

A Paillard's Echophone, stamped 7793, with two reproducers and an aluminium horn, 12¼" long, 31 cm. **£95-125 PJ**

A Columbia Majestic Disc Graphophone in mahogany case with quadruple spring motor, c.1910. **£550-600 CSK**

An ebonised musical box, the ratchet-wind 13", 33 cm., barrel playing 10 airs. **£580-670 KC**

An HMV Model 510 Lumiere Pleated Diaphram gramophone. 43", 109 cm. high. **£480-560 CSK**

An Edison Fireside Phonograph, good Model K reproducer and fireside horn, American, c.1910. **£400-460 SBel**

A Key-Wind Musical Box with sectional comb, playing four airs, 12", 30.5 cm. wide. **£1,200-1,400 CSK**

A Gramophone & Typewriter Ltd. Style No. 6 Gramophone and Typewriter Ltd. 31 Maiden Lane and Imhof & Mukle. **£900-1,000 CSK**

A tinfoil brass phonograph, threaded axis with ivory handle, and a record/reproducer, 9" x 7", 23 cm. x 17.75 cm., probably English, c.1880. **£1,500-1,800 SBel**

A Forte-Piano Key-Wind Musical Box by Nicole Freres No. 33039, playing eight sacred airs (Gamme No. 1464) 25", 63 cm. long. **£1,400-1,600 CSK**

A Key-Wind Musical Box by Nicole Freres No. 37960 playing twelve airs from Mozart operas (Gamme No. 1516), 20½", 52 cm. wide. **£1,200-1,400 CSK**

A Columbia AA graphophone Serial No. 70608, two minute mechanism, lacking parts, American, c.1906. **£90-120 SBel**

A Pathe Coquet phonograph, two minute mechanism, French, c.1904. **£100-140 SBel**

An improved Berliner gramophone, of 'Trademark' design, with 7", 17.5 cm., turntable, 10", 25.5 cm., square, American, c.1900. **£380-460** SBel

A horn gramophone, reproduction Clark/Johnson-type soundbox, 7½", 19 cm., high, lacks winding handle, English. **£80-100** SBel

A gramophone, having a 12" turntable, Alcra large diameter soundbox, 37½", 95 cm. high, English, c.1930. **£220-260** SBel

Phonograph, driven from rear feed screw, large diameter drive wheel, and early reproducer mechanism, 14" x 9", 35.5 cm. x 23 cm., **£130-170** SBel

A good Puck-type horn, with floating reproducer, probably German, c.1903. **£150-180** SBel

An oak upright Broadwood 'Manxman' Piano, stamped John Broadwood and Son, London. 46½" by 56½" by 26½", 118 cm. by 144 cm. by 67 cm., c.1900. **£500-600** SBel

A Cittern by Remerus Liessem in London 1730-1760, **£190-240** PL

A Cittern (English Guitar) with brand of Thompsons, London, c.1780. **£280-340** PL

Victorian Barrel Organ by A.O. Wintle, MA. Lawshall, Bury St. Edmunds, 42" wide, 106 cm. **£980-1,100** B

A Harp Lute Guitar by Barry, London, c.1800, unstrung and requiring restoration. **£440-500** PL

Concertina, probably late 19th C. in case. **£65-75** FA

A Harp Lute by Edward Light — London, **£240-280** PL

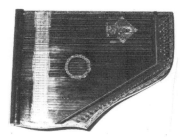

A German Harp-Zither, with 2 tutors. £20-30 PJ

An English Violoncello of the John Betts of London School, c.1800, 29″, 73.8 cm. £1,200-1,600 PL

A Violin by Giovanni Chiaravelli in Falerii, c.1850, with certificate of Messrs. W.E. Hill & Sons, London dated 1902; 14″, 35.5 cm. £3,600-3,900 PL

A violin by Leandro Bisiach, 1897, L.O.B. 14″, 35.7 cm, in shaped case. £4,600-4,900 PL

Violin by Eugenio Degani with makers label. 1891. 14¼″, 36.5 cm. 2 bows, wood case. £2,600-2,800 PL

A Mandolin by Farinia & Figlios, mother-of-pearl and tortoiseshell inlay, in case. £20-30 PJ

A Portable Harmonium by Debain with three octaves and five stops, 25″, 63.5 cm. high, mid 19th C. £300-340 CSK

A Violoncello by Thomas Kennedy, London, 1846, L.O.B. 29″, 74.2 cm. £3,000-3,300 PL

A Harp Lute by Edward Light, c.1815, signed. £220-250 PL

A pair of Stone Greyhounds, 4', 122 cm. long. **£1,350-1,650** HKC

A pair of Lead Urns and Covers, 2'4", 71 cm. high. **£160-200** HKC

A Stone group of 2 putti, 3', 91 cm., **£300-400** HKC

A Stone figure of Autumn, 7'4", 229 cm. **£650-750** HKC

A lead fountain figure of Cupid, base damaged, 34", 86 cm. **£150-170** LC

A Regency Blue-John large Goblet or Bowl, 11", 28 cm. early 19th C. repaired. **£420-480** SBS

A Cold-Painted Plaster figure signed Chere, 24¾", 63 cm. Austrian, c.1900. **£190-220**

A lead water tank with initials BCA and date 1755, 25½" by 12" by 25", 65 cm by 31 cm by 64 cm. **£200-220** LC

An English Coadestone figure base impressed Coade and Sealy, 38", 97 cm. early 19th C. **£400-500** SBS

Lead lion doorstop. **£11-15** PG

An Alabaster figure of a Bohemian Girl, 34½", 88 cm., Italian, 1890's. **£700-800** SBel

An Alabaster figure of a Nymph, signed T.G. Bessi, 37", 94 cm., Italian, 1880's. **£450-520** SBel

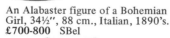

A Cold-Painted Plaster figure, signed Lydown, Austrian, 32", 81 cm. c.1900. **£190-220** SBel

A pair of Matthew Boulton casseolettes Bluejohn bodies with ormolu handles and swags. 13½", 34 cm. high. **£3,200-3,500** HKC

A Painted Plaster Figure of a Boy on an ebonised fluted column, Austrian late 19th C. 63", 160 cm. overall. **£380-460** SBel

A Marble figure of Pauline Borghese, 17″, 43 cm., Italian, mid 19th C. £420-460 SBel

A pair of Marble Lions, 19th C. 10½″, 26.5 cm., £150-200 LC

A Marble Bust, 26″, 66 cm., French, 1890's. £230-260 SBel

A 19th C. Italian Marble Statue, 29″, 74 cm., attributed to J. Gott. £340-440 KC

A White Marble Bust, 28″, 71 cm., late 19th C. £120-140 SBel

A Second Empire Verde Antico Marble and Gilt-Bronze Column, 39¼″, 99.5 cm. mid 19th C. £380-440 SBel

A pair of Veined Yellow Marble Columns with gilt-metal mounts, 40″, 102 cm. c.1900. £540-620 SBel

An early 19th C. White Marble Portrait Bust, 32″, 81 cm. £180-220 HKC

An early 19th C. White Marble Portrait Bust, green marble column, 32″, 76 cm. £180-220 HKC

A Pair of Marble figures, 23″, 58.5 cm., Italian 1880's. £750-850 SBel

A Pair of Large Marble figures, 49″, Italian, mid 19th C. £3,600-4,000 SBel

A Canova White Marble Bust of Sappho, 1817, 21″, 53 cm., with marble column, 3'10″, 117 cm. £11,500-13,000 HKC

A large Meerschaum pipe, 5⅝",
13.3 cm. high, probably Austrian,
c.1885, **£160-220** SBel

A carved wood tobacco sign, 44",
112 cm., English, late 19th C.
£420-440 SBel

A carved wood tobacconist's
sign, 29½", 75 cm., English, c.
1750. **£265-290** SBel

A Novelty Cigar Box in the form
of a Motor-Car, the bonnet as
match-holder, 9", 22.8 cm. long,
maker's mark M & C, Birmingham,
1911, P.O.D.R. number 577091,
38 oz. 19 dwt. 1,209 gm. **£620-720** SBel

A Russian champleve enamel
on silver rectangular case, 6½",
16.5 cm. x 4", 11.1 cm. x 1¼",
3.2 cm. Moscow 1894. **£310-350**
LC

Musical cigar stand, **£24-34**
ORM

An Unusual French Gilt-Metal
Singing Bird Cigarette Box, 4",
10 cm. long, stamped: 'France',
c.1930. **£600-660** SBel

An unusual bathing machine
vesta case/cigar cutter, silver,
4" high, 10 cm., maker's mark
HSB, London, 1892, renovated,
£220-260 SBel

A good set of six J. A. Gilbert
& Co., tobacco containers, 17",
43 cm., English, mid-19th C.
£850-950 SBel

Silver cigar holder Birmingham
1905. **£28-44** GA

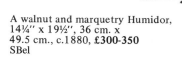

A walnut and marquetry Humidor,
14¼" x 19½", 36 cm. x
49.5 cm., c.1880, **£300-350**
SBel

461

ENAMEL

Enamel is an extremely old form of decoration when applied to metalwork. Three metals were most favoured for this decoration: gold, silver and copper.

Cloisonne is a type of enamelling where thin wires are soldered to the metal to hold the powdered glass. This, of course, varies considerably in quality. Much of the Cloisonne wares available are Japanese and Chinese, many are late examples but can look deceptively old.

Small enamel boxes are highly sought after by collectors and many fine examples were made in Europe in the 18th and 19th centuries. These, however, are very expensive and the collector would find more reasonably priced examples in the boxes produced in England in the late 18th and early 19th centuries.

The European boxes tend to be enamelled on gold or silver, whereas the English boxes tend to be copper.

The main centres for English boxes were Battersea, Birmingham, Bilston and Wednesbury.

Some notes on English boxes.

- very few genuine Battersea boxes, used deep colours, finest boxes made 1753-1756
- boxes made form c.1750-1795 much influenced by Sevres
- many boxes have an inner lid with highly erotic painting. These add greatly to the value of the piece!

A pair of Cloisonne vases, 12", 30.6 cm., late 19th C. **£190-230** SBel

A pair of pale-green-ground Cloisonne Vases, 7¼", 18.5 cm., c.1900. **£230-280** SBel

A large Cloisonne Vase, 18½", 46.5 cm., late 19th C. **£460-520** SBel

A pair of Ormolu mounted Cloisonne enamel vases, on a red ground, 24 cm., 9½", Chinese, mid-19th C. **£330-370** KC

A Large Cloisonne Vase, with pale-blue ground, 22", 56 cm., 1900, **£650-750** SBel

A Cloisonne vase, 10", 25.5 cm., **£62-73** RB

A Blois enamel Watch cover, 2", 5.2 cm., the enamel mid-17th C. **£750-850** CStJ

A pair of Cloisonne vases, on a burnt sienna ground, 9¾", 24.5 cm., c.1900. **£240-290** SBel

A small Viennese Enamel Quatrefoil Dish, silver-gilt mounted, 4½", 11.4 cm. diam, unmarked, late 19th C. **£260-300** SBel

Pair of Enamel Tapersticks. 6½", 16.5 cm. **£380-460** PL

Hyoda Silver-mounted Cloisonne vase and cover in gold cloisons on a pale-yellow ground, 3½", 9.2 cm., c.1900. **£470-530** SBel

A famille rose Canton enamel supper set of twelve spirally radiating dishes, some damage, late 18th/early 19th C., overall diam. 17", 43.5 cm., **£360-400** CStJ

A French enamel tea caddy and cover, 5¼", 13.6 cm. high, c.1900, some chips. **£150-190** SBel

A Cloisonne enamel oviform vase, slightly damaged, early 19th C., 18", 46 cm., **£320-400** CStJ

Pair of silver-shape Tapersticks, unusually in yellow enamel, 6¾", 17 cm. **£360-400** PL

Set of 10 Canton Enamel Tea Bowls and Covers decorated in bright enamels, 3¼", 8.3 cm., mid 19th C. **£200-230** SBel

A small pair of Cloisonne enamel vases, 6", 15 cm., Japanese, late 19th C. **£280-340** KC

An attractive pair of South Staffordshire enamel Taper-sticks. 6¾", 17 cm. **£410-460** PL

A Cloisonne enamel tray, decorated in pale-blue ground, 29.5 cm., 11½" wide, signed, Japanese, late 19th C. **£200-230** KC

A pair of large champleve and bronze vases, 17¾", 45.5 cm., late 19th C. **£420-480** SBel

A 4", 10.0 cm., circular enamel box and cover. £260-300 RB

A Bilston enamel combined scent bottle and bonbonniere, 4", 10 cm., £200-240 PL

Oriental Cloisonne enamel box and cover 2¾", 7.0 cm., £25-30 RB

A 2¼", 5.5 cm., enamelled blue box, £100-120 KC

A Bilston enamel box, c.1780. £130-160 KC

A pinchbeck box, c.1770. £400-480 KC

Bilston enamel Snuff Box, 6.5 cm., 2½", c.1760-70 £410-480 PL

An enamel automaton as singing bird. £340-400 KC

Enamel Box and Cover, probably German, 2¼", 6 cm., mid 18th C. £180-220 PL

Oval Staffordshire enamel box with pink base, with a cobalt blue border, £140-170 KC

A rare miniature enamel perfume bottle gilt-metal leaves and, c.1800 £140-170 KC

A Rare Staffordshire enamel bird bonbonniere, c.1780. £450-520 KC

An unusual Bilston enamel card tray, c.1800. £50-80 KC

A Rare oval Bilston enamel box in dark blue. £420-480 KC

A large Cloisonne enamel tripod deep globular censer and domed cover with gilt copper and champleve enamel, some damage, early 19th C., 21¾", 55.5 cm. £650-720 CStJ

A pair of French enamels, painted in subdued tones, 6¾", 17 cm. long, late 19th C. £340-420 SBel

A Viennese miniature enamel vase, c.1870. **£150-170** KC

A Cloisonne enamel jar and cover, 8¾", 22 cm., Japanese, late 19th C. **£105-115** LC

A Cloisonne Koro and Cover, decorated on a blue ground, 13¼", 33 cm., late 19th C. **£340-370** SBel

A South Staffordshire enamel etui, fittings incomplete, 3", 7.9 cm., **£210-260** LC

A Cloisonne enamel jar and cover 9", 23.0 cm., Japanese, c.1900. **£120-150** LC

An old Islamic 8¾", 22 cm., bottle shaped vase. **£28-36** PWC

An enamel Etui, 3¾", 9.5 cm., **£160-190** PL

A Cloisonne Koro and Cover, decorated with k'uei dragons 14", 35 cm., 19th C. **£310-340** SBel

A Cloisonne Koro and Cover, decorated in bright enamels, 8", 20.5 cm., c.1900. **£200-230** SBel

An enamel plaque, by Elizabeth Matthews, 6¼", 16.2 cm. high, "EM/1926". **£75-95** SBel

An enamel 'Honeysuckle Group' Etui. 4", 10 cm., c.1760. **£240-290** PL

Wrought iron pot hanger. **£12-15** CAL

Iron log fork. **£16-18** CAL

A wooden saddler's clamp, 19th C. **£15-20** HOA

Iron spit hanger **£23-30** CAL

Pair of Chinese metal mandarin irons with wooden handles. **£50-55** LBA

17th C. spice grinder in ash. **£190-220** CAL

A Victorian jack plane, **£5-10** HOA

A high quality mid-Victorian ebony and brass level, 10″ long, 25.5 cm., **£15-20** HOA

Mid-Victorian beechwood dado plane. **£18-25** HOA

Steel measuring yard with War Office stamp dated 1917, **£16-20** HOA

Early army ordnance survey map measuring tape marked in metres and inches (metal tape) **£40-50** HOA

18th C. plough plane. **£20-25** HOA

A Victorian iron and brass coffee grinder. **£20-30** HOA

A selection of Victorian kitchen choppers **£2-3** each. HOA

A wooden 'cat' of the Chippendale period (damaged) **£18-24** PA

A pestle and mortar. **£9-15** RB

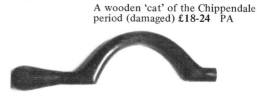

An 18th C. chair maker's brace in beech, **£20-25** HOA

CAMERA EQUIPMENT

- first photographic image produced in 1816
- 1839 Daguerre marketed his box camera
- 1840-1880 wet plate camera; good examples are now highly sought after

- 1880-1920 saw the introduction of Kodak dryplates in 1879 and the development of this much simpler technique led to a large number of firms making their own equipment

- c.1896 cameras developed with bellows which gave the first accurate shutters
- early post-war cameras of the great firms, Zeiss, Leica etc., are now fetching quite high prices, dependant on technical features and new innovations

The 'Telephot' ferrotype button camera, No. 2290, with accessories. 14½" wide, 37 cm., English, c.1900. **£600-700** SBel

A W. Watson & Sons stereoscopic 'Detective' binocular camera, 8", 20.5 cm. high, English, c.1900. **£1,100-1,200** SBel

A wooden cased 'Rover' patent quarter plate camera by J. Lancaster & Son, Birmingham, **£40-50** PJ

An Ensign tropical roll-film reflex camera, c.1925. **£200-250** SBel

A Thorton-Pickard half plate camera. **£45-50** PJ

A J. Lancaster half-plate 'Instantograph' Collapsible camera, English, c.1905. **£58-78** SBel

A large studio camera on stand, the whole 49" high, 124.5 cm., English, c.1900. **£150-300** SBel

A large J. H. Dallmeyer tailboard studio camera, M. Jamin Darlots lens, complete with accessories, English, c.1880. **£500-600** SBel

A No. 2 Planex quarter plate camera, **£45-55** PJ

A W. Watson & Sons Ltd. fullplate tailboard studio camera, English, c.1930. **£190-240** SBel

A good Hewitt & Nettleton Australian whole-plate ambrotype portrait, c.1860. **£95-105** SBel

A stereoscopic Daguerreotype portrait, 1850's. **£60-120** SBel

An attractive stereoscopic Daguerreotype study of silks, lace and brocade, 1850's. **£340-360** SBel

'Fac-simile of an old Printed Page', Talbotype, 23 cm. x 18.8 cm., 9'' x 7½'', c.1845. **£220-240** SBel

Italy. An album of sixty-five photographs, Albumen prints, each 10¼'' x 13¾'', 26 cm. x 35 cm., c.1870. **£85-95** SBel

A group of eight attractive whole-plate contact proof sheets, from Mayall's Studio, Albumen prints, each 87/8'' x 7'', 22.5 cm., x 17.5 cm., 1860-61 **£55-65** SBel

An attractive Nelson & Marshall half-plate Ambrotype family group portrait, c.1860. **£150-160** SBel

Two steroscopic Daguerreotype portraits, 1850's. **£100-150** SBel

Australia. A good album containing seventy photographs, 6'' x 7¾'', 15 cm. x 19.5 cm., 1880's-90's. **£160-180** SBel

SCIENTIFIC INSTRUMENTS

This is obviously a very diverse subject which interested the upper classes from the early 18th century when science became 'a popular study . . . a part of the education of every gentleman'.

Due to the wealth of the instrument maker's clients many beautiful objects were made. It took until 1855 for the first factory to be opened to make a scientific instrument — the telescope. Up to this date instruments were generally made in small workshops and this practice on the whole continued.

In the period when Britain was in control of the seas, much emphasis was placed on the development of new and improved navigational instruments.

The government backed research into navigation and also into land surveying instruments as disputes concerned with land ownership were increasing.

The golden age for instrument makers was the reign of George III as he was fascinated by all scientific matters. This Royal patronage was unnecessary in the Victorian era as the Victorians were great lovers of gadgetry. By now the skills and materials were available which made instruments more accurate and durable.

A Sterling 'Primax' house intercom wall telephone, English, c.1905, 15", 38 cm., **£80-150** SBel

A Gamages morse key in beech case. **£5-10**   PJ

An Emil Moller's magneto wall telephone, stained oak casing, Danish, c.1905, 27", 68.5 cm. **£110-130**   SBel

A set of drawing instruments with accessories, English, early 19th C., 5", 13 cm. long. **£100-120**   SBel

A L.M. Ericsson magneto wall telephone in carved walnut, Swedish, c.1900, 28", 71 cm. **£220-240**   SBel

A L.M. Ericsson magneto desk telephone, English, c.1918, 12½", 32 cm. **£150-200**   SBel

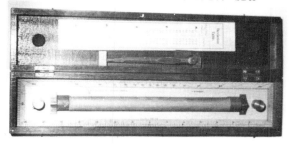

A navigational parallel rule and set of compasses. **£9-15**   PJ

469

Powell & Lealand brass binocular microscope, full mechanical Turrell stage, English, 1859, 17", 43 cm. **£1,300-1,500** SBel

A Culpeper-type monocular microscope, mahogany case and accessories, English, mid-19th C., 11", 28 cm. **£350-400** SBel

A brass dissecting microscope signed A. Rofs, London. Mahogany box with accessories, 19th C. **£220-240** SBS

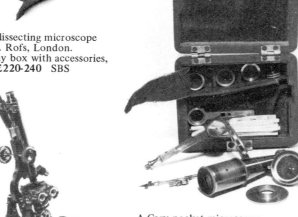

A Cary pocket microscope, mahogany case containing accessories, English, c.1820, 4", 10 cm. wide. **£150-220** SBel

An antique brass large compound microscope, stamped "Ross, London, No. 5178", in box containing accessories, 19", 47.5 cm. **£510-570** RB

Swift & Sons brass binocular microscope, 'Lister-limb' construction, and accessories, English, late 19th C., 17", 43 cm. **£240-270** SBel

A portable lacquered-brass microscope of Cary type with ocular, dividing objective, bullseye, mirror and other accessories, in leather case; and a folding paper shade with brass stand. **£230-250** CSK

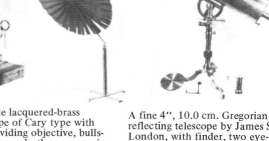

A fine 4", 10.0 cm. Gregorian reflecting telescope by James Short, London, with finder, two eyepieces, two secondary mirrors, altazimuthal mounting and pillow-and-claw stand. **£1,700-1,900** CSK

A brass binocular microscope by Swift & Son of London, mid-19th C., 14½", 37 cm. Mahogany case with accessories. **£450-500** SBS

A brass microscope by Watson & Sons of London in mahogany case. **£55-65** RB

A brass refracting telescope, English, late 19th C., 2½", 6.5 cm. **£190-240** SBel

A William Struthers Gregorian reflecting telescope, English, early 19th C., **£550-600** SBel

A rare brass double sextant, by John Sewill of Liverpool, radii 7¼", 18.5 cm. and 8", 20 cm. **£2,000-3,000** SBS

A Cary brass sextant, English, mid-19th C., 6½", 16.5 cm., radius. **£200-300** SBel

An I.P. Cutts brass refracting telescope, English, mid-19th C., 2", 5 cm. **£240-270** SBel

A John Lilley brass sextant, English, late 19th C., 6½", 16.5 cm., radius. **£190-220** SBel

A brass octant, stamped Black & Murray, Calcutta, English, mid-19th C., 8", 20 cm. radius. **£300-330** SBel

A Troughton & Simms brass refracting telescope, 3", 7.5 cm., length of tube 43", 109 cm. Mahogany case with accessories, English, 1857. **£750-820** SBel

A Heath & Co. sextant, case with 2 telescopes, English, early 20th C., 7", 18 cm. radius. **£190-220** SBel

A brass sextant, English, late 19th C., 7½", 19 cm., radius. **£210-230** SBel

A G.A. Berry brass sextant, English, late 19th C., 7", 18 cm. radius. **£190-220** SBel

A Jeacock ebony octant, mahogany case, English, mid-19th C., 9½", 24 cm. radius. **£310-340** SBel

A good Cary octant, oak case, English, early 19th C., 11½", 29 cm. radius. **£420-460** SBel

A good oxydised brass theodolite, signed Bailey, Birmingham, original wooden case. **£380-420** LC

A brass surveying instrument by Troughton & Simms of London, 19th C., 11⁷/₈", 29.5 cm. **£220-240** SBS

A theodolite by J.Sisson, London, with telescope of canon form spirit-level, compass, vernier and gear-and-pinion controls, on four-screw mounting with integral tripod top, mid 18th century. 9", 23 cm., **£1,600-1,800** CSK

A Thomas Jones brass 'Y' type theodolite, English, late 19th C. **£280-310** SBel

A 19th C. magneto-electric machine stamped S. Maw & Son, London. **£30-35** PJ

A part set of silver drawing instruments, in original silver mounted case, early 18th C., 5¼", 13.2 cm. **£800-1,200** SBS

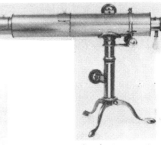

A brass surveying instrument, focusing by screw on side of barrel, 14¼", 36 cm. **£260-300** SBS

A Pastorelli & Co. brass transit theodolite, English, 1857, 11", 28 cm. **£350-380** SBel

A good early Russian brass universal equatorial dial. Signed G. Boelau, S. Petersbourg, diam. of chapter ring 5½", 14.2 cm. **£600-660** LC

An important mahogany angle barometer by Watkins and Smith, c.1763-1774, 35½" high by 26¼" wide, 90.2 cm. by 66.7 cm. **£2,100-2,300** LC

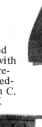

A rectangular silver analemmatic dial, late 18th C., 7¼″ by 4½″, 18.5 cm. by 11.6 cm. **£1,100-1,200** SBS

An orrery with hand-cranked mechanism in walnut base with enamel indicator plate and revolving arm with two bevelled-gear driven shafts. Late 19th C. (incomplete) **£95-105** CSK

A rare Edward Massey brass ship's log, English, early 19th C., 14″, 35 cm. long. **£120-140** SBel

A French mechanical planetarium by Delamarch of Paris, signed and dated 1839, with clockwork motor with worm and fan governor, 49¼″, 125 cm. **£7,500-8,000** SBS

A set of 4 Sand Glasses, 11¼″, 28.5 cm. **£680-740** SBS

A Jydsk 'Telefon Aktieselskab' magneto desk telephone with nickel-plated handset, Danis, c.1920, 13″, 33 cm. **£110-130** SBel

A Negretti & Zambra 'Scotts Patent Stereoscope', English, c.1880, 16½″, 42 cm. **£190-220** SBel

A brass mounted hour glass, possibly 18th C., 9½″, 24 cm. **£420-460** SBS

An unusual Odell typewriter No. 4, manufactured by Farquhar & Albrecht of Chicago, American, c.1890, 10″, 25.5 cm. **£220-240** SBel

A pair of steel-tipped brass calipers by J.Sisson, London, with quadrant scales indicating ¼ part of ye Girt and Diameter in Inches, 24½″ long, 62 cm., **£950-1,050** CSK

A silver model of Marconi's disc discharger, English, 1912, 3½″, 9 cm. **£50-70** SBel

A fine Hall typewriter, No.258, the nickel-plated mechanism with (damaged) rubber typeface, walnut case with panelled lid and leather carrying case. **£320-350** CSK

KRECHOR (Joan de): MEDIUM SALUTARE, 1543. **£70-90** KC

RED ROONEY of The Last of the Crew, 1886, 1st edition. **£20-25** KC

BLOWN TO BITS or The Lonely Man of Rakata, 1889, 1st edition. **£20-25** KC

CHARLIE TO THE RESCUE, 1890, 1st edition. **£20-25** KC

THE BUFFALO RUNNERS, 1891, 1st edition. **£20-25** KC

CAMDEN, WILLIAM: BRITANNIA, trans by Edmund Gibson, 1695. **£600-680** KC

BIBLE, two vols. containing the Old and New Testaments, London 1653, printed by John Field, printer to the Parliament, size 4½″ by 2¼″, 11.5 cm. by 5.5 cm. **£400-500** KC

TIGER TIM'S ANNUAL 1926, cover design, watercolour, signed, 14″ by 10″, 35.5 cm. by 25.5 cm. **£40-50** KC

BUBBLES ANNUAL 1927, cover design, watercolour, signed 14″ by 10″, 35.5 cm. by 25.5 cm. **£40-50** KC

THE BRUIN BOYS ANNUAL 1929, cover design, watercolour, signed, 13¾″ by 9½″, 35 cm. by 24 cm. **£60-70** KC

MRS. HIPPO'S ANNUAL 1931, cover design watercolour, signed, 13½″ by 9″, 34.3 cm. by 23 cm., and the annual for 1932 (2). **£60-70** KC

TEDDY TAIL'S ANNUAL 1936, cover design, watercolour, signed, 13″ by 9½″, 34.3 cm. by 24 cm., and the annual for 1935 (2). **£60-70** KC

JOLLY JACK'S ANNUAL 1937, cover design, watercolour, signed, 12¾″ by 9″, 32.5 cm. by 23 cm., and the annuals for 1937 and 1939 (3). **£60-70** KC

MEYER, HEINRICH: ALBUM AMICORUM, hand-executed by a theological student of Kongsber and Greifswald. **£700-790** KC

A Victorian folding pressed paper lace Valentine card with silk oval panels. **£10-15** PJ

A scrap book containing Chinese paintings on rice paper. **£40-50** PJ

WILLIAM CAVENDISH, Duke of Newcastle. 'A General System of Horsemanship ...', two vols. in one part, London 1743. **£1,250-1,400** LJ

An Ogden's 'New Century' cigarette card album containing portraits of public figures, composers, etc. **£20-25** PJ

Rupert Little Bear Library, 1930-9, complete set of 46 vols. **£320-360** KC

'Mickey Mouse Weekly', a collection of thirty-six editions, English 1936. 11″ by 15″, 28 cm. by 38 cm. **£180-210** SBel

ART NOUVEAU

Art Nouveau was basically a combination of styles which were born in the romantic Gothic revival. It spans the period 1880-1914.

It's departure from classical Gothic styles is best noted in the fact that the 'Gothic' love of straight lines is forgotten in early Art Nouveau and curves abound. In this it emulates much of the baroque. The great inspiration seems to have been an early 'back to nature' and the romance of the non-industrial past and much decoartion is based on flowers such as the lily. The female form in Art Nouveau is based on the concepts of the Pre-Raphaelites.

By 1900 the style had become too decorative and in a reaction against this Charles Rennie Mackintosh brought back the basic straight line form. Much is owed to the London store of Liberty & Co. for extending the artistic nature of the new style onto a commercial basis.

An Art Nouveau vase of solid. agate porcelain, signed, beehive mark and Germany in red, 7¾″, 19.7 cm. £140-180 LC

An early 20th C. Silver Plated Table Lamp in the art nouveau manner, concealed light, inscribed, 1908-9, 38″, 96 cm., £1,050-1,150 LE

Art Nouveau gilded bronze and ivory figure, 10½″, 26.5 cm. £600-700 MH

A turn art nouveau ceramic dish, 17¼″, 44 cm., impressed mark 'Made in Austria', c.1900. £260-300 SBel

Art nouveau patinated metal lamp, 25½″, 65 cm., marked 'Aug Moreau', c.1900. £220-260 SBel

A part gilt and oxidised art nouveau buckle, 3¼″ width, 8.25 cm., stamped 'F. Lassere', c.1900. £180-220 SBel

A centrepiece, Birmingham 1906 maker's mark M & C., 11½″, 29.3 cm., the basket 9 oz. £280-320 LC

An art nouveau wood clock, 13¾″, 35 cm., c.1900. £230-260 SBel

A J. & A. Zimmerman silver art nouveau photograph frame, 11½″, 29 cm., maker's mark, Birmingham, 1903. £190-220 SBel

Art nouveau brass letter rack,
£30-40 CFA

Copper art nouveau inkstand,
£30-40 CFA

A pewter art nouveau mirror
frame, 19¾", 49.5 cm., probably
German, c.1900. **£600-700** SBel

A Scottish art nouveau tea service,
Glasgow 1917 maker's mark
J.W. 40 oz., **£230-260** LC

A Tiffany Studios Bronze Table
Lamp with Leaded Glass Shade,
Shade with panels of mottled
white/green glass and flowers in
mottled pink/white. Bronze Stem.
63.25 cm., shade stamped 'Tiffany
Studios New York', base marked
'Tiffany Studios New York 535',
c.1900. **£1,400-1,700** SBel

An art nouveau bronze and
marble inkstand, 16³/₈", 41.5 cm.
width, dated '03', probably
German. **£60-80** SBel

A large art deco wrought-iron
cheval mirror in the manner of
Edgar Blandt, but signed 'Vua',
6'8¾"; 204 cm. high. **£950-1,050**
PL

An art deco bronze lamp, 20¾",
52.7 cm., 1930's. **£260-290**
SBel

F. Preiss, a 13", 33 cm., art deco
anodised bronze figure, **£780-
880** LJ

A bronze figure signed L.
Alliot, c.1920. **£150-170** SBel

An art deco coloured bronze figure by Lorenzl, signed, 87/8″ high, 22.5 cm., **£150-170**   GC

A Victorian display of five English birds, under glass shade. **£50-70**   AB

An art Deco painted and gilt cigarette box. **£1-5**   RB

A bronze figure, 15½″, 39.5 cm., marked 'Hella Unger', 1920's. **£240-260**   SBel

A mother-of-pearl and lace fan, 9″, 23 cm. c.1885, **£60-70**   SBel

A Duvelleroy fan, ebonised wood guards, with gilt details, 11¾″, 30 cm., c.1900. **£120-140**   SBel

A parasol, the handle of carved green-stained horn, 40″, 101 cm., maker's mark CN, London, 1910. **£90-110**   SBel

A Souvenir Medallion, for the Paris 'Ballon Captif', 1878. 2″, 5 cm. **£50-80**   SBel

A Rare Set of Twelve Buttons, each 1½″, 4 cm. diameter, late 19th C. **£160-200**   SBel

A fine Royal Bengal tiger skin with mounted snarling head, 9′, 280 cm. overall length. **£380-420**   PJ

A 50″ Ordinary Bicycle 4′8″, 142 cm. high, English, c.1880. **£700-800**   SBel

A waxwork and painted card figure of Emperor Nicholas of Russia 16", 40.5 cm. high, beneath a glass dome. **£420-500** HKC

A wax portrait bust of Admiral Sir Thomas Bouchier 6½", 16.5 cm. high, with glass dome. **£30-40** HKC

An early 19th C. travelling set; cruet, knife, spoon, fork and corkscrew, with a beaker, Case 8¼" high, 21 cm. **£35-45** HKC

Russian Icon C.1700 depicting St. John the Baptist. **£800-900** CAL

A rare Hetetalocha Acutirostris, Hen, uncased, 18", 46 cm. from beak to tail. **£200-400** SBel

A George III desk ornament or paperweight marked Weeks R^1 Museum, white marble base, 4¼", 11 cm., c.1790. **£300-340** SBS

A George III Week's RL Museum inkwell in gilt metal, brass and white marble. 5½", 14 cm., c.1790. **£500-580** SBS

Large Cinnabar Lacquer Vase, 20", 51 cm., 19th C. **£210-240** SBel

A Victorian combined pen and pencil by S. Mordan and Co. Designs mark 1868-1883. In a leather case. 3½", 9 cm. **£50-60** DHBN

An electro-plate-mounted ebonised wood inkstand, 16³/₈", 41.5 cm., English, c.1875, **£100-120** SBel

Victorian amboyna inkstand, **£44-54** RB